WILLIAM SCORESBY
ARCTIC SCIENTIST

William Scoresby

WILLIAM SCORESBY
ARCTIC SCIENTIST

TOM AND CORDELIA STAMP

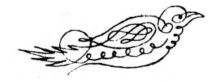

Foreword by the most honourable
the Marquis of Normanby, MBE, HML
Patron of Whitby Literary and Philosophical Society

CAEDMON OF WHITBY PRESS

Published by the Caedmon of Whitby Press

Printed in Great Britain by
Whitby Printing Company Ltd
Set in 10/11 Monophoto Baskerville and printed
on 115 g.s.m. Huntsman Super White Cartridge paper

FOREWORD

The particular interest of this new biography of William Scoresby lies in the fact that the Authors have made full use of the unpublished Scoresby papers which were left to the Whitby Literary and Philosophical Society in 1857.

As the authors of this very interesting book show us, Scoresby was guided throughout his life by a deep religious faith and by a patient search for scientific truth.

William Scoresby's interests were very wide, and this book in consequence should appeal to many, not only in this country but in France and the United States of America. His extensive notes and observations made during his travels throw added light on the social conditions of that period.

MULGRAVE CASTLE
WHITBY   NOVEMBER 1975

CONTENTS

ACKNOWLEDGEMENTS

Unless otherwise stated, all the quotations in this book have been taken either from books written by Scoresby or from documents contained in the Scoresby Archives in the care of the Whitby Literary and Philosophical Society, to whom we owe our thanks, both for permission to reproduce the quotations and for giving us access to the Archives. Acknowledgement to other sources has been given in the text, but we would especially like to thank Sir Alister Hardy and Paul Gallico for permission to quote from their works; the Scott Polar Research Institute opened their snow-crystalled doors to us and gave great assistance; Lady Acland and the Exeter Archivist threw light on Scoresby's Exeter days; Cecil H. Hooper, RN, illumined our nautical ignorance; and Mr J. G. Graham, Honorary Keeper of the Whitby Museum and Curator of the Cook and Scoresby section, has given us helpful encouragement and advice all the way. He read the error-studded first typescript and made many suggestions, all of which we have adopted; his great enthusiasm has made us feel the task has been worth while. We are also grateful to Mr G. E. Gunner for his careful work on the typescript and his many valuable suggestions.

INTRODUCTION

The pages that follow detail the life and work of a whaling captain; an Arctic explorer and surveyor; a pioneer Arctic scientist; a physicist; an educationalist and social worker; a vigorous and active clergyman, and a man whose scientific life extended from the exploring and discovering world of Sir Joseph Banks to the world of energy and electric power that was dawning in the work of Michael Faraday and J. P. Joule.

To do credit to such a man would require specialists in all these fields, and experience of travel, of life and of science to which we can lay little claim. Our chief merit and fitness for the task lies in a life-long study of the history of science and a deep and sustained interest in the lives and works of men of science. We count ourselves fortunate too, that we belong to Whitby and have shared in its seafaring traditions and influences. Added to this, the fact that we live close to the Museum has helped our study immensely, for in order to obtain authentic material and insights into the life of Scoresby, one of us—in the intervals of earning a living—set about the task of arranging, reading, listing and putting into order the papers which Scoresby left to the Museum well over a hundred years ago and which have never before been systematically sorted. This has all been made possible by the kindness of the Whitby Literary and Philosophical Society, more especially by the encouragement and enthusiasm shown by the Honorary Keeper, Mr J. G. Graham and the guidance of Mr Michael Ashcroft, the County Archivist.

We felt that placed as we were and with the opportunities offered we ought to make a determined effort to write a biography of William Scoresby from the standpoint of the last quarter of the twentieth century. Scoresby-Jackson's *Life of Dr Scoresby*, admirable as it is, in many ways is too close to the life and times of its subject to give a satisfactory image. Whether we have succeeded in presenting a clearer image set against a more detailed background must be left to the reader's judgement.

William Scoresby was well known to his contemporaries and held a high place in the esteem of fellow scientists and Arctic travellers. How does such a man come to be undervalued and fall into comparative neglect? Though Scoresby had an investigating mind, no single great discovery stands to his credit. It is in this fact that we have the main clue to the relative obscurity of his present position.

Scoresby was in many respects similar to Alexander von Humboldt and his reputation, like Humboldt's, has suffered from the great concentration on the technical exploitation of the physical sciences. Now that signs of an awakening interest in the global, environmental and natural sciences is apparent, scientists of this type are seen to possess qualities of increasing interest and importance. As well as John Tyndall and Humboldt, Scoresby is seen to represent a quality presenting science as for the friends and not the exploiters of nature; an awareness of science as for all peoples and for the enhancement and benefit of human life everywhere.

Although Scoresby in his younger days engaged in whale fishing with notable success, he came to an increasing awareness of the need for conservation and preservation of natural and human resources, he saw no conflict between religion and science and felt that in the religious impulse lay a necessary and sufficient guide to the right use and application of scientific ideas and technical inventions. This is why in his later years he joined the Church and spent much of his time and effort in educational and social work, guided and motivated always by a deep religious spirit.

Although Scoresby confined these efforts within the conventional religious framework of his time, it is yet possible that such an approach may provide the structure within which mankind may be able to develop a scientific and yet truly religious culture which will support and enhance the quality and dignity of human life.

TOM AND CORDELIA STAMP

Whitby 1975

CHAPTER 1

AN EARLY VOYAGE TO THE ARCTIC

'All that I learnt in nautical affairs was something of steering and the names and uses of all the ropes.'

'Will Scoresby was called my great, great grandfather; great grandf.; grandfather; my Father & self.' The round, childish handwriting in faded brown ink on the scrap of paper states as succinct an ancestry as one could wish for. That of the mother's side is slightly longer: 'Smith my great, gt, gt, gt grandfather was a priest in Cropton about year 1630. John Smith my gt, gt, gt grandfather was a rich farmer, John Smith my great, great grandf. was also a farmer. John Smith my great grandfather a farmer. John Smith my grandfather, farmer, mother's side, his son, John Smith was a Tradesman—my uncle.'

William Scoresby, the writer of the above and the subject of this book, was born on 5th October 1789, the third child of William and Mary Scoresby. The time into which he was born and in which he grew up was a time of change, of exploration and the growth of the British Empire; of the coming of industrialism and of industrial towns; a time when Napoleon's great shadow loomed over Europe. The majority of the population, however, still lived and died in the place where they were born and followed the calling of their fathers and grandfathers (to say nothing of 'gt, gt grandfathers'). But William's childhood was not bounded by the limited horizons of village and small town life, for his father had voyaged far and wide even before William was born and his influence and outlook shaped the family life beyond the narrow confines of the average family of their times.

So the little boy writing at the table in the Whitby of the 1790's had already glimpsed the wide world, and his experiences, and outlook and knowledge was to be wider and more varied than any of his forbears could ever have imagined.

The first two children were girls and were named Mary and Sarah. When William was born his Father had been at sea some nine years, four of them in the whale fishery. He had made his first voyage to the Greenland seas in the *Henrietta* in 1785, and so outstanding were his abilities that in 1791 he was given command of that same ship.

The capital letter usually reserved only for the Deity was always used by William Scoresby in referring to his Father. (In order to avoid

confusion between the two William Scoresbys, the same practice has
been adopted in this book.) There may, or there may not be any significance. Certainly he revered his Father and gave to him a filial
devotion which, even for that time, was remarkable in its subser-
vience. He was nearly thirty before he questioned his Father's authority.

Father's promotion enabled the Scoresby family to move from
Cropton, the Yorkshire village near Pickering where William was
born, to the neighbouring seaport of Whitby from whence the ship,
Henrietta, sailed every spring to the Arctic. They lived in a large house
in Church Street which, though altered in structure, still stands today
and is known as Scoresby's House. Though away from his home for
the better part of six months each year, Father held firmly to the reins
and sent his wife advice and instruction on all subjects, ranging from
the children's upbringing to dealing with the new Income Tax.

'I shall be obliged to you if you will write emediately on receipt
of this to mee at Mr Andrew Gordons Larwick Shetland mentioning
all news and what they charge you for the Income Tax—if they charge
you at no more than about 120£ a year income the Tax on which
will be about 12£ you had best pay them but if it is more you may as
well not pay them nor confess with any money—they may say that
they will sell your goods for it but don't mind them.Yet you must be
cautious when they come to Gather the money that they don't deceive
you in the sum to be paid Yearly for they are to gather it 2 or 3 times.
If they should caul upon you or leave with you A Scedwell, that is a
printed paper in which the yearly income is to be mentioned and ask
you what income you have you may say about 120£, which if they
will put you down at, they may, if not as I said before, tell them that
you know nothing about it and they must Rest until I come home.'

He writes with an engaging frankness, and though at times his spelling is quite haphazard and punctuation almost non-existent, even
so, for a person who left school at the age of nine, the letters are clear,
straightforward, and singularly endearing.

> Braseysound Shetland abord the
> Henrietta
>
> March 27 1797

Loving wife and children,

I hope this will mete you all in good health as it leaves me and
all our crew (thank God) except Tom Hawkins, he is in a sort of
rumatical feavour and very ill but I hope he will soon be better
it appears to have proceeded from cold.

We arrived here on Thursday afternoon 23 March after a very
pleasant pasiage of summer weather. In comp. with the *Volunteer*

and *Lively*. Have parted with the *Lynx* and E. *Fauconberg* off Peter-head in Scotland on Wednesday 22nd. They steered for the Orkneys and we for Shetland—and never saw any ships to molest us. We have heard of a french frigate and privateer being off Whitby but I hope there will be a good account of them.

I hope you will put William to a good school should recommend Mr Mate and he would get company with Mr Allan boys, I darsay two of them goes. As for Arabella any school will do where they are taught to read and learn good manners—and Sarah you may have the choice of a school where you like or your mother thinks proper, but take care and do not spend your time in vain but get all the education you can and learn to be a little polite in company that you may do well for yourself.

William I hope you will be a good boy and learn your book and give over playing under the staithe amongst nauty boys that you may keep yourself clean comfortable and neat, and then you will get respected by everybody that sees you. Arabella, you must also keep yourself clean, learn your book and knitting and never meddle with the pear tree or let anyone else. Sarah must write to both her grandfather and grandmother and let them know that I am well and all our crew except Tom Hawkins and in particular to Mary at Cropton with my love and tell her to learn to write, and then you and her can improve yourselves by accomodateing one another with letters, not by post but by every friend you know of that is going that way.

I have got four more men here and is now all ready for sea, but the wind is not fair, it is Northerly, but as soon as it changes if all's well shall sail emidiatly. There is 9 ships here in all 4 from London 1 from Hull 1 from Peterhead and us three from Whitby, but no Man of War but they are entering men and gives 21£ bounty and one of the *Lively* boys and one of the *Volunteer* boys & a boy of a London ship has taken it and entered.

I conclude with my love to you all and may God bless both me and you in all our doings. My love to you dear wife and believe me to be,

Your affectionate
Husband William Scoresby.

The following year, 1798, Father left the *Henrietta* and sailed from London, in command of the *Dundee*. Mrs Scoresby went to London with him to see him settled in his new ship, but she would not be persuaded to return part of the way with him. It was his first journey in his new ship and she was not going to bring ill luck on it by being the only woman on board, however short the journey.

23 Mar^h 1798   *Dundee*, Lerwick

Loving wife and children,

I hope by this time you are got to Whitby and comfortable settled in your own house and our children along with you. I wish you had stayed by the ship as we came into the Humber, for it would have saved you a great deal of forteague in the length of your journey and believe me I was not certified in my own mind when you left me at Gravesend, and to see you go away in trouble hurt me much and Mr Bailie also for to think that you should go away by yourself amongst strangers, but I hope that your journey was more comfortable than I imagined.

You would wonder that you had no letter from me out of the Humber, the reason was that I got to Hull unexpectedly for I was just going to write when Cap^n Bailie and Cap^n Staverr called on me and took me in one of their boats up to Hull, where we arrived just as the post was going out and the wind coming fair we made no stay but hastened on bord, and I sent Mr Englishes that married Miss Cook of Hunt House and desired him to write you by the next post to inform you that I intended to caul in Whitby Roads and take some men if I could get them. We sailed the next morning March 13th under convoy of the *Prosperine* Frigate that had convoyed us from Yarmouth Roads and in company with 21 sail of Greenland and Streights ships. I asked leave of the Comodore for to caul in Whitby Roads which he granted & I left the fleet off flambro head & steared along shore & was off Scarbro at 6 o'clock the same night and should have come for Whitby, but the wind and sea increased fast and night coming on so that it rendered it impossible for us to get a boat off, so we shaped our course for to join the convoy, which we did at 6 o'clock the next morning & came along with them all the way to Shetland.... I have the pleasure of telling you that we sail fast & is pretty tight. I hope you have brought Mary with you and trust that Sarah and her is making good progress at the school also hope Wm is getting on rapidly in writing and Arabella in knitting. If you please you may write me when you think we are about coming home to the care of Mr Morrison, Lerwick, Shetland but you must put in no seacrets for fear I should not get it.... I trust this will meet you and children all in good health as I am thank God.

I remain your^s affectionately, Wm Scoresby.

William left the dame school where he had learnt the rudiments of education and he suffered much at his next school. The master was a mean-spirited sadist who believed education began with subjugation and strict punishment. His severity branded itself into

William's mind so irrevocably that he remembered every detail of the cruelties twenty years after. Among other perversions, the master delighted in tying the offenders' hands above their heads, by their thumbs, to a bar which he then lifted, by means of a pulley, until only their toes touched the ground. At times he left them suspended for an hour or more.

It was little wonder that Scoresby should write later: 'The years of childhood, so dear and so pleasing in their remembrance to some, had to me but few attractions, and excepting an occasional residence with my grandfather Smith, whose amiable temper and patriarchal manners won the affection and esteem of all who knew him, I scarcely remember any period of either infancy or youth, with any sort of pleasure. Being of a timid and anxious turn of mind and delicate health, I seldom derived that benefit or pleasure in relaxation from my every day routine of scholastic labours which was the privilege of others. If I had a task for the ensuing day, and I was seldom without one, I could never enjoy the recreation of others until it was learnt. This arose from the severity of my early teachers and the timidity of my disposition.'

His parents being strict Sabbatarians, William grew up with a fear of offending on that day in the slightest action; a fear so great that he hardly dared even to stoop and pick anything up which he might find on a Sunday. He once found a beautiful, six-bladed penknife, quite new, but because he had found it on the Sabbath he could not bring himself to keep it and threw it into the river.

As early as 1798, Father was pressing Mrs Scoresby to move to London:

'It is a pleasure to me to know that you have a mind to come to London if I'll meet you, which I certainly will at any place you appoint, and it would be more satisfaction to me if you would concent to come and live in London for it is my intention to endeavour to do all I possibly can for you and the children now in the middle of the day that we may with the assistance of Divine providence rest ourselves in the evening of our days in peace. As the postman's bell is now ringing I have not time to say much more, but I must with patience wate your answer to know if you will come & live here, if so I shal, and am now looking out for a Pleasant situation, which if I here of I mean to engage until I hear from you, but I cannot come for you until the ship gets out of dock and into her moorings. Mr Holme has several ships, 2 of which I have agreed to take a part of . . . they are both brigs and the former is going to load for Bremmin the latter for Hamburg with Goods. This makes me wish you to come to London as my business is likely to be here and I don't see but we may live as cheap in every article except coals and house rent and that won't cost us more extra than your two passiages to and from London did.'

But Mrs Scoresby also was not without firmness of character and she resisted his appeals and stayed in Whitby. Father usually called in on his way north, but in 1799 he was late leaving London as the ships were obliged to travel in convoy for fear of French war ships.

'I am afraid that we shall not have time its so late, for to stop in Whitby Roads for men except they are all ready to come of, our signal in the day will be a Union Jack at the main top gallant mast head and one gun, if in the night 2 lights one above the other & 4 guns. If we are not past before you receive this Sarah may write the signal neatly on a slip of paper and give it to any of the men that will go. They must be sailors. . . . My Dear Children, Be careful to keep good company, serve God with attention and Due Reverence and Read the Scripture Dailie. Attend Church & all public places of worship and walk humbly before God and be at peace with men. I conclude so pray God bless us all. Our men have behaved very well here and kept themselves sober.'

The following year, 1800, he did call in at Whitby with, as we shall see, distressing results for poor Mrs Scoresby. 'He found it convenient,' William Scoresby writes, 'the wind being off land, to call in Whitby Roads, and there to take leave of my mother and the children.

'He invited me, to my great gratification, to go off with him and see the ship. I was delighted with everything I saw. The novelty of the floating mansion; its curious equipment—its labyrinths of passages and berths—and even its unusual provisions, all excited my imagination and interested my feelings. I felt a strange longing to participate in its progress and adventures; and absurd as the idea seemed to me, as to any hope of its being realised, I had pleasure in indulging it whilst the boat remained.

'At length, as evening drew on, the pilots prepared to leave. I heard the stir of the proceedings with trepidation and regret. I strove to delay it. Under the vague and hopeless hope of being forgotten and left behind, I kept carefully out of the way. When silence was no longer likely to be available, I contrived the childlike device of hiding my hat, which, on ascending the companion ladder bareheaded, I let it be understood I could not find!

'My backwardness in obliging the now loudly urged calls from the boat, which was beating with no inconsiderable knocks against the ship's side,—suggested to my Father a sympathy with my feelings and desires, so that, as if speaking to the pilots, he evidently addressed himself to me, saying: "Oh never mind—he will go along with us." The words were delightful to my ears, and being repeated in a manner calculated to get me to give utterance to my wishes, I ventured to look up; but it was with anxious trepidation—for a keen pang went to my very heart when I thought of the feelings of my tenderly loving and beloved mother. Encouraged to speak, however, I anxiously replied to the now distinct enquiry as to my wishes, "But what will my mother say?" My Father's answer settled my very willingly satisfied misgivings,—"She will be the more glad to see you," he smilingly said, "when you come back."

'The pilots were at length made sensible of what they at first could not credit, that I was to remain behind; and they set out for the shore in no small condition of amazement, and with no slight feeling of sympathising embarrassment, on account of the report which they must yield to one, whom they sufficiently knew as an anxious, susceptible and affectionate mother!

'She, indeed, suffered greatly in my absence. On the arrival of the pilot boat with the intelligence of my elopement, she would not credit the information; and when with returning day she was satisfied that the ship had departed, she was overwhelmed with grief. She gave me up for ever. She felt afraid that I could never survive the inclemencies of an Arctic climate; or that if I did, the effect on my delicate constitution must undermine my health and confirm the consumptive habit which already threatened me.'

It is left to the reader to judge of the severity and harshness of Father's character in taking a small child, not strong in health and of delicate stature, away from his mother and on such a hazardous journey. The times, indeed, were hard, and infant mortality a commonplace thing. Though people were used to losing young children it did not mean they felt any less attached to the surviving ones. The reverse was the case, and a child who had managed to survive past infancy was therefore all the more precious. This impulsive act gives us a fair indication of Father's insensitivity. A ten-year-old child could not be expected to realise just how heartless it was.

William Scoresby resumes the story: 'My Father's first consideration after my elopement from my mother was to furnish me with clothing suited for the severity of the climate to which we were bound. The slops provided for the seamen were, of course, too large for me, yet I wanted every article of dress. Fortunately there were several persons in the ship who had not been regularly trained as seamen, but had been apprenticed in various land crafts. Being supplied with material, they set about manufacturing the different articles of dress. In a few days I was in a complete sailor's suit and in the course of the passage I had made for me, in very good style, shoes, boots and slippers, shirts, jackets and indeed, every species of clothing, hat excepted, that I could require.... Not being subject to sea-sickness,— the bane of most young adventurers—I experienced little of what I conceived to be hardship, and was in general not only contented with my situation, but lively, active and happy.

'A voyage to Greenland at the age of ten years could not be expected to conduce much to my improvement either in health or information. All that I learnt in nautical affairs was something of steering and the names and uses of all the ropes. I learnt the ropes in the following manner: I first enquired their uses and finding braces were for turning the yards, reef tackles were for drawing up the edges of the sails etc, I proceeded aloft, and observing the attachments of each rope to the sail or yard, I instantly knew its use and its name, then pulling on the lower part and tracing it to the deck, I noticed to what pin or cleat it was belayed. In this way, visiting many times each mast and yard and frequently conning over the names of the ropes about the deck, I soon became master of the subject. The art of steering puzzled me exceedingly for some time, the use of the tiller and the effect of its movements on the position of the ship were very evident, but it was long ere I discovered the meaning of the phrases: "starboard" "port" "luff" "near" etc. Although by a careful observation of the motions of the helmsman and watching the ship's head and her tracks through the ice, I was eventually not only able to tell the meaning of such expressions, but also to anticipate my Father, sometimes, in his orders to the helmsman when winding through the ice.'

Father had a last-minute qualm of conscience about his son, and when they reached Shetland arranged for him to be left at school at Lerwick, in the care of his friend Mr Andrew Gordon. But young William was just as much a Scoresby as his Father. He hired a boatman to take him out to the *Dundee* just as she was leaving the islands. Father paid the exorbitant fee demanded, quietly rather pleased at his son's enterprise, and William went the voyage.

It was a voyage not without dangers, for it was a time of war, and the risk of meeting French privateers and men-of-war was considerable. The very first day they were at sea an enemy ship was sighted bearing down upon them. Father instantly prepared his subterfuge. When choosing his crew he had been careful to select at least one man adept at beating the drum and one who could sound the boatswain's pipe. The *Dundee* was as well armed as she was well manned, carrying twelve guns and a crew of some sixty men.

'The strategy in this case was to give the surprise of a concealed armament and the impression as of a designed deception in the class of ship assumed. The construction of the ship was well adapted for the purpose, being "deep-waisted" with a high quarter deck and having her guns entirely below, with no outward indication, at a distance, of either ports or armament.

'The men required for the guns were sent to their quarters with orders to make all ready for action, but to lift no port. The hands above were kept as much as possible on the leeside of the deck, where they were in sufficient concealment. The *drummer* and the boatswain, now most important elements in the plan, had their special instructions. The enemy came within hailing distance. Everything visible on board the *Dundee* indicated an unconcerned quietness, and utter unconsciousness of danger from the stranger's approach. The men on deck were laid down flat on their faces. My Father coolly walking the quarter deck, and the helmsman engaged in his office of steering were the only living beings who could be discerned from the deck of the assailant.

'Without showing any colours in answer to our English ensign waving at the mizzen peak, the stranger came down to within short musket-shot distance, when a loud and unintelligible roar of the Captain, through his speaking trumpet, demanded the denomination of our ship. A significant wave of my Father's hand served instead of a reply. The drum beats to quarters, the shrill sound of the boatswain's pipe is heard, and whilst the hoarse voice of this officer gives orders, the apparently plain sides of the ship become suddenly pierced; six ports on a side are simultaneously raised and as many untompioned cannon are run out, pointing ominously toward the enemy's broadside!

'The stratagem was complete; its impression quite perfect. The adversary seemed electrified. Men on the enemy's deck were seen to fall flat; the guns remained silent; the helm flew to port, and the yards to the wind, on our opposite tack, and without waiting for an answer to his summons, he suddenly hauled off, under full sail, in the opposite direction.'

The voyage was a poor one, for the ship became beset, due, we are told, to the chief officer's fault, and they were imprisoned by ice for eight weeks, by which time the fishing season was almost over and they returned to England with only three whales.

'The *Dundee* being bound for London,' writes William, 'My Father again called in Whitby Roads and landed me in the middle of the night. My joy in meeting my dear mother and sisters in health was extreme, and that joy was perfectly mutual. My mother, who had suffered exceedingly in my absence, was quite overwhelmed with pleasure in again receiving me safe. Never before had I found my home so pleasing or experienced maternal affection so delightful.'

In 1802, Mrs Scoresby finally agreed to live in London and accordingly the family went there in the autumn when Father returned from the Arctic. For six months William went to Mr Stock's school at Blackwall Dock, where, he says, it was the 'first instance in which my faculties were brought into exercise. Mr Stock was a rigid disciplinarian, but a teacher of the first order. The advantage I gained was incalculable. On the first weekly examination I was almost at the bottom of the list, my number being below seventy; at the conclusion of a quarter of a year I stood number two. I gained many prizes. The exertion, however, on a delicate frame was severe. I had to rise at five in the morning and pursue the routine of the seminary until the same hour in the evening, with the usual intervals for refreshment, after which, I never failed to have some exercise for my employment at home; and sometimes, which was optional, attended the familiar lectures of Mr Stock, on interesting branches of science, in the evening.

'In these severe and unremitting labours I was supported and encouraged by the incessant attention and persuasion of an Affectionate Mother. If my task was trying I was encouraged by some little reward. If the morning was cold or wet I was seen carefully wrapped up by this unwearied friend. If toils of education produced despondency and the morning gloom an unwillingness to renew them—I also discovered under my pillow, at rising, a sugar plum, or fruit, or some token of her affection to cheer my mind and excite to obedience.'

But Blackwall Dock and London were not for Mrs Scoresby. She was a Northerner through and through and she did not rest until she had persuaded Father to give up the *Dundee* and return to the North.

CHAPTER 2

EDINBURGH UNIVERSITY

'You are on a fertile spot, even the
seat of knowledge.'

Father's new ship, in which he had a part share, bore the same name
as Captain Cook's famous vessel, the *Resolution*. He took William with
him on his first voyage in it; this time with his mother's consent, for
in 1803, at the age of thirteen, he was regularly apprenticed to his
Father to:

> Learn his art and with him (after the manner of an apprentice)
> to serve unto the full end of seven years. During which term the
> said apprentice the said master faithfully shall serve, his secrets
> keep, his lawful Commands everywhere gladly do. He shall do no
> damage to his said Master, nor see to be done of others ... He shall
> not waste the goods of his said Master nor lend them unlawfully
> to any. He shall not commit Fornication nor contract matrimony
> within the said term. He shall not play at Cards, Dice, Tables or
> any other unlawful Games whereby his said Master may have any
> loss. He shall not haunt taverns or play houses nor absent himself
> from his said Master's service Day nor Night unlawfully. But in
> all things as a faithful apprentice he shall behave himself towards
> his said Master, and all his, during the said term. And the said
> William Scoresby his said apprentice in the same art as a Mariner
> which he useth, by the best means that he can, shall teach and in-
> struct ...

For the next twenty years, William Scoresby never spent one
summer in England. The end of winter invariably saw him preparing
for another whaling voyage and before spring had properly arrived
he was heading for the icy seas of the Arctic regions.

In the winter time he went to Mr Routh's school in Whitby where
he 'attended to geometry (plain and spherical), algebra, navigation
and other branches of mathematics; but having in every branch, run
the teachers beyond their usual practice, I found their explanations
of any difficulty that occurred neither satisfactory nor intelligible.
Hence, what I learned perfectly was merely the rudiments of the
science. In the classics I had a better chance, had I had the taste,
but this study was to me complete drudgery and I made no progress

excepting in the first two or three books usually employed in teaching Latin. Drawing and music I was better pleased with, and made some progress in both, as well as in several mechanical arts; but imagining I had no genius for painting I did not persevere in it.

'My Father always evinced the greatest desire for my obtaining information in every kind of useful knowledge. If I asked what use it could be to learn such an art, he would answer: "No one can tell whether it may not hereafter be useful—besides, *learning is never a burthen.*" This principle he carried so far that he would have me taught to beat the drum, believing that this noisy instrument might alarm an enemy in case of attack at sea.' But William disliked noise and equated it with stupidity, and after enduring blistered fingers soon abandoned the lessons. He preferred his violin.

1806 was an eventful year for Scoresby. In the first place his Father made him Chief Mate. This was no act of favouritism—for Father was a stern master—but a reward of merit, for William had shown in the three previous voyages that he had the skill and aptitude which go to make the efficient whaler. In some respects he was 'conscious of being deficient in experience, and especially in bodily strength, for executing this arduous duty. But as it called forth all my attention to the duties of my station—induced me to study the navigation of the polar seas, with the aid of my Father, who was a perfect master, and gave exercise to my judgement, observation, prudence, decision and other faculties of the mind, the voyage proved highly beneficial to me.'

The second notable event of that year was reaching the most northerly latitude which had ever been recorded. As a general rule the whaling ships kept together in one fleet, seldom going far beyond signalling distance. This year, however, when all the rest of the fleet abandoned, as impenetrable, the immense barrier of ice which faced them, Father 'continued with unabated attention until the barrier gave way to his exertions and the *Resolution* was safely conducted into a far northern water. We advanced to the latitude of 81° 30′ north, the nearest approach to the Pole that I conceive has ever been made.'

This was quite true at the time, for Scoresby's account was written in 1820, before Parry went another seventy or eighty miles in 1827. And in so far as it referred to *sailing*, it remained true for much longer, for Parry traversed the ice by sledge.

Their situation was 'singular and solitary indeed. No ship, no human being, it was believed, was within three hundred miles of us. Unquestionably the crew of the ship now occupied the most northern position of any individuals in the world.'

Back from the rarefied solitude of the Arctic, William, who was 'not insensible to the charms of female society' first met his future wife. 'There is no class of men', he writes, 'that enjoy and appreciate

so much the society of the softer sex, as sailors. Deprived of all intercourse with females for perhaps half their lives they esteem the
enjoyment a privilege and value it as a benefit. This is the sailor's
consolation under all his privations—he anticipates the hour that shall
restore him to the society of that sex whose prerogative it is to lessen
and soothe the cares and anxieties of life, and to bestow happiness in
the midst of natural evils, which gives refinements to our manners
and exercise to our best affections.

'It was in the autumn of this year that I accidentally met with Miss
Lockwood, both of us at the same moment going up to the door of
the same mutual friend. The amiable frankness of her manner, pleasing address and refinement of conversation proved to me irresistible
attractions. After the visit I begged permission to accompany her
home', but his youthful bashfulness prevented him from going into
the house with her. There was another chance meeting, when William
was introduced to Mary's brother, George Lockwood, and then for
over a year they did not meet.

William, having outstripped the capabilities of the Whitby
teachers, decided to go to Edinburgh University. Two people influenced him in this decision; the first was John Mewburn, a school
friend who was going there to study medicine, and the second was
John Laing, who had already qualified as a doctor in that university
and who had sailed with the *Resolution* that summer.

Father wrote from London, where he had gone to sell the cargo:

As to Wm he may either come up with you or go to Edinburgh,
I should suppose the latter place as good a school and I've no doubt
but by this time he is well aware that learning is well worth his
attention.

In this I wish to indulge him & have bought him a handsome
trunk covered with black leather, brass nails and iron plate corners,
to hold a suit of clothes, books &c. (It is 31 inches long, 12 deep
and 18 broad, a good size) also the whole of Shakespeers works
in 10 vols neatly bound, wrote by Bensley with his notes and critical
comments thereon. The books Arabella must share with him in
reading. I trust she will be attentive to both letters Figers & Musick
& I shall indulge her in some new pieces for her amusement. I have
also bo^t her a muff and tippet and one for her mother and one
for her sister and I shall not forget little Thomas.

I have sold no oil nor do I see any liklihood of its being sold,
however by this it will not do to be disheartened as this trade is
very fluctivating. Pray write by return,

Yours affectionately,
Wm Scoresby.

William wrote by return, but the letter was delayed by the October gales, which prevented ships sailing from Whitby to London until they had abated, and so Father's reply and sanction to William's plan did not reach Whitby until he had actually left for Edinburgh. But he was fairly certain of his Father's approval.

London 30 October 1806

Dear Son,

I have your favour and observe what you say. I have no objections against your going to collage and flatter myself that you would profit equal to the expense and to the satisfaction of self and your mother, whom I perticularly wish you to be advised by not only as a mother but for the sound advice her piety as well as steady carriage thro life gives a lesson to all who knows her, & I have no doubt but that from your conduct hitherto you will not only endeavour to get learning but to profit thereby in practiscing the good and shunning the eveil: How far it would be wright to go with Mewburn or to hear the same lectors he intends ought to be well considered. Observe his charactor as a gay young man makes his company less desirable & the profession he means to follow is far from your inclination, and as to Mewsick you will not have any time to attend to it at a collage, therefore should recommend you to learn Astronomy in perticular, but not to neglect languages (for you may see by attending to the news papers that the king of Prussia is drided by the French for not knowing their language). Also kmestry is a pleasant science & many lectors of other kinds may be desirable, but above all get religion & read a lesson every day.

I send you a sistom of shorthand, said to be the best composition in the univers & have no doubt but a few hours will make you master of it. The 10 vollumes of Shakespeer I have not bo^t for you to gane a thirst for the theatre, but from the language that runs through the whole in so forseable a manner, (tho poor in itself compared with divine writings) but will be advantageous in learning to read also to get into the way and habit of good English. ...

This was wrote to come by sea, but the wind being out of the way and I being in hopes of getting off in the course of a few days have sent it by Post & taken Taylors shorthand out.

In Edinburgh the seventeen-year-old William was an entire stranger and as 'strangers not introduced are received with extreme caution by the inhabitants' he formed very few acquaintances. His extreme diffidence, amounting, indeed, to bashfulness, made him avoid rather than court society. This arose, he says, 'partly from the want of mixing more with mankind, but more particularly from a most humiliating sensibility to my own deficiencies'.

His first letter home puts on a brave front until the penultimate line, where his loneliness breaks through.

Edinburgh Nov 19th 1806

Dear Mother and Sisters &c,

I received yours yesterday and am glad to hear that you are rather better also of Sister Sarah's recovery. I am very comfortable at my lodgings with John Mewburn. It will be far cheaper than I expected for lodgings, it costs us 4/6 a week each & with the board will be about 15/– a week.

I have got settled at the colledge I attend Chemistry & Natural Philosophy. The former I am very well pleased with, the preparations are extremely grand, also Natural Philosophy but have not got into the heart of it yet. I am just going to see about a French Master. I have bought Arabella some music which will please her better than songs, they are Scotch dances, Reels, Strathspeys & Marches adapted for the piano forte. Here is a new piece of music which I can get if Sister Mary should wish it. It is the Battle of Trafalgar, something of the style of the Battle of Prague, it is much in the fashion here. I find a great want of my Fiddle.

This is a very fine place. The houses in the Old Town are very high, some of them I have seen 11 or 12 stories, but they say there are higher. The new town is built on a very beautiful plan, chiefly of stone and all in the form of squares—there are two bridges going over the top of streets therefore the people are continually walking over one another's heads.

I have not seen Mr Wood yet. Edinburgh and Leith join, there being a row of houses going from one to the other called Leith Walk.

Any music that Sister Mary should want may be got here—but she must have patience till I return. When you send my trunk you must let me know in what vessel &c but you need not say until the day or day before she sails, also pack it up in something thick and strong. I would be obliged to you if you would send me the news paper after you have read it by putting on the name of Mrs Curtis. I am sorry that my Father has not got home yet but hope he will soon.

My love to Brother and Sister Clark, Arabella Thomas and yourself. Remember me to George Lockwood, Edw Steward &c &c. My love, not dry respects, also to C & B Bolton, Sarah Preston & tell her that I should have liked to have seen her before I came away but it happened otherwise, also to Miss Lockwoods, so I remain,

Your dutiful and Affectionate Son, Wm Scoresby.

Be particular about the directions when you write & spell it right
or it will be a chance if I get it.

NB   The girls here have most of them blue eyes.

Excuse this bad writing but if you cannot read it please to send
it back again and I will write it Better—I wrote to George Lockwood last week.

I was very uneasy about your not writing & if you had not wrote
now I don't know what I should have done.

Send me a pillow case to put my dirty clothes in &c.

Though William had already spent five summers away from home
he had in all ways been close to his Father. Realising this, Father
was very faithful in writing frequent letters to him, giving advice on
all subjects:

'I shall have a deal of pleasure in sending you any books you may
point out in your next, also your violin if it will be of infinite service
to you, but I should suppose you have little time to attend to it.'

'Should you, like nine/tenths of young men that go from home to
gain instruction be tempted in an ungodly moment to gratify your
appotite, all the resolution you can summon to your assistance will
be too little to withstand the like temptation, therefore if time would
permitt, I should like you to hear surgical and phisical lectors which
points out the rocks whereon the best of constitutions are wrecked.'

'I did not recommend you to take care of your money for to make
you nigardly, greedy, no, nor that you should not have every book
that was useful to you, but merely to remind you of the value of gold
saved, by carefully avoiding unnecessary expenses; for you would
have been a friend to that man I mentioned that had occasion to sell
his bed from under him to buy food after seeing better days and was
to be pitied altho he had been a prodigal: this I flatter myself you
will always gard against.'

'On learning French at School (Far est ab doceri—E'en from a
foe instruction may be sought. Ovid) The French language abounds
with authors elegant, lively, learned and classical. A scoolar cannot
be displeased at it. To be ignorant of it is to cut off a copious source
of amusement and information. I need not expatuale on its utility
to the man of business and the ornament it adds to the accomplished
Gentleman.'

The journey home being impracticable at that time of year,
William remained in Edinburgh for Christmas.

Revd Mr Mitchells, Edinburgh.
Dec 24

Honoured Father and Mother,
I am glad to inform you that I received safe your trunk and am

very much obliged to you for your Ham &c, which has just come in time for Christmass. I found all things safe in it except a pair of trowsers which you mention which I think is not in. I observe what you said in your last letter respecting French teaching, which is very near the method Mr Pavini uses, for as soon as we get through the verbs we begin to translate Telemacus and Gil Blas, and I think he does all in his power to get us forward, not to keep us back. We attend an hour every lawful day except Saturdays. He has a great number of scholars and is recommended as a very good teacher. I shall at any opportunity read the book you sent also the small tracts. I am glad to hear that my Mother strengthens and hope in a short time she will be able to walk out if it were fine weather although rather a dull time of year—yet it is not so here, for the students make it very lively. I think this place has got a worse name than it deserves with regard to the behaviour of the students, as yet I have never seen anything amiss in them.

I find a very great pleasure in Natural Philosophy and chemistry and I hope if all is well when I return you will find some change in me for the better.

Christmas seems here to be very little notice taken of or not near so much as there is in England. The people here attend the churches very regular and there are very few who do not go once or twice on a Sunday.

I am glad to hear of Mark Bolton & James Brown's safe arrival at Whitby, also of they being well. I have George Lockwood and Mark Bolton's letter together with Arabella's, Mrs Clark's and cousin Wm Jackson's and am happy to hear they are well. Sister Clark's cakes are very acceptable and if one may judge from appearances they seem very good ... [page torn] ... not yet had an opportunity of trying. John Mewburn is very well and received his box safe together with the good things in it which ... I think will make the Christmas very merrily. We have had Mr Wood's two sons at our lodgings, they seem to be two very fine young men and very steady, so I conclude with wishing you all a Merry Christmas and happy new year when it comes, from your

affectionate and dutiful son,
Wm Scoresby

My love to Mr and Mrs Clark, Arabella Thomas not forgetting Wm Jackson. My compliments to Mark Bolton, Geo Lockwood, James Brown, the ladies and all enquiring.

The two boys whom Scoresby mentions were the sons of Mr Peter Wood, a merchant with whom Father had many business dealings and who offered hospitality to the lonely young student from Whitby.

He dined at their home at least once a week and had 'a general invitation to be a guest at their table. The innumerable marks of kindness
experienced under his roof were truly parental.'

Father, however, disapproved of his son's visiting them on a Sunday: 'Beg lieve to observe that we think you have made a mistake
when you say, 'I intend if all is well to go to Mr Woods on Sunday
as on that day I have no lectors to attend.' My dear Lad, I know
that it is too much the custom to visit and take pleasure on the Sabbath
day, which ought to be strictly observed as the wise author of all things
has appointed one day in seven to himself that we may rejoice therein
and serve him according as he has commanded us in the holy
scriptures and has desired us to search therein for wisdom.... As I
have begun, suffer me to offer you my hearty thanks for your steady
conduct up to this time, which I flatter myself will accompany you
thro life.'

At Edinburgh University Scoresby came under the influence of two
outstanding men: Thomas Charles Hope (1766–1844), Professor of
Chemistry, who enjoyed an unrivalled reputation as a teacher*and
John Playfair (1748–1819), Professor of Natural Philosophy, pupil
and friend of Dr James Hutton (1726–1797). Playfair wrote the classic
Illustrations of the Huttonian Theory of the Earth, 1802. Hope, who was
the pupil, colleague and eventually successor of Joseph Black (1728–
1799), as well as being a first-rate teacher was also an investigator
of nature. Through these men, Scoresby came into contact with the
ideas and influences of Hutton and Black, two of the major figures
in the development of geology and chemistry respectively and men of
the widest general and scientific culture. Such contacts with original
minds can be extremely stimulating to a young student of the right
calibre and no doubt these exercised a lasting influence on Scoresby.
Here, too, in the Edinburgh of the early eighteen-hundreds he was
at the centre of the developing sciences and in a cultural and scientific
environment second to none in Europe.

The attitude of the world towards students was very little different
to the present day. 'Let the Whitby people say what they will about
the college,' writes Scoresby, 'I find that it is the best thing I ever
did for my own good, and if I have learnt anything that is bad (which
I hope I have not) I trust I shall learn as much good as will ballance
it and I think if any of them was here sent for a month they would
not say much against it.'

Father continued to bombard his son with advice: 'In chemical
preparations such as lead, Opium, Mercury and any other Pernicious
substances I advise you to be careful & not to get into the fumes if
possible, they are so pernicious to health.'

* It is recorded that in 1823 he lectured to a class of 575 students.

'I submit the perusal of the following letter wrote by the Revd Mr Knox to Charles James Fox ... "No happiness can be enjoyed without health and it will avail you little to become a schollar, a philosopher, and an Oretor to the effectual detriment of your constitution ... Continue not the same studies after a langour seizes you ... use a swing for your hands extended from the scilin of your book room" instead of these methods you may adapt the sword exercise, but with such caution as not to play over long at the first until your arm grow strong, else you will lame your arm. Also be careful to keep your temper when at play which will if broken perhaps be of dreadful consequences.'

'We are afraid you don't take care to air your linen before you putt it on and have comfortable bedding and victuals', here we detect Mrs Scoresby telling Father what to write, 'You perhaps may get cold with your experiments of distilary by going out into the cold air very hot or sitting in a cold lector room when warm with walking.'

'It is with heartfelt satisfaction we hear you are so well amused with what you are learning & trust it will be of infinite service to you. I also suppose you wil have an opportunity to know the best method of giving power to the magnet and charging the needle of a compass. In this (and I trust in all you profess to learn) you will feel pleasure which is the highway to obtain a proficiency in all arts.'

Prophetic words indeed, when we see just how far Scoresby went in his original work and discovery of magnetism by percussion. But more of this and Scoresby's compass needle in their appropriate context.

As the time for their whaling voyage drew nearer, Father instructed his son to: 'Look out either for the same or for another doctor to your mind. I myself recommend one that's steady, sober, and a good scholar, that you may profit by him. His wages should be limited to £4 or at further, guineas p. month & 1 to 2 gns travelling expenses. I had thought of John Jackson that's with Ld Mulgrave now at Lythe, he can bleed from his grandfather teaching him, and he would give you a lesson in landscrip prospective and every other kind of painting; perhaps worth your notice and of infinite service for a seaman that is likely to make a figure in the world, if protected by Providence that hardly every forsake those who trust in him. But I do not know that Jackson will go or Lord M will spare him. If you think well of it I'll contrive to know.'

Scoresby wrote to ask Dr John Laing if he would come with them a second time. He had already proved his worth on the previous voyage, having saved the life of a seaman who was thrown into the freezing sea when a whale overturned the boat. They fished him out, but by the time he was brought on board his clothes were frozen like a casing of mail, and his hair was 'consolidated into a helmet of ice'.

He was brought down to the cabin, stripped and laid on a blanket before the fire. 'His hair', John Laing wrote later, was like so many icicles, and the body exhibited every cadaverous appearance. No pulsation was to be found in any part and I held a mirror before his mouth without producing the least evidence of respiration.' Hot flannels and smelling salts had as little effect and then as a last resource the doctor 'ordered one of the men to blow into the patient's mouth, as strongly as he could'. The kiss of life did the trick and the frozen man recovered. 'All the time I was on board, the poor fellow expressed the greatest gratitude to me,' said Laing, 'and thankfulness to God for thus being providentially rescued from the grasp of death.'

John Laing replied to Scoresby's invitation: 'I have been in many studies since the receipt of your letter, I have many great difficulties to remove. In the first place I remove from this place in May—in the second, I have a great many patients who are not properly re-covered, consequently I have not received my charges, and should I go away I should lose my money; In the third place my wife is very importunate with regard to my staying at home, lest we should fall in with some of Bonaparte's pirates.

'The great distance of Whitby from this place I look on as the smallest obstacle, for in duty bound I must gratefully declare that I would rather pay my travelling expenses to Whitby as to get 2 gns extra from the Liverpool vessels who call in these quarters for men, or to go with any other Captain than your father, who is indeed a Gentleman in the strictest sense of the word.

'Upon the whole, I have come to a determination to go (Deo Volente) and will be at Whitby about the time required.'

Delightful as we may find Father's erratic spelling today, he was very conscious of it himself and continually urged his son to apply himself to his studies and use his time well: 'You are on a fertile spot, even the seat of knowledge and have no doubt you employ every moment of your time in seeking wisdom, which is not easy to be obtained where there wants strength of memory which I hinted to you in my scroll of yesterday and faintly pointed out the great dis-advantage I laboured under on that account. You must know that want of recollection is the cause of my bad spelling and the sole cause of the broils and ferment with everyone I deal with, but these people see with other eyes and suppose it is pride and want of principal, in that I am happy to say they are mistaken.'

'Brother and sisters love to you, not forgetting Arabella, who will be a fine girl if she be attentive to learn her books gramatically and be attentive to her music which she ought to be about, She is now at the Battle of Prague which she attends to in part, but she does not know the value of time so well as I hope you now do. As such I pray you to write her and tell her every branch you are learning, by what masters and lectorers, and in perticular how you divide your time, which I trust will encourage her to imitate. Also paint out a description of Edinburgh together with a view of the College, Castle and any other edifices worthy your notice, all in as expressible language as you are able and address the letter to her.'

It was a wrench to leave the university before the session ended, for Scoresby had soon settled down to academic life. He disliked reading and preferred taking extensive notes in the lectures and then copying them out later. 'Thus I found my notes daily extend, until at length the writing of them used to occupy me three or four hours.' The habit formed in those early days stayed with him all his life— if one may judge from the veritable forest of hand-written papers which remain in the Scoresby Archives.

The whale fishery called him away 'just when Professor Playfair was entering on astronomy—a subject which to me had uncommon attractions. The mandate of my Father, however, was peremptory and I reluctantly quitted my liberal pursuit for the hardy and unrefined duties of a Greenland ship.'

In the progress of this voyage, whilst the vessel was delayed in Balta Sound, Shetland, Scoresby employed his time in 'making a survey of the harbour, of which there was no chart, and in drawing up directions for the navigation. This survey I accomplished by means of an azimuth compass, quadrant and Gunter's chain. I afterwards proved it by means of a theodolite, but found it so accurate that I could make no alteration in it. The extent of coast which I traced and trigonometrically examined was fifteen miles.'

'This voyage proved as prosperous as we could have desired. We procured thirteen very large whales, two and a half of which were in excess of the capacity of our casks, and were taken home in bulk.'

CHAPTER 3

COPENHAGEN. A TASTE OF THE NAVY

'I experienced the most painful privations, hunger, cold and severity of discipline.'

While Arabella was busy pounding out the *Battle of Prague*, its subject, Napoleon, was equally busy helping himself to the greater part of Europe.

There were two treaties made at Tilsit, the second of which was a secret one, from which Britain was excluded. They reckoned, however, without her spies, who soon found out that it was intended to turn the whole of Europe's forces against her and subdue her sea power by the annihilation of her navy. Among others, neutral Denmark was to be pressed into this service.

Against this impending threat, Britain took immediate action. It was decided to disregard the legality of the act and forthwith to seize Denmark's neutral fleet and keep it in a safe place—England of course—until Napoleon had been subdued. With traditional muddle-through inefficiency they asked for volunteers to bring home the Danish fleet. It need hardly be said that the number greatly exceeded the need: nevertheless, the bureaucrats decided to send everyone to Denmark, in any case, and then see what happened.

At first, Whitby men were reluctant to come forward, sure that the scheme was a cunning trap to impress them into the Navy. But when they saw young Scoresby volunteer his services, they followed his example to a man. Father did not see fit to volunteer, preferring to offer his experience only in pen and ink from the security of his own home.

Whitby, 6 Oct 1807

Dear William,

It appears that the Americans will not go to war with this country altho we persist in searching their ships of all descriptions and the Portagee government seems determined to quit Portagel and with their navy flee to the Brascels rather than bend to the French yoke, and I must confess that I feel highly gratified that our present ministers has acted with such courage as to break the neck of the framed confederacy between Denmark and France, which to all

appearances was to have been joined by Russia, who together was
to have forced the Swedes to have come forward with 10 sail of the
line and make up a fleet composed of the ships of the above nations
to 50 sail of the line, then to come out of the Baltick by way of
Holland whose ships would be ready to join them to make it a fleet
strong enough to cope with the English Navy. I say if that was one
of the secret articles of Tilsit it is done away. The French prohibit
all English Goods being sent to the continent and by way of retaliat-
ing our Government has I think very wisely ordered all vessels
whatever that's bound to the continent with goods to be brought
into our ports, for you must not deem this piracy. I hope every
true Britain sees the necessity for it and will be ready to a man
to support the cause till a permanent Peace can be made.

I flatter myself you will not pity J Hall who would not volunteer
his services and had a protection when I tell you he is pressed....

We are all well thank God as we trust this will meet you. By
writing at all opportunities you will oblige your loving F & M

Wm & M Scoresby

Lockwood &c compts.

At first, Scoresby fared well, despite a very uncomfortable night
on board the *Texel* where there was no room to sling a hammock and
he was obliged to 'spread my bed upon the deck, where six of us were
crowded between two guns. I was dreadfully squeezed; the truck of
a gun carriage formed my pillow and my situation was so uncomfortable that I never closed my eyes all night. It was a great relief when
the boatswain's mate piped all hands at day break. I arose and felt
refreshed by walking the deck.'

Mr Gourley, flag lieutenant to Admiral Vashan, was their officer
in charge and he befriended Scoresby and invited him to join him
at his meals. He fully expected to be put in charge of a Danish vessel
and promised that Scoresby should stay with him in his command.
But when they reached Copenhagen on the 9th October, 'where we
anchored in the midst of a fleet of near a thousand sail of ships', he
was disappointed, for all the commands had already been disposed
of.

The Whitby men were taken aboard the flagship where Scoresby,
with his intensely active mind and acute power of observation, with
the ability to notice every slightest detail—and what is more, to remember and record these details later—was able to explore a man-
of-war.

'The magnitude of the vessel—the great number of men—the
numerous decks—yet the order, quietness, cleanliness of the whole,
excited my surprise and admiration. Rambling about and exploring

every place to which I could gain admission, I traced six different decks, three of which, besides forecastle and poop, were occupied by the guns, the number of which on board were upwards of a hundred.

'When all hands were called in the morning, I quitted my hammock and after strolling about the decks for a few minutes, being still weary, uncomfortable and unrefreshed, I sat down upon a gun in the *waist*. While involved in thought, and unconscious of what was passing around me, the rising of the sun notified the time for the *daylight gun*. The gun immediately behind me was selected for this purpose and the preparation being intentionally made with great silence, it was fired before I was aware of it. The noise in that confined place was so deafening that I did not recover my hearing for some hours afterwards.'

As the response to the call for volunteers had been so far in excess of the need, in order to give the men something to do, it was decided to take the small Danish gunboats away, instead of sinking them as had been intended at first. They were only river craft, and Scoresby could see right away that they were quite unfit for a sea voyage, especially at that uncertain time of year, when stormy weather might be expected.

Before the fleet left, while the ships were loading stores and preparing for the voyage, Scoresby slipped ashore unnoticed and took a look at Copenhagen and the effects of the bombardment 'by which, chiefly, the Danes had been induced to capitulate. To witness hundreds of houses in ruins, some that had been set on fire smouldering in ashes—to observe churches demolished—and one reduced to a pile of rubbish—while it made me sympathise with the homeless inhabitants and regret the calamities of war, it excited my thankfulness to a merciful Providence that my country was almost the only one which had escaped the ravages of conflicting armies.

'Turning my eyes from the desolate and ghastly spectacle of smouldering ruins, I expected to find in every countenance I met, that woeful and mourning expression of which I experienced the lively sympathy, and that the justly indignant patriot would wear on his brow the marks of determined and revengeful hatred towards the authors of these calamities. But my surmises were not well founded; the prevailing physiognomy indicated rather gaiety, carelessness, or phlegmatic indifference. Everything I saw seemed to express insensibility.' He noted that shops were open, the quays were busy, the taverns overflowing with noisy drinkers and to crown all, a lottery was being drawn in the public street.

Returning to his ship, Scoresby had a narrow escape from imprisonment when caught by a crowd of angry Danes in a part of the city that was 'out of bounds', and he secured his release only when he produced a forged passport. One of his crew was less fortunate and was put in prison, but managed to bribe the jailor to release him.

On the 17th October the ships were put under orders and the fleet sailed into the roads. During this preliminary trial Scoresby records: 'Among other stores which we had on board was a large quantity of gunpowder in boxes. Directly over the place where it was stored was our fire hearth, consisting of a match tub lined with bricks (the contrivance, I believe, of Admiral Hood). During one of our passages from the beach, the vessel was discovered to be on fire! The heat of the fire, penetrating the bricks, had already consumed the bottom of the tub and set fire to the deck. By the good providence of God we got it extinguished, when there was scarcely an inch of deal between the fire and the gunpowder!'

The tiny gunboat was fated. Constructed to be rowed by sixty-four men in shallow waters, it drew only three feet of water, and Scoresby had the gravest doubts about putting to sea. His protest, however, was ignored and they were put in tow by the *Alfred*. 'The whole of the day we were towed at the rate of nine or ten knots. The sea made a free passage over the deck, washed out the little fire we had ventured to make and kept the watch continually drenched. But this was the least evil, the vessel plunging into the sea started the bow-port, and admitted such a quantity of water that the pump was kept continually going.

'As we could not get anything cooked, we could only eat bread and raw pork, and as our clothes could not be dried, we were obliged to remain continually wet. Night again approached and it appeared to be the intention of Captain Bligh* to continue us in danger. As the water now gained rapidly on the pump, and as it was impossible we should survive through the night, we made a signal (a blanket in the rigging, having no flag) which was observed by the sentry on the *Alfred*'s poop. The ship now made more sail, and after running us almost under water for two hours, she *hove to*. We immediately set our sails and ran under her lee. We had previously taken our clothes upon deck, which were readily taken on board of the *Alfred*, and we quickly followed. The vessel was by this time so nearly filled with water that the sailors were unable to get below to save any of the stores. As soon as I had taken a little refreshment, I slung my hammock between two guns and, retiring to rest, slept more soundly than I had done since leaving home.'

Scoresby and the other Whitby men had no reason to complain of Bligh's treatment of them personally, though they witnessed very severe punishment meted out for the slightest misdemeanour. 'The

---

* Not Bligh of the *Bounty*, however. He was Governor of New South Wales at this time.

morning after the gunboat was abandoned, the boatswain summoned all hands to witness punishment. Among the rest I approached the gangway where I saw a man stripped to the skin and about to be *flogged*.' The italics are Scoresby's own. Rough as life was on shipboard, no whaling captain would ever think of such a brutal act. The crew of a whaler worked together as one unit and had a pride in their ship and the number of whales they could catch by their combined skills. Scoresby was sickened by the sight of a strong man lashed to a gun and having to suffer this inhuman torture from another human, while the ship's officers calmly looked on, and after watching the man's back bleeding after three lashes, he turned away and hastened from the spot.

There was worse to come. The seven Whitby men, Michael Young, Matthew Light, Hugh Burnsides, Matthew Moon, John Dale and Thomas Westall, together with Scoresby, were transferred to the *Seyeren*, a Danish ship under the command of the *Alfred*'s first lieutenant, 'Mr Cs Grey', whom Scoresby refers to as 'Charley'.

'Here we were most uncomfortable, ill-treated, insulted by most of the crew, could get no where to mess and always in danger of losing our provisions or cloathing; we could find no where to hang our hammocks without being threatened to be cut down. The *Alfred* was extremely orderly. This ship all confusion with soldiers, women and children.

'The morning after we came on board the *Seyeren* I entertained no favourable opinion of our Commander for he flogged 3 or 4 men before breakfast as he said for drunkenness but I could perceive nothing of the kind, but now I found he was a mere savage for he used to flog continually without any evident cause, and used to call it *for skulking* if a man was half a minute after the rest. One day he ordered one boatswain's mate to flog another because the tackle fall got foul when lowering an empty water cask down. He refused to strip himself, then Charley got a small sabre & cut about him such a manner, swearing at the same time he would run him through the body, by God; He was forced to strip and received 36 lashes for nothing.

'The man also that was killed was supposed to be careless of his life, for he was flogged three times in three weeks for the faults of the fore-top men when he had not the least command over them.' This man fell from the fore-top mast and was instantly killed. The body was taken below and the next day 'he was thrown overboard with no more ceremony than if he had been a Dog. Indeed, there was few that knew of it.'

'Does it not break the spirit of our seamen,' Scoresby asks, 'to be punished with such severity for faults scarcely worth naming, and sometimes for no fault at all? Is it not most trying for manhood to be struck, or perhaps kicked, as well as cursed for an idle scoundrel, by a boyish midshipman of neither years nor discretion? And if the man, conscious of his integrity and his own irreproachable conduct and acknowledged seamanship, ventures to give way to his indignation by a rash word, is it not painful to humanity for him to be lashed to a gun and flogged? And perhaps if he be brought before a superior officer and dares, in the manliness of his heart, to look undaunted instead of cringing, is it not destruction to every principle of natural dignity and courage to flog him for *looking contemptuous?*'

In the *Seyeren*, Scoresby, a young man only just past his eighteenth birthday, and used always to being with his Father, was 'excessively uncomfortable, ill-treated, insulted, robbed by the crew and refused redress by the officers, and endured continual hardships'. To add to this the very men who should have showed him kindness, the Whitby sailors, used him badly. On the 21st November he wrote to his parents: 'lately I have been ill treated by some of the Whitby men who came in the gunboat with me, particularly Matt. Moon, although since I came from home I have conducted myself as their equal except in cooking and for which I have always repaid them'.

At home, rumour was rife about the whereabouts of the volunteers. Although Father writes on the self-same date as his son—who is still in Yarmouth Roads—he has 'heard' that they have arrived at Portsmouth. In fact it was another ten days before they reached Spithead.

Stockton, 21 Nov 1807

My dear Son Wm,

I have been attending a sale of casks at Shields and bought 100 tons. As I hear you are arrived at Portsmouth I write it plain to say you may by all means come by land and if in good health stop in London to have my ans. by you writing to say where you will be found as I have passiage paid from Snowhill. If you want money you may draw from any place whatever. Pray write as soon as you get this. We expect you have lost all your clothes but hope to the contrary.

I am, yours Wm Scoresby.

But long before the *Seyeren* reached Spithead there was a dreadful storm and the ship was nearly wrecked, mainly due to what Scoresby nicely calls the 'inebriety' of the commander, who was so drunk that he did not realize the ship was in any danger and 'ordered "all hands below" to enjoy themselves on the remnant of their rations, such as they had, of coarse biscuits and water'. Scoresby fell asleep and was awakened by shouts above. He rushed up on deck and with inconceivable horror saw *broken water* within a hundred yards of their lee. 'Nothing could exceed the awfulness of our situation; the heavens poured down torrents of rain, the wind seemed loosened for destruction; the sea was thrown into prodigious turbulence, while the darkness was such that nothing was visible save the luminous breakers which shone with phosphorescent and terrifying lustre. The ship now entered the breakers—the sea raging and foaming about us with awful vehemence—and instantly struck! "She strikes, she strikes!" was the involuntary and universal shout—the effect was appalling.'

Fortunately, however, the *Seyeren* was washed into deep water away from the sandbank. 'All was in a moment joy and gladness.' The ship returned to normality and Scoresby went below to his hammock. He 'stumbled over a person rolled in a blanket; urging him to remove from a situation where he must be liable to be trampled on, I accidentally laid my hand on the marble-like face of a corpse! It was the body of the man who was killed. Shuddering at the circumstance, and shrinking back from an object so repugnant to youthful sensibilities, I retreated too far, and fell down the open hatch into the hold. Falling on the chine of a cask I stripped off the skin and broke the small bone of the leg. I lay for some time motionless, but aroused by a sentry above me crying out: "Hollo there; are you killed?" I crawled out of the place and with difficulty found my way to my hammock, where I lay in great pain till daylight and then applied to the surgeon for assistance.

'During my stay in this vessel, which was fifty days, I experienced the most painful privations, hunger, cold and severity of discipline. The hardships, indeed, that we endured were such that my companions became insensible to personal safety. I have seen them take a lighted candle to the door of the magazine in search of any trifle, and on my cautioning them of the danger, they would reply, "What matter?"—they cared not if the ship were blown up and we were all destroyed together.'

From a safe distance, Father tried to pour oil on the troubled waters:

Whitby
26 Nov 1807

Dear Son Wm,

Since yours of the 13th we have seen two letters wherein the writers bemorn their situation in the late tempestuous weather under a harsh master. They should give latitude to a commander who from all accounts has an uncomfortable ship with only 200 instead of 500 seamen on board, makes your ship work heavy and the men appear as if they were backward in their duty mearly because they have not strength of men to work briskly, this together with being left behind may frustrate and break the temper of a good man.

We have every reason to believe you have considered the above which has been the cause of your delicacy in writing for which you have great credit by being content in your winter situation which we are aware of and do feel for you, as we suppose you lost your clothes when you abandoned the gun boat and I am afraid you will be perished for want of them, if so we request you will indulge yourself with a fresh sute if they to be had on board, if not borrow of your ship mates rather than let your clothes dry on your back for no constitution can bear it.

Tho we direct this to Yarmouth, we hope you will be at Portsmouth before it reach the above place, therefore have directed another of the same time and date to the latter place from whence we beg you to write as soon as you arrive to say when you come off. On your arrival in London we recommend you to go to the Lodgings of Mr John Jackson No 32 Haymarket where you will meet a note from us enclosing a note for your passage from Snowhill London to York, and also a meteorological journal of our last Voyage &c to lay before Sir Joseph Banks &c.

We flatter ourselves that you place due dependance on the wise author and governer of all things.

Your loving Father and Mother,
W & M Scoresby

The harbour at Portsmouth could only manage to take two ships at a time, and so there was much delay before it was the *Seyeren*'s turn. The crew returned to their own ship, the *Alfred*, and men from the *Pompey* came on board 'to assist us into the harbour. They cared not for our Commander and he using them very roughly, they began singing and making a great noise one evening about six o'clock. He came out, apparently *half seas over* (a common case) and asked why they made that noise, then told them to put out all lights & go below. Instead of this they all went up on deck, he turned into the cabin and brought out his sword, which he drew and flourished about in a very dangerous manner, saying, "You scoundrels, how dare ye disobey my orders."

'Then they all went below but a Black Man who stood upon the top of the ladder & seemed to take no notice of what passed but looked calmly at him with his drawn sword, which incensed him so much that he struck him over the head, but having on a tarpaulin hat, it only cut him about an inch, & did not injure him. Still he did not stir and the Captain, recollecting what he had done, instantly grew quite calm, when the seamen were saying that they would inform their Captain of him. "You will my lads will you" says he, "you'll tell your Captain." "Yes we will," answered they. "O you are very welcome," says he. "But you had better say no more about it. Let it drop, do, & I'll allow you to do as you like, you shall have liquor in what quantity you like" (A thing never allowed in the Navy) "You shall have women and your own way." Then they seemed satisfied & went quietly below.'

The captain's behaviour towards the volunteers had greatly altered during the last weeks owing 'to his having received a letter signed by 12 volunteers complaining of bad usage, headed by one of the pilots who got clear at Yarmouth'.

As soon as the ship docked Scoresby went ashore, expecting a remittance from his Father. Unfortunately it was only an order on his London banker and was not negotiable. Without a farthing in his pocket, he wandered up and down the town the whole day in a 'truly pitiable state of disappointment'.

'At length, almost exhausted by hunger and fatigue I entered a tavern, meaning to offer my watch for security until I could pay for refreshment. But as I entered my courage failed me; my eyes became dim with rising tears; and I hurried from the bold, inquisitive gaze of the waiter. Never before had I known the want of a shilling, now I personally felt what the anxieties of one must be who knows not where he shall satisfy the cravings of hunger.'

He returned to the ship and 'once more entered with joy a place I before deemed the counterpart of the abode of the wicked in eternity'. On the 21st December they were paid off and Scoresby received £11 19s. 2d., wages, travelling money and bounty for three month's service. The past was forgotten and Scoresby treated the six Whitby men to a dinner and 'other refreshments' before taking the London coach. Arrived in London, he found his Father's letter awaiting him.

12 Dec 1807

Dear Son,

I purposed to have sent you this through Mr Jackson but I hear he is still in the country, but should he have arrived in Town I trust that you will meet a Brother and a Friend who will introduce you as a visitor to the acadamy of painters and other lector rooms that he attends.

I have been at Greenland 23 voyages and have found the wind to blow from the NNE NE & ENE and blows fresh with frost April & May after which, viz forepart of June, less wind but mostly same way as above and fine weather; latter part of June and forepart of July enclined to calms and foggs, Barometer high and wind southerly SW or WSW. The latter part of July frequently brings strong NW winds. As the ice almost always sets off from the east land about the latter part of May, forming the same shape as Capt Phips lays down in his chart, fresh NE winds with the flush of the water against the points, wheel them round into the bights and turn the washed ice into the pack and the fields and flows to the outside where the whales like to play or more properly speaking they are prevented getting under such large pieces and all of them that comes past such fields is forced to come along the edge.

You may tear this off if you be inclined to lay the other side before Sir J. who is a judicious philosopher and a rearer of science. If you call on him you must have a short note to send in by the porter you will meet by a rap or a bang at the front door. This note must specify your business with Sir J.

Time is short and I would end by telling you that we are all well Thank God as we trust this will meet you ...

Wm & M Scoresby

CHAPTER 4

NORTHERN LIGHTS AND SNOWFLAKES

'I was enabled to converse very freely on the phenomena of the Arctic regions which have no parallel in any other country.'

Sir Joseph Banks (1744–1820), whom the young Scoresby had to seek out, was a formidable figure in the social and scientific life of London in the early nineteenth century. He had sailed in the memorable first voyage of Captain Cook in 1768, when he was twenty-four, and had later financed, organised and led an expedition to Iceland. He had been President of the Royal Society since 1778. He was a friend and benefactor of all who strove to advance natural knowledge by travel, observation and investigation, and Captain Scoresby (Father) had no doubt made a favourable impression upon him. Banks, too, had a kind side to his nature and was ever eager to assist men of scientific ability, and to use his influence to further the work of young men of promise. The celebrated botanist, Robert Brown, was one of his protégés and owed much to Banks's help and encouragement.

Banks grew a little autocratic in his later life (he has been called the autocrat of the philosophers) but he had spent a life of useful service in science and his influence had been exerted on behalf of many able men and worthy scientific causes. He was one of the leading Englishmen of his time. At 32 Soho Square, Banks kept open house to all engaged in science; his weekly breakfasts were famous and his Thursday formal receptions often brilliant social and scientific gatherings. Here, distinguished foreign men of science could often be met with, talking to their English colleagues; Cuvier or Linnaeus with a Wollaston or a Priestley.

So we may imagine the young William Scoresby—'having exchanged my sailor's garb for a dress more suited to the refinements of the metropolis'—making his way to 32 Soho Square in some trepidation, yet not unhopeful, to meet this famous man, for in meeting Banks he would be taking the first step towards entering the scientific society of the capital. He had already been greatly stimulated at the start of his student life in Edinburgh by the intellectual atmosphere created by the Northern Lights (Hutton, Black, Hume and their circle); now he was to meet Sir Joseph and to gain entry into the scientific life of London. The door of 32 Soho Square was the entrance to a new world.

'To overcome my natural diffidence, and call upon a person to whom I was an entire stranger was to me an extraordinary *trial*. Having, however, prepared the way by a note which I delivered to the porter, I was shown into Sir Joseph's study, and received by the benevolent man with that frankness and cordiality for which he was so remarkable. His freedom of manners soon dissipated the timidity I felt on being first introduced, and I was enabled to converse very freely on the phenomena of the Arctic regions which have no parallel in any other country. The worthy baronet was exceedingly kind; he invited me to his weekly breakfast on the ensuing Thursday morning, when I was introduced to Mr Home, Professor Carlisle and several other gentlemen.

'These interviews led to a correspondence which was continued pretty regularly, until within a few weeks of his lamented death; and gave rise to a personal intercourse, from which I derived very great mental advantages.'

Scoresby returned to Edinburgh University after his next voyage, a much more mature person than two years before. His experience in the Navy had given him a new confidence, as well as a most decided opinion never to enter the service. The fact of his not being a naval man was to hinder him later from the point of view of discovery expeditions and more especially in his relations with John Barrow, secretary to the Navy Board. Nevertheless it was a very firm decision which Scoresby never regretted.

'Excepting a little deficiency in cleanliness, an article for which lodging houses in Edinburgh are not famous, and abating a small want of conscientiousness in my hostess respecting her right to my stores, I found my quarters at Mrs Schearer's exceedingly comfortable.' Here, Scoresby planned his course of study: 'Having for some time cultivated a habit of observation and enquiry, and by occasional reading (very occasional and very excursive, for as yet I had never read a book of science through) made myself tolerably acquainted with the rudiments of general knowledge—the attendance to several branches of learning was now to me a matter of comparative ease to what it was on my first entering college. I therefore took out tickets for natural history, two classes of mathematics and logic; in all, four daily classes. These, with anatomy and some gymnastic exercises, completed the routine of my studies.'

'Professor Leslie, two of whose classes in mathematics I attended, showed me several civilities. I twice breakfasted and once or twice dined with him. I generally found him alone, absorbed almost in

those abstruse and original investigations that have greatly contributed to render his name eminent in science.'

John Playfair's successor in the chair of mathematics and subse-
quently in that of natural philosophy, was John Leslie (1766–1832).
He passed through Edinburgh University as a student of mathematics
and then of divinity. He spent a year as a private tutor in Virginia
and after in the family of Josiah Wedgwood, where he devoted his
leisure to natural science, translating Buffon's *Natural History of Birds*.
Returning to his native place, Largs in Fifeshire, Leslie devoted ten
years to scientific research and then settled down at Edinburgh University. He received the honour of knighthood shortly before his
death.

Leslie's name is especially associated with his researches on radia-
tion, and his differential thermometer was for a long time a useful
piece of scientific apparatus.

Father, however, was not greatly impressed with his son's facility
in this direction: 'You say you are a master of filling a thermometer.
I am glad to hear this, but you will by and by perceive that every
German Jew traveller with such things manufacture them themselves.
Now I should wish you to make yourself master of all arts and sciences,
but first aim at the usefull part, such as apportains to Astronomy &
a marratime life, Distillation, Electricity, Galvansianity. I am far
from wishing you to over burden yourself with learning overmany
classes at once, but as you say nothing about Algibera suppose you
don't get a lesson in that useful art ... could you do it on Saturdays?'

Another man who became Scoresby's firm friend at the university
and afterwards was Robert Jameson (1774–1854), an enthusiastic and
kindly man who had a great gift for arousing enthusiasm in others.
He started out to become a doctor, but having been fond of natural
history from boyhood, he felt his true life work to lie in natural science.
He was educated at the grammar school in his native town of Leith
and later at Edinburgh University. After a short apprenticeship to
a doctor in Leith, he left for Germany to study under the celebrated
Werner at Freiburg. He returned to Edinburgh in 1804, when he was
appointed to the chair of Natural History in the university.

Jameson was a brilliant teacher, and the first great exponent in
these islands of the Wernerian system of geology, but it is greatly to
his credit that he abandoned the views of Werner and embraced those
of Hutton, frankly admitting the latter to be a better system.

Such was the large-minded and enthusiastically learned man who
became Scoresby's friend and mentor. He describes their meeting:
'In taking out my ticket for admission to the natural history class,
Professor Jameson enquired my object in attending the University,
and the profession for which I was designed. He was surprised when

Robert Jameson

Reproduced by kind permission of the Royal Scottish Museum

I announced myself as a sailor (being, I daresay, the only one in the college), and still more so when he understood my usual voyage was to the whale fishery of Spitzbergen. This led him to make many enquiries respecting the natural history of the Polar Sea and especially of the whale.' Scoresby was not found wanting. He was a scientific observer by nature and had made extensive notes and drawings of marine life on all his voyages, as well as detailed meteorological tables. All these he showed to Professor Jameson, who was greatly interested. He invited the young student to dinner. But Scoresby's 'extreme diffidence rendered my introduction into a party consisting of scientific men of eminence, with accomplished and intelligent women, at first inconceivably painful. I felt such a degrading sense of my own inferiority, that I could not summon vanity enough to imagine that I could be the object of any attention. The free and encouraging manners of the professor and his friends, however, and the frankness of the ladies, soon dissipated every painful feeling, and enabled me at length to enjoy the uncommon treat that such a party presented.'

Between the lines of Scoresby's writing we see his very sweet and gentle nature. He was obviously quite unaware of his own attractiveness—especially to the ladies. Perhaps it was this very innocence which was so appealing. He was tall—5′ 9½″—yet slightly built and delicate-looking. His eyes were dark, and his clear, penetrating gaze revealed the fine mind that lay behind them. He was not handsome, but he had an extraordinary quality. The one word that springs to mind is the most apt in this case, for his personality was undoubtedly *magnetic*.

'To my great surprise', he continues, 'the civilities of the kind professor and his family did not terminate here. I was repeatedly invited to dine with him, and invariably met that kind of refined and intelligent society for which Edinburgh is so eminent, and from which I derived incalculable advantages. My natural timidity or even bashfulness, wore off, and I could eventually enter these august societies without fear, until I was perfectly at my ease. Having a taste for music, an accomplishment in which the professor's nieces excelled, I never failed to be delighted.'

So Father had been wrong when he supposed William would not have time to play his violin. There were other things to study besides natural philosophy in the stately city. Scoresby's affection for the absent Mary Lockwood faded in comparison with the blue-eyed Scottish girls of 'amiable manners, great accomplishments and beauty'.

Scoresby's studies in Edinburgh, his contact with first-rate minds, and the stimulating atmosphere of creative activity, bore fruit in one of his most original and altogether charming insights and observations; his first drawings and descriptions—both astonishingly accurate—of the very beautiful and varied forms of the snow crystal. Not till the invention of the photographic microscope—and especially in the work of W. A. Bentley—were these studies surpassed. There were very few attempts to describe and illustrate the snow crystal before Scoresby; one of the earliest occurs in a curious work by Olaus

Magnus, Archbishop of Uppsala, published in Rome in 1555, but here the woodcuts are so poor as to be valueless. Later, pioneer workers like René Descartes and Robert Hooke turned their attention to the snow crystal, but not till the young William Scoresby voyaged in the Arctic did these minute miracles of nature find a patient observer and skilled draughtsman of the highest integrity. We may imagine him on some very calm and still Arctic day, seated partly under cover on the deck of his ship with pencil, paper, hand lens and black cloth, and we may marvel at his patience and exactitude and share too his sense of the beauty and wonder of these crystal forms.

Today, representations of the snow crystal are so familiar as to be very nearly commonplace. One place where it is rightly reproduced is the Scott Polar Research Institute in Cambridge, England, where it has been cut into the large glass doors, so that the form of the snow crystal—so faithfully recorded by William Scoresby—forms a fitting introduction to this Mecca of the polar student.

No one today has described their beauty in words better than Paul Gallico in a small book called, appropriately, *Snowflake*:

> Snowflake knew that she was beautiful. She was made up of hundreds and hundreds of pure, shining crystals, like fragments of glass or spun sugar. She was all stars and arrows, squares and triangles of ice and light, like a church window; she was like a flower with many shining petals; she was like lace and she was like a diamond. But best of all, she was herself and unlike any of her kind. For while there were millions of flakes, each born of the same storm, yet each was different from the other.

The drawings were first publicly shown at a meeting of the Wernerian Society in January 1809. This society was formed by Jameson in 1808 in honour of his great teacher and it later became the Royal Physical Society. The usual method of election—nomination and introduction by several Fellows, followed by a ballot—was entirely suspended in Scoresby's case, and he was unanimously elected a member of the Wernerian Society after reading his account of the voyage to latitude 81° 30′, which included drawings of the whale and the snow crystal. This voyage was made when he was only sixteen.

Not only the snow crystals, but everything around him in the Arctic interested the young Scoresby. The polar ice came under his scrutiny and he amazed the sailors by making lenses of it: 'The homogeneous and most transparent pieces are capable of concentrating the rays of the sun so as to produce a considerable intensity of heat. With a lump of ice, of by no means regular convexity, I have frequently burnt wood, fired gunpowder, melted lead, and lit the sailors' pipes, to their great astonishment; all of whom who could procure the needful eagerly flocked around me, for the satisfaction of smoking a pipe ignited by such extraordinary means. Their astonishment was increased on observing that the ice remained firm and pellucid, whilst the solar rays emerging therefrom were so hot, that the hand could not be kept longer in the focus than for the space of a few seconds.

'In the formation of these lenses I roughened them with a small axe, which cut the ice tolerably smooth; I then scraped them with a knife and polished them merely by the warmth of the hand, supporting them during the operation in a woollen glove.'

Shy and diffident as the young Scoresby was on shore, on a ship he was very much at home. This became abundantly evident on a voyage which he made from Leith to London in a packet, when a tremendous storm arose, 'in which above 100 vessels were wrecked on the eastern coast of Britain'. Had it not been for Scoresby it is probable that the twenty-five passengers would have lost their lives, for the vessel grounded on the Maplin Sands and sprang a leak. Seeing this, the sailors prepared to take the only boat and save their own skins. Scoresby's own words, written in the third person, tell the story: 'The confusion which prevailed on board, increased by the terror of several females among the passengers, was extreme. All order and authority was at an end, the Captain's orders disregarded, and the sailors, suspending their care about the vessel, began to haul out the boat for themselves. At this critical juncture, Scoresby, perceiving that the tide was rising and that, were the sails set, she might probably be forced off the bank, went among the seamen and in a spirited remonstrance, urged them to return to their duty. They at first continued their efforts with the boat, saying, "That they were determined not to sink with the vessel." "Very well," replied Scoresby, "do as you please. But as you will have time to secure the boat when the water comes along the cabin deck, you may surely help us to clear the vessel of her anchor and set the sails for us, and we will do the rest; the passengers will work the pump, and we shall be able to take her up the Swin."'

'Surprised with the justice of the remarks, and at the confidence expressed by a mere youth—whom they had mistaken for a landsman—one of the principal of their number turned to his comrades, saying to this effect: "Come, let us set the sails and get the anchor and we can take the boat after all." Forthwith they returned to their duty, set the sails, and as the packet began to float, hove up the anchor, and in a short time they were in deep water and under way. By the continuous exertions of the passengers at the pumps the vessel was kept afloat, whilst Scoresby himself took the helm and steered up the channel until they had passed the Nore. The water then gaining on the pumpers, they ran the vessel, at near the time of high water, upon a mudbank on the side of the Thames where she lay whilst the tide retired, and before the return of the water, the water was got out and the leak sufficiently overcome for getting the vessel into safety.'

We are not told what the captain was doing all this time, but the story—which was quite true, for Scoresby was not given to exaggeration—gives us a fair indication of the young man's character and bearing of authority.'

Shortly after the incident on the Leith packet the man the sailors had mistaken for 'a mere youth' received his twenty-first birthday present. It was no less than the command of the *Resolution*.

Father had for some time been negotiating with some Greenock merchants and after the voyage of 1810—the last one in which Father and son sailed together in the same ship—he went into partnership with them and moved to Greenock with his family. Visiting him later Scoresby wrote: 'The delicate olfactory nerves of the Greenock folk renders my Father's occupation unpopular here, they considering the smell of the oil unbearable. It is laughable to see the behaviour of the ladies who have occasion to pass by the oil yard; long before they reach it they apply a scented hkf to the nose and set off at full speed and run until far beyond the reach of the effluvia, scarcely allowing their lungs the necessary respiration, *suffering* as much from fear of perceiving the smell as from the actual sensation. My Father laughs at their prejudice and tells them he would build a dwelling house within the walls of the yard were it not for the intolerable smell of an adjoining tan yard!'

Father sailed from Greenock in the *John* whilst Scoresby made his first voyage as captain of the *Resolution*. Of this he writes: 'Notwithstanding the encouragement I had experienced from men of science, and the flattering reception I had met with from the various respectable families I visited during the preceding eight months, I was still extremely diffident of my acquirements, and entirely unconscious of any superiority over the most ordinary capacities; and having no confidence either in my talents or experience as a fisherman, I entered on the command of a ship with much apprehension for the result.

'Our first fish not having been taken until the 30th of May, which was thought rather late, the officers and crew became uneasy and fearful of the issue. My youth, and the still greater rawness of my chief mate,—whom I imprudently engaged in consequence of his belonging to a respectable family—for he was very little acquainted with the fishery and on the whole a very indifferent seaman,—encouraged these suspicions so detrimental to the spirit of a fisherman.

'One of the principal men, the specksioneer, was so discouraged (not from what he saw, certainly, for we were generally the leading

ship of the fleet, which were almost all in the same predicament as
ourselves) that he did not scruple to make his fears pretty public. He
was often heard to declare, "We can get no fish, there is no hope of
it—for what *can you expect from a couple of boys?*"'

But despite the specksioneer's fears the voyage, though 'without
much adventure', proved extremely prosperous, for the *Resolution*
returned to Whitby with 'the largest cargo that had ever been taken
into the port in one vessel', no fewer than thirty whales.

CHAPTER 5

WEDDING BELLS

'My happiness was beyond expression and now admits of
no description.'

The prosperity of this voyage, together with his new command,
encouraged Scoresby to think of marriage, for he could think 'of no
real enjoyment independent of domestic and connubial happiness'.
But all had not been plain sailing with Mary Eliza Lockwood, for
in January of the same year she—dissatisfied with William's apparent
indifference to her charms, and his excessive attention to the beautiful
newcomer Miss Shipton—had become engaged to Another; an un-
scrupulous young man by the name of Chadwick who, despite the
outward cloak of respectability—a theological student—was in reality a
wolf of the first order, for he was already 'in the sight of heaven wed-
ded to another'. As if this were not enough, he also had epileptic fits.

Until the engagement, Scoresby had thought his feelings for Mary
were only friendship. Suddenly he found he was in love. Thoughts
of Miss Shipton and the blue-eyed Scottish maidens faded. So did
the roses on his cheek; his 'rest and appetite forsook me and I became
pale and ill'.

The panic-stricken Miss Lockwood was 'obliged to flee the house
and town', but she was recalled and Chadwick was 'eventually dismissed, protesting he could never marry'. Within a month he had
married the former lady who lived in York, and how she coped with
his fits and his preaching is not recorded.

Having obtained Father's concurrence—no mention is made of
mother's—William Scoresby married Mary Eliza Lockwood on the
25th September 1811. Faithful to his meticulous scientific habit of
recording the minutest detail, Scoresby kept a journal of their marriage tour. Throughout his life he kept a journal of any tour or new
place to which he travelled; he did not, however, keep a regular daily
journal, so that of his day-to-day ordinary life there is little record.
The habit of keeping a log of the ship's progress was formed early
and persisted into later life in the form of notes whenever he made
a journey, long after he had left the sea. If this book should appear
to have some blanks in its course, that is because there are no written
records of these times and we feel that it would not be right to fill
in the blanks from our imagination. We leave that to the reader.

The marriage tour lasted two months. First of all they went to 'Alston in Cumberland, to the house of Mr Stagg, treasurer and paymaster of the lead mines belonging to Greenwich Hospital, who was a particular friend of my wife'. Here, Scoresby occupied himself in visiting the lead mines and making extensive notes of their workings, output, conditions of labour and the like. His was a restless mind, driven by a force which compelled him to observe and record each slight detail of whatever happened to be under his notice at the time. Throughout his whole life this attention to minute detail, so characteristic of the scientific mind, persisted, and is very evident in the immense pile of paper which he left.

The tour of Stanhope mill, where he noted the slag furnace, the lead infusion, the refining process for the 'oar', and the pack horses, was followed by a visit to the Vale of Whitfield. 'There are no mines in the vicinity of Whitfield,' he wrote. Did the young bride heave a sigh of relief?

Their evenings were enlivened by music. Scoresby had brought his flageolet and 'Mr Bryen accompanied me in singing and playing several pieces'.

A summons from Father was not to be ignored, and they left Alston after only a week to make their way north, stopping at Penrith where 'we were very comfortable, spent the Sabbath being twice engaged in religious public exercise and early retired to rest'. The journey was a tedious one, in a jolting coach, uncomfortably packed by a large woman 'who had lately been imported from Jamaica' and an equally large man, a 'lump of healthy looking flesh', and Scoresby and his bride were obliged to sit on opposite sides, which was not to their liking. But, eventually, the coach 'stopped outside our lodgings, we got out and were soon entranced in the embraces of our dearest relatives. All were kind, they wept for joy at our arrival—even an Indian parrot greeted us with welcome.'

Mary and William were little different from other newly married couples: 'Surely we are favoured, highly favoured. Such is the strength of our enjoyment that an hour's separation is an hour of pain, an hour of vacancy and an age almost to look at and count the passing moments. From most feelings we are little inclined to conform to the custom, the fashion of this spot, where partners of life are scarcely ever seen together, where it is almost reckoned vulgar for a man to walk out with his wife, or to sit by her side at a party. Such a strength of attachment outvies all ceremony and form, it almost shows itself in the attraction which draws us together—yet we are averse, notwithstanding the mutual feeling of our bosoms, to the public foolish fondlings which some *new fangled*, *new married* folks often exhibit.'

The November weather was unsettled: 'This very day we have ex-

perienced these peculiarities: High winds, rain, snow, hail and lightning & in the evening had a delightful walk with my Mary under
the bespangled canopy of a starlit atmosphere.'

'Peculiarly situated with the Dear object of my choice, no hours
of dullness are felt; no time hangs heavy on my hands. The vulgar
hony moon has long been past, in a few days two months will have
passed since the morn of delight, and happy am I to say that a weary
moment or an instant of uneasiness with my Dear Partner I have not
yet experienced.'

Scoresby conveyed his momentous news to Professor Jameson in
the following terms:

'I have two excuses for not writing sooner, the first a sufficient one
I had little or nothing worth your notice to communicate, the other
that I have lately been engaged in a scheme which gives rise to an
era of connubial import. My partner in the matrimonial excursion
is now with me exploring the beauties and curiosities of this part of
Scotia.' The letter then goes on to give details of his voyage and his
bride is not mentioned again.

Jameson replied with an invitation to visit Edinburgh—'I congratulate you with all my heart on your marriage, which I hope will
prove a source of numberless comforts and delights to you. I heard
of your very prosperous voyage before I received your letter; indeed,
I anticipated a full ship—for wherever skill, intrepidity & indefatigable perseverance are combined as I know to be the case with you,
success must follow.'

The young couple returned home by way of Edinburgh. 'We took
our seats in the Glasgow coach at 8 am, with regret we parted from
our dear mother, who with tears in her eyes bid us adieu; dear parent,
affectionate and good, what I owe to thee: Cowper in his lines on
receiving his Mother's Picture expresses more finely than I could hope
to describe my feelings, my affection, my regard. We parted—My
Father accompanied us to Edinburgh.

'At Glasgow, where we arrived about noon, we called on the
Admirable Crichton (so called by some) he is by business a Thermometer maker, but quite an eccentric, as well as a genius. He showed
us some curiosities of his own workmanship.

'The students of Glasgow college all wear red clokes; we were surprised to see these clokes so old, threadbare and torn, but our surprise
ceased when we were told that an old one was made more valuable
and esteemed more because it proclaimed the wearer an old student.'

'In the Edinburgh coach we found a little boy not 8 years old, who
had been at sea, was shipwrecked and had with his shipmates rowed
in a boat to Ireland, from thence he came to Glasgow in a small
brig. The little fellow told his tale so simply and yet so correct and

connected, you would have thought he had been taught what to say. Says he, "When I came to Glasgow I wished the Master of the Brig to bind me, but he told me I was too young & not strong enough for him." On being asked what money he had to pay his exps to Berwick, where his father wrought as a shipwright, he replied, "I have a note (20/–) which the master gave me at Glasgow and I gave this man 10/– to let me go to Edinburgh." On being asked by the 3rd coachman for something, he looked simply up to my Mary and said, "I have given them two sixpences." '

Father nearly had a stand-up battle with a very fat man who joined the coach and took more than his share of seat 'beside the boy, he actually pushed him quite off. The poor little fellow looked up to my wife and whispered, "I have no room". My Father threatened to put him off the coach if he did not make the little boy plenty of room. He was obliged to comply and vented his spleen by a contemptuous silence. We were at length happily parted on our quitting the coach at 10½ pm at door of Mackay's Hotel, where for a couple of days we took up our abode.'

Here, Scoresby was on familiar ground, and he delighted in show-ing Mary 'the beautiful new town of Edinburgh; for simple elegance excelling any other place in the known world. I am partial to Edin-burgh, the society is sociable, the inhabitants genteel. Their parties are particularly agreeable; no more ceremony than is admissable with true politeness.' This last, the young Mrs Scoresby was able to experi-ence for herself when they were entertained by Professor Jameson and his family.

From Edinburgh, the young Scoresbys returned to a very short interval of residence in the Lockwood home at Whitby, now occupied by Mary's brother-in-law, Mr Arundel, 'a dissenting clergyman' who was also executor to her late father; his wife, Mary's sister; Charlotte, the youngest daughter, and Richard, the youngest son; and their maternal grandmother, Mrs Richardson, 'whom we found greatly in-disposed and in fact upon her death bed'.

'Early in the succeeding year a disclosure took place which threw the whole family into confusion, and occasioned in a few months the breaking up of the house and the sale of the property. It was intimated to Mr Arundel that Charlotte was not what she appeared to be— an unmarried girl—but that she had for some time past been a wife! Mr Arundel in great anxiety and trepidation summoned the agitated Charlotte into the drawing room. "Charlotte," said Mr A. with un-usual gravity, "is your name Lockwood or *Gray*?" "It is Gray," was the candid and trembling reply.'

Michael Gray, an American, had come to Whitby with Chadwick—of whose amorous entanglements we have already heard—a year before. They were students of Divinity at a seminary which demanded strict celibacy of its students, and Gray's courtship of and marriage to Charlotte Lockwood had necessarily to be kept a secret. Young Mrs Scoresby knew of this, though she was an unwilling party to the deception.

The consequence of the disclosure was Gray's dismissal from the seminary and the 'casting of himself and his wife on her little portion only (amounting to £400) on the world. Mr Gray's prospects in England being now blasted, he turned his eyes to America, where he had a considerable amount of landed property, (but of very small value) left him by his grandfather, Colonel Johnsone. For that country they soon afterwards embarked and remained there during part of the last American war; but the dissatisfaction of Mrs Gray in being totally separated from her friends made her so unhappy as to induce them, in connection with the scanty income which his grand-patrimony and ministerial services provided, to return to England in the summer of 1814.'

Meanwhile, Scoresby prepared for another voyage and 'on the 28th March the *Resolution* again put to sea under my command. It was a new trial to me, this separation from a beloved wife, and to her the effect was most severe. I have every reason to believe that she knew not happiness until my return.' On the back of a little 'Common Place Book' in extremely small writing, Scoresby has put the words 'Halcyon Days'. One of the items within refers to this time. He calls it 'Curious Dialogue':

In the summer of 1812 Mrs Clark and Mrs S., having occasion for some article kept by Mr Webster, the Quaker silversmith & watchmaker, called at his shop. Some silver was offered by Mrs S. for payment, amongst the rest was a shilling on which was engraved very neatly the two letters WS. Mrs S. requested it to be returned as she had given it by mistake.

Mr Webster: Now does thee really value that shilling because it has thy husband's initials on it?
Mrs S: Yes I do and would not part with it on any account.
Web: I fancy it was his gift?
Mrs S: It was.
Web: Is not the rest of the money in thy purse likewise his gift?
Mrs S: Probably so.
Web: Then thou valuest this shilling because it is marked with WS, and that is the only reason thou wilt not part with it?
Mrs S: Even so. The veriest trifle from an absent friend, especially one so dear, is valued far above its intrinsic worth.

Web: Then thou lovest thy husband?

Mrs S: Why need of such a question—could you doubt it?

Web: Nay, I did not think differently—(considering, hesitatingly) But does thou really love him now, as well as before thou wast married?

Mrs S: Unspeakably more.

Web: Thou has been so candid with me. I'll be plain with thee in my turn. Many years since I had thought of taking to myself a wife, but I durst not venture. Now, tell me honestly, hast thou never found any thing in thy husband which thou didst not expect, any failings, faults or bad temper which thou wast ignorant of?

Mrs S: Nothing of the kind. I can truly affirm that my most sanguine expectations have been exceeded, my happiness has constantly increased until now that his absence has become a source of regret and the weeks of our separation are to me a heavy trial.

Web: So thou loves him better, thy happiness has been increasing and thou hast never discovered a failing in him! Well ... I must confess it passeth belief! Thou hast pleased me much ... I begin to think I shall dare to venture on matrimony. Give me that shilling and as thou valuest it because of thy husband's name being upon it, I will place thy initials on the back—what was thy maiden name?

Mrs S: Mary Eliza L.

Web: M E L. If I recollect right that is either the Latin or French word for honey—a sweet name, truly—I should have felt loth to part with it if I had been in thy place. Here is thy shilling, maybe thou mayest esteem it still higher, now that the two names are joined. Really, thou hast persuaded me to change my opinion and I think almost gives me courage to venture on the serious charge of a wife.

'Again the voyage was prosperous', Scoresby wrote, 'and was attended with some circumstances that were thought particularly creditable to me personally. At this period of the fishery we had little expectation of success after the middle of July. The fishery, indeed, generally closes in June. About the 14th of July I was tracing the skirts of the ice in a gale of wind from the eastward blowing upon the ice, in company with several ships, some of them belonging to Whitby. Perceiving a slack part in the ice, I conceived the idea of running into it, which, by the bye, was thought a very bold, if not imprudent measure, and accordingly penetrated the sea stream and gained shelter. None of the ships ventured to follow our example, fearful of getting beset; but after cruising a day or two off the ice, with bad weather and a heavy sea, they all bore away for England.'

They brought home the tale of Scoresby's imprudence, saying that

he already had a cargo of twenty-three whales and would in all probability remain in the Arctic for the winter. What then was their surprise when the *Resolution* entered the port only two days after this intelligence, with this cargo and another three large whales in addition,
making theirs, once more, the largest cargo brought to Whitby that
year. Nor was that the only cargo. There was also a polar bear for
Professor Jameson, who later wrote, after receiving the animal: 'I
found your valuable present, the polar bear, in perfect health. I return
you many thanks for this mark of your attention and kindness. I have
brought the animal to the college where he is now lodged in a commodious den. I wish to know from you what you consider is the best
food for him—he has been fed on liver and horse flesh.'

Scoresby's reunion with his wife, in her last month of pregnancy,
'after such an absence and on such a hazardous business, was beyond
anything I ever before witnessed, felt, or had conceived. She received
me in a private room—and rushing into my arms remained for some
minutes either incapable of speaking or uttering the most rapturous
but scarcely coherent expressions of welcome, delight and thankfulness. My happiness was beyond expression, and now admits of no description; but hers, owing to her warmth of affection and exquisite
sensibility, was still superior inasmuch as her capacity for enjoyment
was greater than mine, or indeed, than that of almost any creature
living. The agony of parting, the gnawing anxiety and distress attendant upon our separation, were thus fully compensated by the feelings,
the delights experienced on our re-union.

'This extreme sensibility, whilst it subjects its possessor to pain and
anguish unknown to coarser minds—reaps, when circumstances are
favourable, a mighty and full return in an ecstacy and weight of
enjoyment which minds of other moulds can neither participate in
nor understand. If the stoical soul is insensible to these delicacies arris-
ing from wounded feelings that often occasion a keen distress to the
truly sensitive—it is on the other hand equally insensible to those
refined perceptions of pleasure.'

'The 5th of September following was a day of extreme and pro-
tracted anxiety, but terminated in joy and gratitude in consequence
of the happy birth of a son. He was named William, both because
of the earnest request of my wife, and because of this having been
the christian name of the first born of my Father's family for a long
succession; he now making the fourth of the name all living.

'This appears to have been a year of such considerable indolence
that I cannot now ascertain how my leisure on shore was occupied.
In science I seem to have done little or nothing, and in the higher
knowledge of the Gospels I made no advancement. But forms of religion were kept up. Family prayer in the morning was occasionally

attempted, but on my part it was a business of formality and a mere
soother of conscience.

'The only passing event of the year 1812, of a personal or family
nature that remains to be noticed was the marriage of my third and
youngest sister, Arabella, with Captain Thomas Jackson of Whitby.'
He was a cousin of Scoresby and a gallant sailor, once having risked
his life in saving a boy who fell overboard in the Arctic seas. They
were boyhood friends and went to the same school. He was later to
show how deep that friendship was when Scoresby was in trouble in
the Arctic.

CHAPTER 6

THE SHIP *ESK*

'It was the mutual opinion of all ... that it was impossible to save
her. But I, still urged by hope, held a different opinion.'

A fine new ship for the whale fishery was launched in 1813 in Whitby,
the *Esk*, and Scoresby accepted her command. He was reluctant to
leave the *Resolution*, but the offer was tempting.

The *Resolution* was known as the 'lucky ship', for under the two
Scoresbys it had always brought home larger cargoes than any other
Whitby vessel, and wagers on the amount of the expected cargo were
frequent. In consequence of this Scoresby was 'much reflected on by
those at all inclined with superstition, and these in Whitby were not
a few, who imagined that my change must doubtless be to my dis-
advantage'. They were wrong, however, for the voyage was a great
success commercially.

Scientifically it was also successful, for Scoresby continued his work
on the temperature of the Arctic sea and proved that it is warmer
below than it is at the surface. He had first used a primitive apparatus
consisting of a ten-gallon cask with home-made valves at each end.
When the results were communicated to Sir Joseph Banks he, in the
typically kind way in which he helped all those engaged in original
scientific work, offered to have an instrument specially made for the
purpose.

Soho Square,
Sept 8 1810

Sir,

I thank you for your letter and for the observations contained
in it, which prove that you continue to exercise your talents and
your industry in a way that cannot fail in due time to make you
usefull to the Public & Respected by them in proportion as they
find your application and study have improved the knowledge of
Science.

I am sorry to have disappointed you last year in failing to provide
for you a proper apparatus for obtaining the temperature of the
sea at considerable depths. I myself was disappointed in procuring

it by the unexpected death of Mr Cavendish* who had undertaken to superintend the contrivance & afterwards by the death of Mr Gilpin who overlooked the execution. The loss of these two admirable men, for such they were, both of them, made me at the time too negligent of & indeed unfit for my usual pursuits. I find however that the instrument is now Ready for Delivery, as I saw it a few days before I left town & gave then the final directions to Mr Carey, instrument maker in the Strand to finish it for me. He promised to have it done without delay. I shall be glad if you come to London to have the pleasure of seeing you that I may instruct you personally in the use of it. If you do not I will have it delivered to your order wherever you please with the best account I can provide of the management of it, which however is by no means difficult. I confess I am at a loss however to guess how your bucket could have been broken by the force of the water if water was able freely to pass through it, nor do I comprehend how the pores of the wood could be filled with congealed water, when the temperature of the sea was only 20° and that of the water in the bucket warmer.

I have often noticed the varieties you mention in the colour of the sea, but as I have been sometimes able to ascertain that they have depended on accidental circumstances, I have my doubts of any usefull conclusions arising from them, perhaps however, it may be different in the chilly latitudes you have visited.

Your very obdt sert,
JOS BANKS

Banks's occasionally erratic spelling, together with his complete indifference to punctuation of any sort—which has here been inserted for the sake of clarity—is more readily understood by the following quotation from a letter declining membership of a Belles-Lettres Society:

'I am scarce able to write my own language with correctness and never presumed to attempt elegant composition either in prose or verse in that or any other language. It is fitting therefore that I should continue to confine myself to the dry pursuits of Natural History.'†

Hindsight is fatally easy, but it is interesting to remark Banks's failure to notice the importance of the varying colours of the sea, for

---

* Henry Cavendish (1731–1810). The foremost English scientist of his day, discoverer of the gas hydrogen and the composition of water. He left behind him a mass of unpublished work, the importance of which was not realised until long after his death.

† Quoted by H. C. Cameron in *Sir Joseph Banks, the Autocrat of the Philosophers.*

it was Scoresby who deduced that they were produced by 'minute animalcules', or what today we call plankton—the food of the whales.

Banks's apparatus was 'made chiefly of wood, and bound with brass'. But the first time it was sent to the depth of 300 fathoms, the wood swelled and the glass broke. After this, Scoresby made 'a model of a similar instrument and got it cast in brass. This I fitted up with the assistance of an ingenious mechanic, and applied to it the valves made by Carey, which then proved an elegant and useful apparatus.' He called it a *Marine Diver*. It weighed twenty-three pounds and never required any load for sinking it.

Later he altered the diver so as to bring up small fish and to send down various specimens, suggested by Professor Leslie, in order to note the effect on them of extreme pressure. But alas, in 1817, as he wrote to Leslie:

'Having a favourable opportunity on the 28th June, I procured a variety of lead lines and sent the marine diver, the two iron vessels, a six's thermometer and about twenty articles, consisting of the specimens of various kinds of wood, bone, jet, metals &c, to the depth of 7,200 feet. After an interval of about 2 hours we began to haul the apparatus up, when to my extreme mortification, one of the lines, apparently the strongest of the whole series, *broke*. Thus finished my experiment. The apparatus and 1050 feet of line which accompanied it were of 20£ value.'

And so Scoresby's Marine Diver now lies on the bed of the Arctic Ocean.

Scoresby's active mind was seldom able to rest. When beset by bay ice, he was tantalised by seeing whales in the midst of it without being able to capture them. He devised a pair of 'ice-shoes', very similar to ski—though he himself had no previous knowledge of ski and had never seen anything of the kind before. By this means he was able to cross the brittle ice and three whales were caught in this way.

'Some of the sailors having attempted to follow me over the ice without any extra defence, all broke through; and indeed, being obliged to have the men occasionally on the ice when we were getting the dead fish to the ship, all hands, at one time or another, fell in. I was the only one who escaped without breaking through, whilst several of the men broke in two or three times in one day. As each one who got wet was entitled to a glass of rum, it was suspected that some of them who were very fond of this refreshment wilfully neglected the ordinary precautions that they might become entitled to the premium, though at the expense of a wetting and at the risk of their lives.'

For many years now, Scoresby had been observing, noting and

writing extensively on all he saw. The drawing of the snow crystal was no isolated event, but just one of his many observations in the Arctic. On his return from the 1814 voyage he concentrated on compiling a paper on the polar ice, to be read to the Wernerian Society. This paper was not only important as being the first detailed scientific description of the polar ice, but it also contained an original suggestion for reaching the North Pole over the ice. It took into consideration all the obstacles which might be met and suggested ways of overcoming them. Not the least of these was the idea of a light-weight amphibian craft which could be both sailed on water or drawn by dogs or reindeer, assisted by sails, over the ice.

He advocated an early start, for 'soft snow would diminish the speed and augment the fatigue of the animal; to avoid which it would therefore be necessary to set out before the close of April before the severity of the frost should be too greatly relaxed'.

The great coldness was a drawback, but, 'The injurious effects might be avoided by a judicious choice of woollen clothing; the external air being met by an outward garment of varnished silk, and the face defended by a mask, with eyes of glass. The exterior garment would be water-proof and thus capable of shielding the body from accidental moisture.'

There was a widespread belief, in the last century, that the North Pole was entirely ice-free and surrounded by open sea. To Scoresby, who had voyaged in Arctic waters for so long, the idea was simply ludicrous: he dismissed it in this paper on the polar ice in a few words:

'From the pretended excursions of the Dutch, many have believed that the sea at the Pole is free from ice; were this really the case, the circumstance would certainly be an extraordinary one; but I consider it too improbable to render it necessary to hazard any opinion concerning it.'

This statement, however, from a mere man of the Arctic was by no means enough to convince the world. As late as 1876 we find references to 'the open sea which, it is believed, surrounds the Pole, but a barrier of ice has invariably arrested progress'. The same writer* also says: 'A properly equipped English expedition will carry the British flag into the waters of the circumpolar sea. With this view, the Admiralty have fitted out the *Alert* and the *Discovery*, under Captains Nares and Markham.' We may also note in passing that John Barrow believed in this open Polar sea to the end of his days.

The working out of all the details in the paper on the polar ice was an immense task and it occupied Scoresby—who was also busy

* The writer is anonymous, but the book is a lavish production entitled: *The Arctic World* published by Nelson in 1876.

fitting out the *Esk* for her next voyage—for a considerable time. When
he showed his results and the outline of the paper to Jameson, before
it was actually presented to the Wernerian Society, he urged him to
think very seriously about becoming an explorer. The idea appealed
very strongly to Scoresby, who would have been only too glad to give
up whaling, for which he 'had no very decided preference or regard'.

None of the family could be made to see it in the same light. Father,
always the dominant figure, was proud of his son and would have
liked him to lead an expedition, but he insisted that any Arctic voyage
should be combined with whaling. It was mere madness to go there
in a ship and watch whales sporting around it without even trying
to catch them.

But the loudest protest came from Scoresby's wife. He had a wife
and family to keep and keep them he must. There was to be no more
talk of discovery and exploration. She gave him no rest and Scoresby
wrote to Jameson when he sent him the completed polar ice paper
early in 1815:

'My paper on the ice I am happy to say is at length brought to
a close ... I hoped to have handed you the paper some time ago,
but the ship and other engagements really left me very little leisure.
You will observe that I have failed to comply with your wish by volunteering my services, under equivalent emolument, but on proposing
it to her who is most dear to me, my personal interference was so
peremptorily negatived by one and all, that I could not satisfy them,
without promising that I would not become the adventurer without
their concurrence.

'Mrs S. joins me in heartfelt remembrances of your hospitable
domestic circle, and flatters herself that you will feel grateful for the
great regard which our financier bears to the happiness and welfare
of bachelors!'

In this letter is found the complete answer to the question of why
Scoresby did not lead an expedition to the North Pole. Had he been
a free man it is more than likely that he would have done so. He might
even, despite his *Seyeren* experience, have emulated Cook and joined
the Navy, but the combined resistance of Father and wife was too
strong. Well might Baron von Buch write: 'He is also known as one
of the most courageous and skilful of the captains who frequent the
Greenland seas; he indeed is a man worthy of being placed along
with a Hudson, a Dampier, and a Cook.' Had Mrs Scoresby con-
curred, her husband might well have reached the North Pole nearly
a hundred years before Peary. But this book is not a collection of
might-have-beens; we are concerned with facts.

Scoresby was not able to present the paper on the polar ice to the
Wernerian Society personally as he was preparing for his next voyage.

Jameson wrote to tell him of its reception at 'the most numerous meeting we have had this season.

'We had all the Naval people about Edin^h and the Captains of the diff^t ships of war present, also Profs Playfair, Leslie, Dr Thomson &c, and I was desirous to learn particularly the general opinion of your plan. The plan was considered as most luminously and satisfactorily explained & it was suggested that the Society as a public body should apply to Government for their support and countenance to whoever should undertake the proposed expedition. Nothing, however, will be done until you return, as you of course must be the person best qualified to judge of the best way of setting the whole a-going.

'As naturalists are great beggars I have to request of you as a particular favour to endeavour to procure for me the head of the sea unicorn—and also of the saw fish & if you could add to these the head of a horse & two or three seal skulls it would be increasing the obligation tenfold. You know I long much for the skins of some of the Greenland birds, particularly the fulmar. I would also use the liberty of directing your attention to the finny turtle? Perhaps your surgeon might be induced to look after birds and fishes.

'The bottles of sea water came safe to hand and are now in the hands of Dr Murray. I wish you would add a few more bottles during your next voyage, and also two or three with diff^t sheets of ice—in order that the water from them might be examined.'

The letter ends with Jameson's wishes for 'a prosperous voyage'. But, alas, for the first time, in 1815, the catch was a poor one, although the work Scoresby did while looking for whales bore a more lasting result, for he 'stretched across to the coast of Spitzbergen, and as I traced it along for 120 miles in search of whales, amused myself with making a survey of its hitherto imperfectly sketched outline. I discovered errors in the latitude of some of the principal headlands and bays of 10 miles, and in the longitude of Point Look Out, the southern cape, no less than *four* degrees.'

The beginning of the winter was spent in London, where Scoresby visited Sir Joseph Banks several times, at whose house he 'met with men of science and received some attention from Dr Thomson, Professor in chemistry at Glasgow University, Sir Everard Home and some other men of science. But my chief and most obliging friend was the liberal President of the Royal Society.'

But, since Mrs Scoresby's brother—with whom they stayed—lived in Cannon Street Road and 'his connections in general not wealthy, we saw little society'. They spent a great deal of money and 'it was indeed a visit without profit'.

Another summons from Father called them north. 'Accordingly, we set off about the middle of December, and being desirous of seeing

a friend in Newcastle, I took my wife so far, where I left her and proceeded to Greenock alone. The business for which I had been sent
being accomplished, I returned in a few days.

'Being a high admirer of female beauty, and indeed, what man of
any affection is not, I cannot omit mentioning an acquaintance that
I made in my journey from Edinburgh to Newcastle, who exceeded
in elegance anyone I had ever before beheld or even could conceive
of, excepting by the aid of romance.' The lady slept with her head
on his shoulder the whole night long and it was not until morning
that he was able to catch a glimpse of her. He was 'astonished at her
perfect loveliness. Her features were somewhat small and delicate, but
with as much of sharpness indicative of intelligence as was compatible
with sweetness of expression. She was not a *tame* beauty; but full of
character, energy and animation.

'Young as she was, only twenty, she was already a widow. Her husband, Captain Hansard, fell in one of the hard contested struggles
of the Duke of Wellington, with the armies of France in the Peninsula.

'On my arrival in Newcastle I had to separate from this delightful
companion, who in so short an acquaintance made an impression on
my feelings that has not to this day worn off.

'It was perhaps well for me and my wife too, that I was so soon
parted from this enchanting female. Though my wife was beloved
with sincere affection, I yet found the external attractions of Mrs Hansard so pre-eminent as to throw every other lady I had ever known
into the shade. And although I had hitherto, since my marriage,
maintained a general correctness and propriety of conduct, this rectitude was not to be relied upon.'

The beginning of the year 1816 was 'occupied in removing from
a house I had rented in Church Street,—a low part of the town and
not genteel—to the New Buildings, an elevated situation and fashion-
able neighbourhood. I here took a lease of a house, at treble my former
rent,—which, however, was still low compared to other towns, being
only 34£ a year for a handsome house (with 11 rooms) in the best
situation in the town, having in the front a very pretty flower garden,
facing the south and separating the house from the high road—with
a very commodious well stocked kitchen garden behind and extending
backwards 30 or 40 yards.'

The voyage of that year proved to be the most hazardous of all
Scoresby's adventures in 'this inhospitable region'. Within a month
of leaving Whitby, having caught but one whale, the ship *Esk* became
completely embayed by ice in a storm 'that was truly terrific'.

'While the wind howled through the rigging with tempestuous roar,
the sea was so mountainous that the mast-heads of some accompanying ships, within the distance of a quarter of a mile were rendered

invisible by the swells. At the same time we were rapidly approaching a body of ice, the masses of which, as hard as rocks, might be seen at one instant covered with foam, the next concealed by waves and instantly afterwards reared to a prodigious height above the surface of the sea.

'Dangers which occur unexpectedly, and terminate suddenly, though of the most awful description, appear like a dream when they are passed; but horrors which have a long continuance leave an impression on the memory which time itself cannot altogether efface. Such was the effect of the present scene.' They steered a course into an opening, or slack part of the ice which 'promised a safe and permanent release. But in this we were grievously disappointed, for when we attempted to ware the ship, she refused to turn round, notwithstanding every effort in a space which, in ordinary circumstances, would have been twice sufficient for the evolution. She fell to leeward into a close body of ice, to which we could see no termination. We were obliged to drift more directly before the wind, in consequence of which we began to receive prodigious shocks on the broadside and had great difficulty in preserving the rudder. It did receive one blow, indeed, which broke almost the whole of the braces (all of them were injured but one) and started the upper part of the stern port.

'In this dreadful situation we lay beating against the opposing ice, with terrible violence, during *eight* successive hours, all of which time I was stationed at the mast head, directing the management of the ship, to avoid the larger masses of ice, any one of which would have perforated the side of the ship. This was far from being an agreeable position. I was perpetually swinging from side to side by the rolling and lurching of the ship, and now and then received such violent hurls when the ship struck a hard blow or threatened to throw me out of the crows nest upon the ice. The gale was so heavy and the rolling of the ship so great that on the one hand I could scarcely make myself understood and on the other the sailors could not stand upon deck to obey my orders; to overcome this the mate was stationed on the companion with a speaking trumpet and the crew were seated upon the deck and thus enabled to "rear and haul" as was required.'

The storm eventually abated and they were able to repair the damage to the *Esk*. They resumed the fishery and Scoresby was able, 'when not employed in fishing, to pursue my experiments with the marine diver, on the temperature and specific gravity of the sea at great depths. On 20th May (lat. 79° long. 5° 8′) the marine diver was successively sent to the depths of 13, 37, 100 and 400 fathoms. The temperature at the surface was 29°; at 13 fathoms 31°; at 400 fathoms 36°.'

But the calm of these few weeks was deceptive. Very soon after mak-

ing the above observations the wind, 'blowing strongly from the south-
ward, forced a swell into the ice which, though quite imperceptible
to the sight, broke the fields of ice—12 to 20 foot in thickness—around
us into numbers of pieces, and brought the fragments so closely
together that my ship, along with the *Mars*, commanded by my
Father, and three others were soon immovably fixed. During the succeeding week we never moved, excepting occasionally a few yards,
which we effected with great labour, to avoid the terrible crushes of
the ice that were apparent all round us. On several occasions we had
recourse to sawing and in some cases wrought for many hours with
our whole force and ingenuity without being able to move an inch.

'At length, on the 12th June we happily escaped.' They continued
with the fishing, but on the 29th of June they were unexpectedly
caught in a nip of ice, although 'the pressure on the ship was by no
means heavy, nor to appearance, dangerous'. But a tongue of ice had
damaged the keel badly. When the ice relaxed, the ship sank two or
three feet. 'The carpenter then sounded the pump and discovered to
our infinite concern a depth of $8\frac{1}{2}$ feet of water in the hold. This amazing flow of water in so short a time was most alarming.

'With despair pictured in every face the crew set on the pumps
whilst a signal of distress being hoisted, immediately brought us a
dozen boats full of men from a number of ships that were around
us. With this assistance, the two principal pumps and a spare pump
in the fore-hatch way, fixed temporarily, with buckets and tub at the
companion, were plied with such energy that the water diminished
rapidly.'

After this initial success the water slowly started to gain on them.
As the leak could not be found on the inside, fothering was suggested,
that is to say, drawing a thrummed sail over the outside of the ship
so that it would be sucked into the hole.

'But what was our astonishment to find that a large piece of the
after keel was entirely detached from the floor timbers to the distance
of nearly two feet and a large portion of the garboard strake was torn
from its place. This extraordinary damage we could clearly see from
the stillness of the water.' Fothering was impossible because of the
spike of the protruding timber.

'Having consulted several captains who visited me without finding
them at all agreed or offering any plan that was possible, I was left
entirely to my own resources. The most effectual plan, it appeared
to me, was to allow her to fill with water and then to turn her bottom
upward, by means of tackle fixed to the ice, and to repair the damage.'

This plan was thought by everyone else to be quite impracticable.
The general impression was that the ship was a write-off and must
be abandoned. Nothing could be done with so large a hole in the

very bottom of the ship. Far from helping, the men from other ships made things worse 'by their open declarations that the state of the ship was without hope. These inconsiderate men did not even scruple to converse, in the hearing of our people, on the subject of plundering the ship the moment they had the opportunity. One fellow had the impudence to demand of our blacksmith for some iron-work which he found in the ship, saying that in a short time it would be the prize of anyone. Another pilfered a musket—others were observed examining some small sails which lay on the ice, with a view, doubtless, of seeing how far they would suit their convenience.

'Instead of pumping, I could observe them treating it as a mere jest. The men on one side would frequently baulk the stroke of those on the other by an untimely jerk; then the whole gang would express their amusement by bursting into a laugh. I was so grieved with their conduct that I was on the point of ordering them to leave the ship.'

Against this general opinion, Scoresby proceeded to have the entire contents of the ship removed on to the ice, preparative to turning the *Esk* upside down. This took them about forty-eight hours of incessant labour. 'By this time the people were weary of helping us and my own crew was completely worn out. Whilst the water, therefore, quietly flowed into the ship I sent my exhausted crew to erect tents upon the ice and seek a little rest. I had already been fifty hours upon my feet. My legs swelled and became so painful I could scarcely walk. Spreading, therefore, a mattress upon a few boards, laid on the snow, within one of the tents, notwithstanding the coldness and the excessive dampness arising from a thick fog, I enjoyed a comfortable repose of four hours and arose considerably refreshed.

'Assisted by about 150 hands that now came to us by signal, we attempted to turn the ship over ... The extraordinary buoyancy and stability of the ship rendered all our efforts futile.

'It was the mutual opinion of all the Captains and officers who visited us that it was impossible to save her. But I, still urged by hope, held a different opinion. I thought that the ship could never be lost so long as we could keep our hold of her.'

After much difficulty, they managed to remove the piece of keel—no less than 22 feet in length—which had prevented the fothering sail from being sucked into the hole satisfactorily. A second fothering sail was then applied and 'the effect was as happy as we could have anticipated.

'Whilst these operations were in progress, the weather became favourable for fishing and all the ships excepting the *John*, of Greenock, commanded by my brother-in-law, Thomas Jackson, deserted us to pursue the object of their voyage. If the *John* left us also, we had little or indeed no hope by numbers of accomplishing all the labours that lay before us, the ship at the time being a mere wreck—and the stay of the men by the ship could not be secured if we were likely to be totally deserted. I therefore entered into an agreement with Mr Jackson to give him nearly half of my cargo if he would assist us with boats and men and then attend upon us as far as Shetland homeward. To this proposal himself and the ships' companies agreed, and we now with increased energy set about the completion of our operations in the hold.

'In two days from this time, the ship was completely rigged, the hold restored, the needful water as ballast filled,—stores all taken on board, and the ship in readiness to get under way.

'These laborious exertions performed by 90 to 100 men I still view with astonishment. For my own part I was greatly cut up by fatigue. During 120 hours I only rested 12, or one hour out of every ten, so that the swelling and pain of my legs and exhaustion of my bodily strength became such that I could scarcely move about.

'Under a moderate breeze of wind we left the place, but what was our astonishment and grief to find that the ship could not be guided. The rudder, from the loss of the after keel throwing the ship out of equilibrium and the eddy water produced by the fothering sail, was become perfectly useless. The *John* "took us in tow" and conveyed us a few miles to the eastward into a place of greater safety, where both ships being moored to the ice, we applied a large temporary addition to the rudder and made such other arrangements as happily proved sufficient (though only just sufficient) for the performance of the evolution necessary to our being able to accomplish the passage homeward.

'Whilst these matters were in progress I retired to rest, determined to have a comfortable sleep if possible, and I do believe I slept with little intermission for nearly twenty hours.

'A passage to the eastward was discovered among the floes, toward which, in tow of the *John*, we made the best way that a contrary wind would permit. We were happy to find that the ship was in some degree manageable and the flow of water diminished nearly four-fifths. After much arduous and anxious navigation among fields, floes and crowded drift ice, we escaped from all these entanglements without accident.

'Various contrivances were now adopted to our further security on which our lives in the proposed passage evidently depended. A spare pump was borrowed from a ship that we met with which was of great use to us. Being now fairly at sea, we received 12 men instead of 20 or 25 that we had hitherto generally had of the *John*'s crew, to assist with pumping.'

A storm arose and the fothering sail was torn away. It was all hands to the pumps until a new one could be fixed and fortunately the following day was calm. 'Having prepared a new fothering sail, by the use of cross ropes, chains and warps stretched fore and aft to press closely over the wounded part of the ship, we took this opportunity of applying it; but on the following day, having again a fresh gale of wind with heavy swell, this sail shared the fate of the former and was torn away. The leak immediately began to increase.

'The next day the accumulation of water alarmed us, but it was fortunately overcome. On the 22nd blowing a gale of wind and the ship scudding with great velocity the pressure of the helm stranded a new wheel rope and carried away the wheel stanchion. This obliged us to take in all our sail and allow the *John* to drag the *Esk* through the water. But the greatest fear now was in the stern post. In the early part of the voyage all the rudder braces—one only excepted—were broken and it was hung entirely by the bolts through the transome. It now began to "work" and became leaky. There was reason to fear it might be torn out; if so, the ship must have foundered instantly.

'On the 23rd we came within 15 miles of Hangcliff, Shetland. The *John* having fulfilled the several articles of agreement, they left us for Greenock, with three cheers and the usual display of colours. Fortunately we had fine weather for the remainder of our passage. At daylight on the 27th we were rejoiced with a sight of our port; we pressed toward it with every sail that we could set and grounded at $5\frac{1}{2}$ am in a place of safety.

'Intelligence of the distressed state of the ship and the hopelessness of her situation reached Whitby the day before us, and in consequence of exaggeration respecting the loss of the crew, involved every interested person in deep distress. Throughout the town and neighbourhood the event was considered as a general calamity. My dear wife, from whom the disaster could not be concealed, was overwhelmed under her agonising feelings and immediately was taken with a series of dangerous fits of epilepsy.

'The hearty congratulations I received on landing, from every acquaintance, were almost overwhelming, and these, with the enhanced endearments of my affectionate and enraptured wife, amply repaid me for all the toils and anxieties of mind I had endured.

'The effect of the sudden transition from the depth of anxiety and sorrow to the heighth of certainty was well nigh proving more dangerous to my wife than even the first communication of our disaster. When I met her, she flew into my arms and for some time was incapable of utterance excepting the exclamation frequently repeated,—"Oh! Are you safe!" "Are you safe!"—"Thank God!" "God be praised!"'

Though the owners of the ship—which was worth some fifteen thousand pounds—were 'disappointed with the sacrifice of so much of our cargo', they expressed their gratification to Scoresby by giving him fifty pounds.

CHAPTER 7

DISAPPOINTMENTS

'I do conceive there is sufficient interest attached to these remote
regions to induce Government to fit out an expedition.'

A naturally devout man, made the more so by his strict upbringing
and his profession, living, as sailors do, closer to perils than most men,
and aware of the insignificance of man, Scoresby's religious consciousness was heightened by his observations of the wonders and order of
the natural world.

He felt deeply responsible for his sailors' spiritual welfare and
always held a religious service on Sunday, often reading a sermon
to them and sometimes preaching extempore. He was most particular
to 'keep the Sabbath holy' on board and no fishing was allowed. Indeed, very little activity was permitted—except, of course, in emergency. On one occasion scores of little auks were killed by flying into
the ship's rigging, but Scoresby would not allow the men to launch
a boat to pick them up, for it was the Sabbath, so they had to content
themselves with fishing out as many as they could with a bucket and
rope. Sometimes they sighted whales on a Sunday and it was difficult
to control the crew's anxiety to catch them, but the captain remained
firm. No good could come of breaking the Sabbath, and they were
in no position to tempt Providence.

A new preacher, the Rev. Richard Holloway, came to Whitby and
caused a great stir by his preaching, but his 'evangelical zeal and Cal-
vinistic sentiments rendered him obnoxious to all the good, *moral* sort
of people'. Scoresby, who 'had seldom heard in the church anything
but dry morality and that delivered with total want of feeling',
went to hear him preach and was deeply impressed. Holloway
preached 'with an energy of manner and a spirituality of matter that
made his sermons a new language and placed religion in a new
light'.

But it was no instantaneous conversion. After a while, Scoresby's
cold, scientific eye began to analyse the preacher's style, and detected
a certain sameness in his oratory and 'the novelty and earnestness
which had first struck me, produced a gradually weaker effect, until
at last I attended his ministry with considerable indifference'. Later,
however, he came to know Holloway personally and he was charmed
'with his frank, pleasing and gentlemanly manner'. In every

subsequent interview with this excellent man, who soon became an intimate and beloved friend, I found myself encouraged, and saw religion in a favourable light, attended with cheerfulness and evident happiness. The fearful gloom of its professors and their supposed rigid severity were not to be seen in my friend.'

The catch of the 1817 voyage was a poor one, but science profited once more, for Scoresby visited the little-known Jan Mayen island and afterwards wrote a paper for the Wernerian Society on his discoveries. 'This island, which had rarely been visited of late years, and never scientifically examined, proved extremely interesting. I discovered it to be volcanic, the beach being covered with magnetic iron sand, and the foot of the cliffs with burnt clay, slag and lava. Two craters of volcanoes were also discovered and examined. One of them was a fine basin of considerable size. I obtained specimens of rocks and plants, and of animals, as far as we could accomplish their capture.'

He also surveyed the island, and found the existing latitudes and longitudes to be incorrectly mapped. He gave the name of *Jameson Bay* to the place where they landed.

The fishing was poor. Scoresby 'gave up all dependence on my own judgement for near two months together, and followed my Father. Hitherto I had always made a practice of acting independently. I avoided, as far as possible, other ships; and rather than follow a fleet or proceed in the midst of them, I often struck out a new path and proceeded alone.' Father caught six whales while the *Esk* got none.

On the way home, the view of the English coast 'along which we were sailing, produced a train of reflections on expected happiness, checked by the recollection of our scanty cargo, that was productive of much mortification and disappointment of soon gaining a comfortable independence. Methought God was working against me. My labours for three years had been increasingly unprofitable. They now hardly promised to me the supply of my necessary wants. "I will leave off the sea," thought I, "the little property I have acquired will produce £120 or £150 a year, and on this I may live, in an economical manner at least, entirely on shore. I shall then be no longer exposed to the freaks of fortune and unsuccessful voyages and may have the continued enjoyment of domestic intercourse and blessings of the land."'

But his hopes of a speedy independence were soon dashed to the ground. His 'little property' consisted almost entirely of a substantial loan which he had made to his brother-in-law, George Lockwood, to set up as a linen draper, and it was the interest from this which Scoresby expected would keep him modestly. Lockwood, however, was up to his neck in debt and went bankrupt. 'It was a most iniquitous business,' Scoresby writes, 'There was a degree of baseness in the conduct of George Lockwood that nothing but the most abject selfishness could palliate. I lent him a considerable portion of the sum in which he was indebted to me only about twelve months before his failure, to relieve him from some present difficulties. It was done in the confidence of his honour that his embarrassment was only partial, his property being stated at considerably exceeding his debts. It was lent on the express condition that I should have any security I pleased, and be promptly and certainly informed of the real state of his affairs should there be any cause for apprehension of a failure.

'Relying on his word and honour, I made no use of my securities as he continually declared he was fully solvent and should soon be able to pay me by instalments—yet such was his baseness that he actually *concerted* with one of his creditors (his father-in-law) the act of bankruptcy, by which I was made to suffer. He said that if he paid me he should have little or nothing to give to the manufacturers who were his creditors, who, therefore, when he should again set up business, would not allow him goods on credit!

'Attending a meeting of the Commissioners, I proposed myself, with Mr Thos Simpson, banker, as joint Assignees, which, on account of the great proportion of my debt to the whole amount, was carried. In this arrangement, Lockwood and his father-in-law opposed me, but without effect. I immediately chose another solicitor and set about selling the property, which was done to the best advantage.' It was some considerable time before the matter was cleared up, and even then Scoresby only recovered half his original loan.

It looked as if the Lockwoods were born to trouble as the sparks fly upward. First there had been the trouble with Charlotte and unpleasantness when the home was broken up. Now George had let him down. Scoresby no longer found his other brother-in-law, Mr Arundel, an effective preacher and even went so far as to have his little son, William, re-baptised by Mr Holloway, and he now 'attended most chiefly the ministry of Mr Holloway under whom I found myself more benefitted. He became my most attached and valued friend. I sought but little society beyond his and that of his family, and I found his advice generally prudent, christian-like and proper.'

When Scoresby returned from the whale fishery in 1817 he 'made known to the public, through the papers of the day, that a remarkable diminution of the polar ice had taken place, in consequence of which I was able to penetrate in sight of the east coast of Greenland, in the parallel of 74°. A situation which for many years had been totally inaccessible.' Sir Joseph Banks saw the report:

Letter from Sir Joseph Banks to Scoresby

                              Soho Square, Sept 22 1817

Dear Sir,

  I have read in the Liverpool paper that you have this year seen
the coast of West Greenland free from Ice and have sailed along
it for a considerable distance.

  You will oblige me much if you will give me a letter stating such
particulars as you have observed relative to the decrease of the Polar
Ice, a matter in my judgement of greater importance to the prosperity of this country if, as I conceive to be the case the frosty springs
and chilly summers we have been subject to for many years past,
so much so that it is now 16 or 17 years since we have had a full

crop of apples for cyder, are caused by the increase of Ice which seems to have accumulated for many years past.

It is said that islands of ice have been this summer seen in far greater numbers than usual in the Atlantic and the floods in all the mountanous [*sic*] parts of Europe of which our newspapers have given us continued accounts seem to prove a diminution of cold in the upper regions of the air.

I hope your Good Father is alive and well. Lady Banks has not forgot his obliging present to her of white bear skins which she uses in the winter to her great comfort.

An answer to this directed to me at Revesby Abbey near Boston will be thankfully received by,

Your faithful & Hble Servt

JOS BANKS

In reply to this letter, Scoresby sent Banks a copy of his printed *Treatise on the Northern Ice* and in his letter said:

'I found on my last voyage about 2000 square leagues of the surface of the Greenland sea, between the parallels of 74° and 80° north, perfectly void of ice, which is usually covered with it. . . . Had I been so fortunate as to have had the command of an expedition for discovery, instead of fishing, I have little doubt but that the mystery attached to the existence of a north west passage might have been resolved. There could have been no great difficulty in exploring the eastern coast of Greenland.

'I do conceive there is sufficient interest attached to these remote regions to induce Government to fit out an expedition. . . . In case of any whales being taken—and the fishery might occasionally be prosecuted without detriment to the other object of the voyage—the expenses would be proportionably reduced and might possibly be altogether defrayed.'

Banks's next two letters studiously avoid all reference to Scoresby's suggestion of a discovery expedition; he maintained a discreet silence on the subject, for he knew only too well from his own bitter experience that it was government policy always to have naval men in charge of such expeditions. He had quarrelled with the Navy Board forty years before and had financed his own private expedition to Iceland, instead of accompanying Captain Cook a second time, all because he could not persuade the Navy to see his point of view.

Banks thanked Scoresby for his 'very intelligent letter' and asked him why it was that no one had yet tried to win the reward offered by the government:

'You are aware no doubt that an Act of Parliament, the 16th Geo 3 Ch 6 offers a reward of £20,000 for the discovery of a N W passage and £10,000 for the ship that shall first reach the 89th degree of North Latitude.

'These rewards have not produced a single effort on the part of any Whale Fisher to accomplish either of these great purposes. Allow me to ask your opinion whether an act offering a thousand pounds for the reaching every degree of latitude from 82 to the Pole would be likely to induce the masters of ships to make a trial to reach at least some of the unknown degrees of Latitude.'

Scoresby's reply to Banks's enquiry was somewhat delayed because of the bankruptcy business, but in November 1817 he wrote to him:

'I am aware of the premiums offered by the Legislature for the attainment of certain situations on the polar regions, but am not surprized that they have not produced a single attempt, neither do I believe they ever will. Several reasons operate against them.

'1st   Few of the commanders of Greenland ships have either a taste for discovery or sufficient nautical knowledge for effecting them.

'2nd   The expenses of a fishing ship are so considerable that no owner considers himself justifiable in sinking these expenses and foregoing the advantages which may reasonably be expected from the fishing, to pursue objects of discovery in contemplation of a reward, the conditions of which are not known to be even possible. Besides, if we view the so called NW or NE passage as practicable, we shall find the expense of outfit, trials, insurance, hire of the ship and wages of the crew and Captain, would swallow up at least half of the premium offered. Now it is evident to those who visit the Greenland seas that were such a passage once accomplished it might not be again practicable in ten or even twenty years—it is evident that no premium could be adequate to the expense.

'I do not mean to imply that there is no such thing as a northern passage to India, for I do think the point has not been satisfactorily determined; yet I firmly believe that if such a passage does exist, it will be found only at intervals of some years; this I deduce from attentive observation of the nature, drift and general outline of the polar ice.'

Scoresby describes his first meeting with John Barrow, the Secretary of the Navy Board. He did not know at this time that Barrow had taken all credit for suggesting the polar expedition, wilfully suppressing Scoresby's name, and this mean act coloured all their future relationship. Barrow was a mean-spirited sycophant who had wormed his way upward by devious means and he was determined not to give way to anyone, least of all a whaling captain; he had made one journey to the Arctic in a whaling ship when he was a lad and that had been enough for him.

'My Father, who was then in town and had several conversations with Sir Joseph Banks, was advised to send for me, with a view to my being employed in this interesting service. Accordingly I left Whitby on the 11th of December and proceeded immediately to London. The day after my arrival I had an interview with Sir Joseph Banks and Mr Barrow. I found Mr Barrow was particularly anxious that my Father or I, or both of us should go in the proposed expedition; yet to my surprise he evaded conversation on the subject and generally avoided me in the room until, provoked by his conduct I watched an opportunity and put the question plainly to him—was it decided that I should have an employment in either of the expeditions, and if so, what situation it was that I must expect? He answered shortly and indirectly that if I *wished* to go in the Discovery, I must call the next day at the Navy Board and give in my proposals, and then turning sharply, he left the room. More than ever amazed by this ambiguity and general mystery that there seemed to be respecting this matter, I determined to ask an explanation of Sir Joseph Banks, of whose conduct and good will I had no doubt. The first interval that I observed him to be disengaged, (it was in his library at one of his conversaziones) I stepped up to him and put the same question to him. The substance of his answer was that they much wished (himself and the admiralty, I presumed) I should embark in one of the expeditions but he was very sorry to say that all his endeavours to obtain me a command in one of them failed, as the admiralty, having taken up the matter, *could not* employ any but their own officers as leading men. But it was hoped I might be disposed to go as a master (namely a pilot) having the charge of my own ship and crew; subject to the direction of the naval captain.

'The worthy president then, in as delicate a manner as he could, conveyed to me the information I wished and repeatedly and I doubt not with perfect sincerity, expressed his dissatisfaction with the arrangements. He stated moreover that he believed the commanding officers of the four proposed ships were already appointed.

'I was greatly disappointed with the result of this interview, from which it clearly appeared that I had undertaken a journey to Town for nothing, and had been called upon in such a way that I could have no claim for my expenses.

'Spurning the idea of embarking in a subordinate capacity on a service that I was better capable of, from my experience in the icy seas, than any Captain in the Royal Navy could possibly be, I declined the proposed arrangement suggested by Mr Barrow and neither appeared at the Navy Board, nor made any further enquiries on the subject. Indeed, I well knew had I been disposed to so disrespectful (to say the least) an arrangement, that the Navy Board would have stared at me in surprize had I requested 1000£ for my voyage; and

yet in my usual occupation a very successful voyage, with my high
wages and perquisites might bring me in as much, and with share
of a ship, much more.'

Thus began the long and largely ill-organised search for the north-
west passage by British naval commanders of little or no Arctic experience, which could have been completely avoided by the appointment
and adequate support of Scoresby, whose knowledge, experience and
scientific insight into Arctic problems fitted him uniquely for the task.

Had Banks been at the peak of his power and influence, instead
of within a year or two of the end of his life, the story might have
had a different and more satisfactory ending.

This was Scoresby's first brush with Barrow, and it does seem
singularly mean that his expenses were not met.

The weather in the British Isles was no better in the early nineteenth
century than it is today, and even then its inhabitants were busily
looking for the reasons. Sir Joseph Banks thought it might be due to
the 'Ice Islands in Strait Davis'. 'Be so good', he asked Scoresby, 'as
to make enquiry among your Greenland friends whether they have
been much more seldom seen formerly than at present. Should this
be the case, it will account fully for the diminished heat of our summers.' His letter made it clear that he regretted Scoresby's absence
from the Arctic expedition:

'The discovery ships are fitting out with much diligence The
Dorothea and the *Trent* are those intended for the Polar research. Captain Buchan commands the *Dorothea* and Lieut. Franklin the *Trent*.
I have mentioned to both of them your intention of communicating
with them in case you should meet them at sea, and impressed them
with the value of your experience and observations. I heartily hope
you may see them as I am sure that you will do them good.

'Let me know at what time you intend to sail and whether your
good Father attacks the whales this season. Oil is dear and I fear fish
will be scarce.'

The Lieut. Franklin whom Banks mentions was, of course, John
Franklin—later Sir John—the ill-fated commander of the 1845
attempt to find the north-west passage, lost with two ships and their
crews; a tragic consequence of the failure to enlist informed and experienced support for such enterprises.

Father, in the fullest confidence that his son would be asked to lead
the expedition to the Arctic, bought a ship for the voyage and gave
his son a thousand pounds towards a share in its ownership. The
Fame, a 'fine old teak built vessel', was docked at Liverpool and
Scoresby went there in February 1818, to equip it for its Greenland
voyage.

Time was short in Liverpool for they were 'late in starting and were greatly harassed in getting ready in time, and after all we were obliged to sail in a very disordered condition'. The *Fame* put in at Shetland for more men and from Balta Sound Scoresby replied to Banks's letter:

'Your particularly kind attention to my wishes with regard to a dipping needle demands my warmest acknowledgements. As an instrument of this description cannot be procured for observation on my anticipated voyage, I must of necessity defer my proposed experiment unto a future occasion. With much pleasure and gratitude therefore do I accept your estimable offer of superintending the construction of a dipping needle against another year.

'Were I, Sir Joseph, to attempt to express to you the grateful sense I entertain of your goodness in stimulating me to scientific pursuits by the many means on your own hands and the commanding influence you possess with others, my humble tribute of feeling & of praise might assume the garb of parasitic adulation and destroy the effect it was meant to produce. As such, I shall refrain, but I cannot withold the sentiments of others. An artist of some eminence from Lincolnshire called on me with some specimens of his performance in November last. In the course of conversation I asked him if he knew Sir Joseph Banks. "Know him," replied he with emotion, and tears started to his eyes, "Yes, to that great, that kind man I owe *everything!*"

'As the expeditions for discovery in the Polar seas have excited so much interest with the public, it may not be amiss to offer an opinion as to the probability of success. Though the Polar seas were navigable in an uncommon degree last summer, I conceive it very uncertain whether the ice may yet remain the same, and whether the navigation of these seas still continues equally open. As to reaching the Pole, I confess myself sceptical ... I shall be much surprised if they pass the eighty-fourth degree of latitude.

'The success of the expedition intended for the north-west is still more equivocal. Indeed, the nature of that voyage is wrapped in so much uncertainty, that in my opinion, it cannot warrant even a conjecture. I am persuaded a north-west passage exists—that is, as regards any obstruction from land; but how far it may or may not be blocked up with ice, so as to be always impervious, can only be determined by repeated trials.'

The results of the expeditions were precisely those which Scoresby had anticipated. Captain Buchan returned home from attempting the pole having only reached 80° latitude and the other ships were also prevented from navigating the then hypothetical north-west passage by ice. It took Amundsen three years to do this at the beginning of the twentieth century and not until 1969 was the north-west passage finally crossed in one year, when the massive ice-breaker, the *Manhattan*, smashed its way through the solidly frozen icy barrier.

The voyage in the *Fame* proved, 'according to the general average of the fishery—which was indifferent—prosperous. We obtained eight whales.'

Looking from the alleged enlightened age of the twentieth century it is extremely difficult to view the wholesale slaughter of whales and seals and other Arctic creatures which took place in Scoresby's time, with anything but revulsion; but we must remember he was a man of his time and he accepted the carnage as being in the natural order of things. Indeed, thirty years after he had left whaling he wrote:

'We are led to reflect on the economy manifest in respect to the hugest of the animal creation, whether on earth or in the ocean, whereby all become subject to man, either for living energy or the produce of their dead carcasses.

'The capture of the whale by man, when their relative proportions are considered, is a result truly wonderful. An animal of a thousand times the bulk of man is constrained to yield its life to his attacks and its carcase a tribute to his marvellous enterprise.

'Why this result should take place is satisfactorily explained on the simple principle of the Divine enactment. It was the appointment of the Creator that it should be so.' He then goes on to quote chapter and verse of scripture to prove his point.

The *Fame* returned safely, but just as she entered Whitby a sudden squall drove her off course and she was damaged. The repairs to the ship occasioned the first open difference between Scoresby and Father. For nigh on thirty years he had remained subservient to Father's domination, but the final straw came when Father interfered and ordered not only the repairs, but also expensive and quite unnecessary alterations to the vessel.

So much unpleasantness arose that Scoresby 'found our confidence and affection and my duty daily injured and was convinced that we should be more happy were our co-partnery dissolved. I therefore submitted to him two propositions, the first I considered to be strictly just—the second I considered as a personal sacrifice, and consequently in my Father's favour. They were as follows:

1. That I should resign the command of the ship to him and leave the management of everything to himself, reserving to myself the share I already held of the ship, which would, of course, entitle me to a proportion of the benefit of any profits, or to a contribution toward any losses.

2. That I would resign the command and likewise the share of the ship I then held, thus returning to my Father the gratuity of 1000£ with which he had presented me, provided he would allow me, for the recent voyage, in addition to my wages as Captain, one third share

of the profits of the voyage, to which I was justly entitled, free, however, from incumbrances with the expense of repairs.'

Father chose the more favourable alternative, pocketed the thousand pounds and left his son without a ship.

CHAPTER 8

AN ACCOUNT OF THE ARCTIC REGIONS

'One of the most remarkable books in the English language.'

For many years, in the intervals of the fishery, Scoresby worked on collating his vast collection of notes, drawings and journals relative to his Arctic experiences and observations with the intention of putting them all into book form. Jameson, to whom he eventually dedicated the book, gave much valuable advice:

'It gives me great pleasure to learn that you are so far advanced in your account of Greenland. I see by the curious facts mentioned in your first letter how much interesting information we are to expect from you. I agree with you on the propriety of sending a notice of your projected work to Dr Thomson, but I do not so much approve of your plan of publishing by subscription, because it has always a bad appearance, particularly when the plan is projected by the author himself. It looks as if he were in straitened circumstances and is about making a book merely for the sake of money. Now although this is very far from being your case, yet still one cannot prevent the world from believing it to be so.

'As to Prof. Gieske's book, I know it is already finished. It is entirely confined to West Greenland and will not interfere materially with your work. I rather think it will be useful to you as it will afford you a good deal of curious information in regard to the mineralogy, botany and zoology of that country.'

Jameson also wrote to his friend Archibald Constable, the founder of the publishing firm of that name, who wrote to Scoresby: 'I should feel much pleasure in undertaking any work of yours. If I had an opportunity of seeing the *MS* & drawings of the intended plates, I should very soon be enabled to give you terms. Lizars is now a very excellent engraver & I should think the plates might be extremely well done by him, and I would take the liberty of recommending the Octavo form for the letterpress.'

In the meantime, there was the matter of employment. Offers were not wanting, but Scoresby was cautious. He did not wish to rush into the first opening that offered itself. He was not anxious to enter into partnership again with anyone, least of all with any members of the family, several of whom suggested it. The previous trouble with

George Lockwood—from whom, incidentally, he never recovered more than half of the loan—had made him extra wary and he determined only to join with people of 'pious and conscientious character'. His friend, Dr Holloway, was now in Liverpool and so when Messrs Hurry and Gibson wrote from there offering a ship, Scoresby (after careful enquiry having found that Mr Hurry was 'a deacon of the most respectable of Independents' and Mr Gibson was 'a zealous and consistent Methodist') felt that it was an answer to prayer, for he was an intensely devout man and by the time he was thirty, the 'mere outward form' of his younger days had developed into a personal knowledge of God and a sincere dependence on his will. Of the Liverpool offer he wrote, 'the hand of God seemed in it'.

Mrs Scoresby was expecting her second child and Scoresby waited for its arrival before going to see about the new ship. 'On the 5th of November my second son was born. He was a very small, delicate child, whereas our other son was a plump fine lad. As soon as I was satisfied that my wife was in a promising way of recovery, I set out for Liverpool.' They named the boy Frederick Richard Holloway, in honour of their friend the Rev. Richard Holloway, to whom they were greatly attached.

In Liverpool there was much talk and discussion with the ship owners. Scoresby was not happy with the ship they proposed and eventually it was agreed that Messrs Hurry and Gibson would build a whaling ship especially for Scoresby and that he would draw up the plans for its construction. He was to have a one-third share in it and it was to be laid on the stocks the following spring, when Scoresby would move to Liverpool to superintend the building of the new ship.

Having settled all these details Scoresby went to stay in Edinburgh to attend to the other ship he was about to launch—his book. He wrote to Constable's accepting their proposals:

'That in consideration of the sum of 250£, payable to me by your bill on London @ 6 mo. from the date of publication, and 25 copies of the work free of charge, twelve of them to be printed on fine paper and hot pressed, I agree to sell you and Messrs Longman and Co, who are to have the offer of a share of the work from you on the usual footing, the right and benefit of an edition of 1000 copies (the copyright of the book, however, to remain with me) of the proposed work, entitled "A View of the Arctic Regions" &c, including an account of the "Northern Whale Fisheries" &c to be completed in 2 Oct° volumes of about 400 pages each, and to be illustrated with various engravings, amounting in all to about 20 plates; the book to be printed at the office of Mr Patrick Neill and the retail price about 30/– in boards.

'I further agree to use every exertion on my part, that the work may be ready for publication early in the spring of 1820.'

Even before the book was published, the scientific world in Edinburgh recognised Scoresby's worth, for on 25th January 1819 he was elected a Fellow of the Royal Society of Edinburgh.

Scoresby's stay in the northern capital was cut short by the death of his mother in February of that year. He writes:

'The dreaded intelligence has at length arrived. Our dear, affectionate, our beloved mother is no more. How pleasingly painful is the recollection of her tender care! When we were in pain the only sympathising friend was our mother,—when we were in grief, the consolatory friend was our mother—when we were the subjects of pleasure, the participating friend was our mother,—yea, there was a time when the only dear object of our affections was our mother.

'We were in some measure prepared for the distressing news, nevertheless we feared the event and dreaded the post every day during the interval since she was taken alarmingly ill. But all these events are in the hand of God.'

In May 1819 the Scoresby family, with their two children, William and Frederick, accompanied by their faithful nurse, Betty, removed *en bloc* to Liverpool, which now became their permanent home. They already had friends here, for Mr Holloway now lived in Liverpool and Scoresby had become acquainted with Dr Traill*—whose lectures he had attended—when he had been based there in the *Fame*. Another friend was Dr Thomas Raffles, the minister at Mr Hurry's chapel, whose subsequent illness, though not relevant to this biography, is interesting for the picture it gives us of the hit-and-miss style of medicine in the early part of the last century. In a letter to Scoresby in 1823 Raffles says:

'You may have heard perhaps that I am quite an invalid & entirely confined to the house. The affection proves to be that of the liver partially inflamed—I have taken mercury inwardly—but am now applying it to the part in the form of an ointment. The complaint is accompanied (I believe it is an invariable symptom of it) with great depression of spirits, and almost entire frustration of all intellectual energy.'

A very neat description of mercury poisoning, showing similar symptoms to those suffered by Faraday in his illness, though his mercury was not deliberately self-administered, but absorbed unconsciously during his work.

The new ship, the *Baffin*, named 'in honour of our long neglected navigator, whose hardihood, skill and perseverance in crossing the Atlantic and navigating and discovering the circuit of Baffin Bay, in a vessel of only fifty-five tons burthen, cannot be too highly estimated',

* Traill. See Chapter 9, p. 92.

was laid on the stocks shortly after their arrival in Liverpool and was built entirely to Scoresby's design. The plans of the ship, drawn by his own hand, may be seen in Whitby Museum today, together with a scale model of the *Baffin*.

For the first time in nearly twenty years Scoresby spent the summer in Britain. But he was not a man to be idle. There was much to be done at the shipyard and correspondence to be attended to, especially with regard to the forthcoming book. In September he attended his Father's marriage to Hannah Seaton, which took place at Trinity Church, Hull; and in October he went on holiday to Ireland with his friends Dr Traill and Mr Rathbone. His active mind took note of the details of the steam packet, the *Robert Bruce*, her measurements and dimensions, her speed and consumption of fuel, and he recorded her course and the state of the wind and weather. Though Scoresby himself was almost entirely without any sense of humour—his one great lack—some of the entries in the journal have an unconscious humour; for instance, it was 'blowing a brisk gale; sea on the increase' and then, in the next paragraph: 'A comfortable dinner, *for those who could enjoy it*, was provided at 3 o'clock.'

Nothing escaped his notice. The state of the Irish roads; the white-washed cottages and the 'gentlemens residences'; the cultivation of the land; fences, stone walls; the peat stacks outside the cottages; his observant eye took everything in. He lost his heart to Ireland on this first journey and afterwards returned again and again.

The principal part of the tour was a visit to the Giant's Causeway, for which they hired a guide, John Cory, who took them along the coast in a small open boat rowed by four men. Scoresby, needless to say, was not content to sit, he 'took a slight survey of this interesting coast' which is appended to the diary of the holiday. The party was duly impressed by the amazing formations in the Causeway and at the end of the three-day tour paid their indefatigable guide '31/6 for which he appeared grateful. Our boatmen's demands, though extravagant, were complied with. We paid 4 men for their services and the use of the boat 40/– and /4 for whisky. This excessive charge must militate against their general employment in similar excursions. About half this sum would probably prove in the end a greater emolument to them.' But the Irishmen had the last laugh, for the resourceful John Cory sold the tourists six joints from one of the pillars of the Giant's Causeway for three guineas, which they paid quite gladly.

By the end of February 1820 the book was ready for publication; 'but', wrote Constables, 'the cost has greatly exceeded our original calculations. We do not think the selling price can be under £2— at 36/– it would do little more than cover the bare cost. We would much rather it had been a cheap book.'

An Account of the Arctic Regions shows us Scoresby at the peak of the purely scientific part of his career. Although he was still to do much useful work, especially in terrestrial magnetism and magnetism in relation to marine navigation, it is in this work on the Arctic that we find his gift most fully employed. It is not too much to say that this book is Scoresby's greatest achievement.

It forms a landmark in the study of the Arctic, and on reading it we are led to reflect on the loss sustained by Arctic study and exploration when Scoresby failed to obtain command of an Arctic expedition—the fatal break in the natural continuity of his career which had occurred two years earlier. He was a descriptive and exploring scientist of the type so well represented by Alexander von Humboldt. In Scoresby we see an investigating mind, more at home in the great open spaces than in the laboratory, and whose gifts require to be well supported and encouraged before they can come to fruition in large projects. In the second half of the twentieth century the parallel type of scientific endeavour is centred in space research.

The two volumes have lately been brought out by David and Charles in an excellent reproduction. We agree so wholeheartedly with every word which Sir Alister Hardy says in his admirable Introduction to the 1969 edition that we feel we cannot do better than quote his comments verbatim; we are indebted to him and his publishers for permission to do so:

'For many years William Scoresby's *An Account of the Arctic Regions* has been out of print, one of the rarest items in the catalogues and shops of dealers in second-hand books. When found, what a price one was asked to pay for it; but then, what a treasure to possess.

'It is not only a classic of whaling literature, giving a reliable history of the early Arctic fisheries and vivid first-hand accounts of the methods of hunting in the old days; it is also an account of Arctic exploration and a quite outstanding pioneer work on the science of the sea. The late Sir Sidney Harmer, who was director of the British Museum of Natural History and our greatest authority on whales and whaling, rightly referred to it in his Presidential Address to the Linnean Society in 1928 as "one of the most remarkable books in the English language"; it is described in the *Dictionary of National Biography* as "the foundation stone of Arctic science".

'The two volumes are equally important, but for different reasons. The first volume is concerned with the geography of the Arctic regions, an account of early exploration, and then with Scoresby's truly surprising scientific investigation of the Arctic ocean with only the most primitive equipment. His chapter on the Hydrographical Survey of the Greenland Sea is as much a classic of early oceanographic literature as is his second volume in the field of whaling adventure. He describes the varying distribution of waters of different colour, particularly distinguishing the blue more transparent water from the more opaque green water which he shows to be coloured by the presence of innumerable minute organisms. While he does not realize that these are the minute plants of the sea, he actually describes through his microscope what are clearly chains of diatoms. . . . He then refers to a number of planktonic animals which are clearly recognisable in his drawings and knows that some of them are the food of the whales which tend to congregate where they are abundant. This must be the first account of the Arctic plankton.'

Sir Alister Hardy next remarks on Scoresby's chemical analysis of sea water; his marine diver; his work on Arctic current systems, ice formation and on Arctic meteorology and his important observations on magnetic variation. We are told that our knowledge of the Greenland whale is largely based on Scoresby's account of it in this book.

He then goes on to say that in his opinion the second volume is the finest account of the Arctic whale fisheries ever written, and he concludes his Introduction by recalling that the name of William Scoresby has, in this century, been carried into the polar regions at the opposite end of the world, for that was the name of the Royal Research Ship on which Sir Alister had the honour of serving as

The RRS *William Scoresby* pictured at Lagos in 1950

scientist, as well as on the RRS *Discovery*; the full account of the exploits of these two vessels in Antarctic seas is given in his enthralling book, *Great Waters* (1967).

The *Baffin* was launched on 15th February 1820 amid much celebration, for she was the first whaling ship ever to be built by Mottershead and Hays, the Liverpool shipbuilders. In only a month from this date she was ready for sailing, and Captain Scoresby and his new crew—some of whom he had recruited in Hull when attending his Father's wedding—sailed down the Mersey on the 18th of March. Only a few weeks after they left Mrs Scoresby was delivered of 'a fine boy' who, alas, only lived long enough to be christened Henry.

Scoresby had to wait until his return from the Arctic to hear what reception his book had, though shortly before he left he received his copies from the publishers and sent them to all his friends, including Sir Joseph Banks, who was just able to see it before his death in June of that year. Professor Jameson was one of the first people to receive a presentation copy; Dr Traill, Mr Gibson and Mrs Scoresby had theirs in Liverpool while Father had seven copies sent to him at his new home in Hull. Four were sent to 'Mr Philips' for the royal household.

The *Baffin*'s first voyage was extremely prosperous and she returned home with a full cargo at the end of August. A letter from his publishers told Scoresby: 'We have every reason to be much pleased with the sale of your book—it has gone further than we could have anticipated. Upon the whole the sale has been very creditable to the author, at the same time, it would be wrong to flatter you with a new edition—that cannot be thought of for some considerable time yet to come, and even then with great caution.'

But there was little need for this hesitation. *An Account of the Arctic Regions* was universally acclaimed; it was undoubtedly the foremost book of its kind. In a report upon it to the French Government, Rosily and Rossel wrote: 'We have examined the work and can assure you that for a long time we have not read a more substantial and methodical nautical work. . . . Captain Scoresby appears to us to have united to a mind incomparably more enlightened that genius for observation which rendered the accounts of Dampier so interesting and instructive.'

The reviewers, as always, were reluctant to give praise; the reviews of that day gave more of a résumé of the book than a direct criticism, and Scoresby's two volumes of 600 pages each, took up a good many pages of the reviews. Sometimes there was an unkind barb in the tail. After twenty pages of condensed résumé, the *Monthly Review* wrote:

'We rise from the perusal of the work with the pleasing reflection, that the commander of a Greenland whaler has here displayed much judicious and active observation, combined with no ordinary share of acquired knowledge and scientific attainment, and prompted by an ardent and generous zeal for useful discovery. In consideration of such estimable qualities, we may well pardon in a sailor a certain disregard of refinement of style and accuracy of language.'

An illustration from *An Account of the Arctic Regions* which Scoresby entitled 'Dangers of the Whale Fishery'. The critics called it 'a Munchausen-like picture of a whale playing at Battledore and shuttlecock'

The *Eclectic Review* confined itself to twelve pages. Deploring the 'Munchausen-like engraving of a whale playing at battledore and shuttlecock with a boat and its crew' they said they 'took up these volumes with very low expectations of gratification. They have somewhat of a clumsy look about them; and it was an awkward circumstance that we had it strongly in recollection that Capt. Ross's publication, notwithstanding its formidable apparatus of silver icebergs, carmine snow, leaping bears and Esquimaux beauties, was a very dull and unprofitable book. Mr Scoresby has, however, pleasantly disappointed us, although his work is not very dexterously put together, and a more judicious selection and compression of his materials would have given them a more general interest.'

They could not resist the sting in the tail and they concluded: 'Mr Scoresby writes, if not with the finish of a professed author, with the simplicity and precision of an intelligent man who is master of his subject, and more anxious to communicate important information in a distinct and impressive manner than to give himself the airs of a fine writer.'

An unknown hand, very probably Mrs Scoresby's, has copied out favourable reviews from Liverpool and Inverness journals, but one from the *European Magazine*, which refers to Scoresby rather slightingly, is broken off half way with the words: '(I have no patience with this review)'.

But Scoresby did not need any reviewers to commend his book. Its worth and his name far outlived their feeble ineffectual comments.

CHAPTER 9

NEW FRIENDS

'Advantages and information may be derived from his experience
and judgement not to be met with from any other source.'

The successful voyage of 1820 was followed by a holiday in Wales
with the ladies, 'Mrs Topham and her daughter', together with Mrs
Scoresby, who left the children with their devoted nurse, Betty. They
hired a landau which they were able to take across the Mersey in
the *Etna*, steam packet, 'a great acquistion to the river navigation
of Liverpool'. They found the hotel at Wrexham 'not a little uncomfortable' for a party of cavalry officers 'after dining at a late hour,
revelled through the night and only ceased their unhallowed noise
on the rising of the sun', and so they went on to Llangollen where
they 'enjoyed extreme comfort at the King's Head. Our sitting room
was very large and fronted the river in a charming situation; our lodgings were good; the provision excellent; the attendance punctual and
pleasing; altogether giving a first-rate character to this public mansion. I never, indeed, was an inmate of an inn where I felt more real
comfort.'

Their evenings were enlivened by the performance of a blind harp-
ist, Edward Jones—the details of whose harp Scoresby carefully noted
in his meticulous fashion—and Miss Topham entertained them by
singing 'several beautiful airs with much delicacy and sweetness'. After
which, they danced a reel to 'a spirited highland air'.

The days were spent in walking and exploring the district. When
it rained the ladies stayed indoors but Scoresby, the man of the Arctic,
was undeterred and went out alone. He admired the aqueduct at Pon-
tysyllty, 'the bold design of Mr Telford the engineer', and noted the
depth of the dungeons at Chirk Castle. They went to visit Mrs
Topham's youngest daughter at her seminary and Scoresby enjoyed
being the only man among '25 or 30 ladies, among whom there were
but one or two that could be called children'. There was more singing
by the inexhaustible Miss Topham, and more dancing.

At the end of the week they all returned home 'considerably benefitted as to their health'.

The voyage of 1821, though not prosperous, was one which
Scoresby enjoyed more than any he ever remembered. This was
due to the presence of Captain Manby, who came to Liverpool

bearing a letter from Dawson Turner,* the celebrated amateur naturalist.

My dear Sir,

Our friend Capt Manby is not satisfied to present himself before you without being the bearer of a letter from me & I comply with his desire, not because I am either vain enough or childish enough to suppose that anything which I would say would lead to the recommendation of such a man.

Of the merits of Capt Manby's invention it would be presumptuous to attempt to form an opinion, but to his great energy I am competent to bear testimony, and I am sure that whatever may be the fate of the attempt, you will have a most pleasant companion in your voyage. His being with you will lead, I trust, to a friendship between you; and in that case I may be so fortunate as to see you in Yarmouth and to form a personal acquaintance with you. Few things would give me greater pleasure than to receive you under my roof. . . . In the meantime it would make me very happy to contribute by any means in my power towards the furtherance of those literary and scientific pursuits which have done you so much credit, & I at all events rejoice at the opportunity thus afforded me of repeating the assurance of that respect and interest of,

my dear Sir, Yours most faithfully,
DAWSON TURNER

Yarmouth, 17th March 1821.

George William Manby (1765–1854) was at that time fifty-six years old. He had been an army captain and was a friend of Nelson. Twenty years before he had invented a life-saving apparatus which had proved most effective in rescuing shipwrecked seamen. It was an early form of the breeches buoy which fired a line to the ship by a rocket gun. Like Scoresby, he too had a restless mind, forever seeking out new truths. Even in his seventies he remained mentally active, for we find him writing to Scoresby twenty years later pages and pages about cod fishing off Greenland and related topics. He lived to be nearly ninety and was a most interesting character. After the voyage with Scoresby, Manby published his journal, which in its way is quite a classic, and in a letter to Dawson Turner, he says of his host:

'Captain Scoresby appears to me to be one of the most extraordinary men that ever came under my attention. I feel in his society as if I knew nothing; but I feel also that advantages and information may be derived from his experience and judgement not to be met with from any other source. To look at him with the eye of scrutiny

* Dawson Turner (1775–1858), wealthy banker of Norfolk, a patron of science and a naturalist and collector of great ability.

Captain G. W. Manby

there is no particular clue to discover his great mind and vast scientific acquirements. The habits and conduct of his life possess uncommon evenness, and in the truest sense of the word he is a real good man, most religious and extremely amiable.'

Manby had perfected a harpoon gun and wished to try it out on the voyage. He did not reckon, however, with the Luddite crew, who saw in the weapon an end to skilled harpooners—and incidentally an end to the bonus money paid to them—and did all in their power to demonstrate that the gun was of little use, even going so far as to pour water into the mechanism when no one was looking. Fortunately for the whales, they had another fifty years before their only enemy perfected his method of wholesale slaughter and whaling ceased to become a matter of skill, daring and enterprise, but merely an extension of the butchery trade, where the work of the slaughter-house is carried on at sea; but with this tremendous difference—stock is bred and constantly replenished in the land butchery, whereas the whales were not, until very recently, even allowed to breed and increase their number, but were shot indiscriminately,

But, harpoon gun apart, Manby enlivened the lonely Scoresby, who had never previously sailed with a close companion. He was a great raconteur and had had a varied and interesting life; he had much in common with Scoresby, being, like him, no mean artist.

The catch of that year was not good and reflected the general decline in the whaling trade. Father and Scoresby determined to ask the Board of Trade to look into the matter and see if they would institute an expedition to search for fresh whaling grounds. Together, they prepared a Memorial, which they sent to Barrow, the all-powerful Secretary to the Admiralty and the persistent thorn in Scoresby's flesh. It need hardly be said that Father's idea was for the *Fame* and the *Baffin* to be the sponsored ships in the voyage of discovery. But once again Scoresby was baulked by Barrow—a highly skilled member of the circumlocution office—who wrote to Father:

Admiralty.
5th Jan 1822

Dear Sir,

    Having sent your memorial to the Hon. Fred Robinson, the President of the Board of Trade, I have received the enclosed; and you will perhaps think it advisable to let your son wait upon him.

Yours, my dear sir,
very faithfully,
JOHN BARROW

Thus, very neatly, he put the onus of bringing Scoresby to London entirely on Father's shoulders. The 'enclosed' letter from Robinson only said, 'I think this proposition well worthy of consideration and I shall be very glad to see these gentlemen. I shall be in town the end of next week, and if you will take the trouble to invite them to London, and meet them at the Board of Trade, we will see what can be done.'

Scoresby was not immediately able to comply with this request, since he was delivering a course of lectures at the Liverpool Royal

Manby, who drew this picture, calls it 'A bear attacking a boat'. The bear appears
to be outnumbered

Institution, but at the end of the month he 'left Liverpool in the mail coach and reached London on the evening of the following day'. The next day he went to the Board of Trade and 'sent in my card. Mr Robinson was not within, but the secretary would send me word when it would be convenient for me to see him. I waited two days, and called again. There was a cabinet at the time, and he was engaged. The next day I called again, without success. I then addressed a note to Mr Robinson. At length I received a reply and, at Mr Robinson's request, arranged with Mr Barrow to accompany me to the Office for Trade on the Wednesday following.'

The story has a strikingly familiar ring. Breathes there the man who has not had a similar experience with the circumlocution office? When the meeting eventually took place, Scoresby was astonished to find that, 'instead of speaking favourably of the proposal, as his correspondence implied, he now seemed altogether to waive any arrangement with me on the subject. He said that our proposal was only suited to individuals, not to public boards—that though the trade showed decline it would soon find its proper level; and intimated that the loss of private property was a matter of private, not public consideration, and that the whole fishery had already received too much of the national support! I was quite amazed with his reasoning which was completely in opposition to what his letter had led us to expect. I found, however, that his object was to get rid of me and our proposal in the best way he could! Mr Barrow happened, in the course of the interview, to suggest that the Board of Longitude, of which he was a member, had it in their power to spend £5000 annually in valuable discoveries, and he stated that he would throw out a hint at the next meeting of the Board, that a premium of £2000 be offered for circumnavigating Spitzbergen. On this hint, Mr Robinson immediately seized, and through it took the opportunity of disengaging himself both of me and my proposition. I was therefore compelled to submit to be dismissed without recompense or even apology.

'This was now the second time I had been invited to London by a public board, on public service, and the second time I had been involved in the expense of my journey without any remuneration whatever.' It goes without saying that Barrow's proposal to the Board of Longitude was turned down also.

There was one advantage gained from the visit to London, however. Scoresby met Sir Humphry Davy. In the death of Sir Joseph Banks, Scoresby had suffered a severe loss. This genial and gifted man had been a good friend and powerful support to the young Scoresby and had provided for him an influential voice in the scientific circles of the day. Banks was, of course, deeply interested in the kind of scientific work Scoresby pioneered in the Arctic, and the two volumes of

Arctic Regions showed how fully justified he had been in seeking to further the young man's scientific career.

His death marked the end of an era in British science. A different type of scientist—more professional and specialist—gained control of the Royal Society. These men were more interested in the discovery of new substances and new phenomena; they were chemists and physicists, laboratory workers, with narrow and more specialised outlook. They had not voyaged with Cook nor hunted the great whale amid Arctic icebergs.

The science Banks had fostered and which had contributed so much to the development and enhancement of British power in a great overseas empire passed largely into the hands of a group of professional scientists, headed by Sir Humphry Davy, who hoped to harness the new chemistry and physics to the Industrial Revolution—the promise of a new Britain that was to be the workshop of the world. In such changing circumstances the scientific type so well represented by William Scoresby came to be undervalued and to lack encouragement and support. Davy himself was personally friendly and well disposed towards Scoresby, but his background and interests in life and in science were very different from Banks's, and his friendship lacked the potency and power of the Autocrat of the Philosophers.

Scoresby sent Davy a note requesting his "acceptance of a paper relating to an instrument for measuring magnetic attractions and finding the dip of the needle. Some of the laws determined by this instrument, when iron was rendered magnetic, & by electricity may be considered I apprehend as the mere mechanical effect of the shock, similar to the influence of a blow. These are consequently distinct from the electro-magnetic laws, which were so satisfactorily developed in your recent experiments.' He offered to show Davy the magnetimeter, for such it was, and Davy, replying by return, like the great man he was, invited Scoresby to demonstrate it—'tomorrow evening at $\frac{1}{2}$ past 9'.

After the indifferent, almost insolent, treatment which Scoresby had received at the Board of Trade, Davy's kindness was balm to his wounded feelings and he felt that his visit was not entirely in vain for he had made the personal acquaintance of the new President of the Royal Society in his own house. Davy was 'much struck with the experiments and requested me to furnish a paper for the Royal Society on such of the experiments as had not previously been communicated'. On his return to Liverpool Scoresby wrote this paper and sent it to Davy only a month before sailing; at the same time he asked if it would be possible to borrow some instruments:

'You were so obliging as to say that besides the dipping needle which the Board of Longitude propose to commit to my care I might

Sir Humphry Davy

probably obtain from the same source the loan of any other instruments which might be useful in a scientific or nautical view. I therefore take the liberty to submit whether the Board of Longitude might be inclined to furnish me with a chronometer and one of Capt. Kater's azimuth compasses. I do not ask either of these instruments for my private use as I have already a chronometer & azimuth compass of my own; but as none, almost, of the lands within the Arctic circle are correctly laid down, I should be happy to undertake, at all opportunities, to ascertain the position of any headlands or coast near which we might happen to navigate; this could not be satisfactorily accomplished by the use of one chronometer, particularly as few opportunities occur of correcting its rate either by the proximity of lands whose precise longitude is known, or by lunar observations, the moon being three-fourths of the time beneath the horizon and seldom visible when above.'

Davy's approach to the Admiralty only elicited the following curt reply from Barrow:

'I have shown Mr Scoresby's letter to Lord Melville, but he observed merely that we have no authority to dispose of His Majesty's property to private ships; and I believe the Board of Longitude has as little. Mr Scoresby must therefore do the best he can with his private means.'

Despite the repeated rebuffs Scoresby received from Barrow's hands, he was still anxious to pursue his scientific studies in the Arctic, to survey uncharted coasts and to perform any useful work he could in these directions, as well as answering the many calls on his time and energy as a whaling captain. Herein he showed his true stature; he was a dedicated scientist, interested primarily in obtaining results and adding to the store of knowledge slowly and painstakingly accumulated by devoted and disinterested men; it mattered little who did the work, so long as it was done, so long as the new pathway was trodden and the road made for others to follow.

After the rude dismissal in Barrow's letter, it is all the more remarkable that Scoresby did actually manage to map the east coast of Greenland while on this 1822 voyage despite his lack of instruments. Right down the coast he mapped and measured and charted the position of the land, giving illustrious names all the way, starting with *Kater's Bay*, in honour of the man whose azimuth compass he used. Another member of the Board of Longitude, Wollaston, together with its Secretary, Thomas Young, were also 'put on the map'. Nor was Davy's kindness forgotten, for *Davy's Sound* was almost as long as *Scoresby's Sound*, which was named after his Father.

The map was sent to Davy shortly after Scoresby's return to Britain and it was published that winter in Scoresby's *Account of a Journey to the Northern Whale Fishery*, which was dedicated to the King. And yet, the only names which survive on modern maps are Traill, Jameson and Scoresby. It is not quite clear why this should be so, for he was undoubtedly the first person to survey this particular part of the coastline correctly. The only fact which is quite clear is that he was not a naval man. On his original chart, now in the Whitby museum, the following note appears at the bottom:

Remarks: The northern part of the coast comprised in this chart was visited by Capt. Clavering RN Admiralty research, in 1823, who, being late in the season was enabled to get close inshore, and so as to correct the coastline from lat. $73\frac{1}{2}°$ towards the north. Considering that my nearest approach to the land was a distance of from 40 to 45 geographical miles & that I had but one chronometer and that a second rate instrument, the accordances between lat. 73° 30′ & 74° 20′ must be considered as very remarkable. The position of Jackson Island with the headlands of Gale Hamke's Bay and Cape Broer Rays being all but identical. Thus Capt. C. having landed on Jackson Isl. found it lat. 73° 56′ the *precise* latitude given in my published Journal p 464.

It is remarkable that Capt. Clavering makes no mention of my observations on these northern coasts in his journal till his arrival at Cape Parry, though my Voyage was published two months before his departure. The points of coast laid down by me betwixt C. Broer Rays and C. Parry are obviously so accordant with the determination by Capt. C. as by no means to justify any alteration of the names attached by me.

Wm Scoresby.

Quite by chance we came upon a letter from Clavering which made it clear that he most certainly had read Scoresby's account. This was in the Scott Polar Research Institute, and we are grateful for their permission to reproduce part of that letter, written on 6th February 1823 to one John Smith. He writes: 'I have read some of Scoresby's papers. The old man, tho clever, is I am told a great rogue. Capt. Colquhoon of the Artillery accompanied him to make experiments with Congrieves Rockets for the purpose of killing whales, but the old man made him do the duty of a common seaman.'

It is difficult for anyone with a knowledge of Father's character to credit Clavering's statement with any degree of truth and at once this gives us an insight into the sort of man he was. It is obvious he was telling the story for effect, adding his own little embellishment to make the story more striking. If there was the faintest shadow of truth in the story, then why should John Laing wish to go a second time to the Arctic with Father and write, in 1807: 'I would rather go with your father than any other Captain. He is indeed a gentleman in the strictest sense of the word.'

From Loch Ryan, before leaving for the Arctic, Scoresby wrote to

Dr Brewster* enclosing a paper 'On the Errors of the Sea Rates of Chronometers by the Magnetism of their Balances and Chronometrical Compasses'.

My dear Sir,

The accompanying paper has been some time written, but I have not had opportunity of copying it until now. I was induced to draw it up partly because my former experiments with the magnetimeter suggested a means of destroying the magnetism of the balance of Chronometers & partly because Mr Barlow in his laborious investigation of the effects of iron on the rates of Chronometers seems to have neglected to note the direction or position of the Chronometer he used when the rates were ascertained before they were brought near the iron, whilst this circumstance must have had a most important effect on the whole of his results. I cannot indeed perceive from his paper that he has at all considered the superior importance of terrestrial magnetism over that of the iron in ships.

Dr Traill mentioned to me that the article *Polar Regions* for your encyclopaedia would soon be needed. If I have opportunity during my voyage I shall get it into a state of forwardness.

Brewster's position as Secretary of the Royal Society of Edinburgh laid him open to the whimsies of cranks, one of whom he describes in a letter to Scoresby: 'Your paper on the impregnation of wood with water &c is printed in our journal now at press. Mr Deuchar, a lecturer in chemistry here has sent me a long paper, the object of which is to shew that at great depths in the sea the water will pass through a Glass Bottle hermetically sealed. I have told him that I could not think of putting such a paper when an experiment can be so easily made to confirm or refute his notion. Your experiment with a conical cask impervious to water would at once decide this question, if such an idea merits being put to the test of experiment.'

Among the many papers which Scoresby contributed to the journal of the Royal Society of Edinburgh one of the most interesting is the following:

Electro-Magnetic Experiments and Observations
By Thomas Stewart Traill, M.D., F.R.S.Edin.
and William Scoresby jun. Esq, F.R.S.Edin.
(Read May 6th 1822)   *1823*

His collaborator, T. S. Traill (1781–1862), was an Orkney man who had been a fellow student of David Brewster. He settled in Liver-

* David Brewster (1781–1836), noted Scottish physicist who helped to found the British Association, inventor of the kaleidoscope, discovered Brewster's Law in optics. Knighted in 1832. Lived at 10 Coates Crescent, Edinburgh (the house where Cordelia Stamp was born!).

pool in 1803 and continued in practice there until 1832, when he was appointed to the Chair of Medical Jurisprudence at Edinburgh University. Dr Traill took great pleasure in lecturing and delivered many in Liverpool, and thus it was that Scoresby met him and formed a friendship which lasted to the end of his life. Traill was a prime mover in founding the Liverpool Literary and Philosophical Society, of which he was its first secretary. He assisted in founding the Liverpool Royal Society and the Liverpool Mechanics Institute. He was editor of the eighth edition of the *Encyclopaedia Britannica*, to which he contributed many articles, but ill health forced him to entrust much of his editorial duties to others.

The discovery in the winter of 1819 by the Danish physicist Oersted of the true connection between electricity and magnetism started off a whole new series of researches in physical science. Davy, Arago and especially Ampère repeated and extended the important observations of Oersted and founded the new science of electro-magnetism.

Scoresby and Traill, like most of their scientific contemporaries, were greatly stimulated by the new discoveries, and electro-magnetism became the centre of interest for research in the physical sciences much as Volta's battery and the new phenomena of the electric current had been twenty years earlier.

The two investigators are mainly concerned in their paper to stress the direction in which the needle is deflected with various arrangements of simple conducting wires and with helices, and they do not record here anything new, indeed, the discovery was so completely presented by Oersted and so brilliantly developed by Ampère, that nothing in this respect remained to be elucidated. A number of experiments, however, are recorded using a thin brass tube, which appears to have been 6 inches long and 2 inches in diameter, with a magnetic needle suspended within it; a current was passed through, varying the direction and position of flow, and the movement of the needle was observed. Here, the experimenters observe variable results and state (p. 7):

> We remarked singular irregular motions of the needle in its axis which were not easily reducible to any general law.

Later, on page 14, we find these observations:

> The degree of deflection [of the magnetic needle] appears to be subject to sudden variations and irregularities, of which the cause was not always apparent. If we may be allowed the expression, it seemed as if the electro-magnetic current moved through the tube with difficulty.

The fact that the experiments with simple wires and helices were consistently reproducible and not subject to unexplained variations, shows the galvanic arrangement to have supplied a steady current during the experiment. The observations with the thin brass tube would seem, therefore, to have provided effects arising from electro-magnetic induction, later again obtained in the well-known experiments of Arago and Barlow and Christie (magnetism of rotation). Unfortunately, although our authors remark on these irregularities, they do not follow the clue provided by them. Even later, when the results of Arago and the theoretical analysis of them by Herschel and Babbage were before the scientific world in 1824–1825, the correct interpretations were not forthcoming. These had to await the physical insight and experimental ingenuity of a Faraday (1831).

Even a scientist as penetrating as Ampère—who, in September 1822, working with Auguste de la Rive, obtained effects arising from electro-magnetic induction—failed to follow out the clue offered and so missed the great discovery. So we can hardly blame Scoresby and his friend Traill for their failure; but they do seem to have been among the first experimenters to have obtained these effects. Their paper was read in May 1822, so their experiments must have been performed before those of Ampère and de la Rive. Had Scoresby been able to carry on his researches with Traill at leisure during the summer months of 1822 instead of having to voyage in the Arctic whale fisheries, who knows?—perhaps a major discovery might have been made by the two investigators. The history of science gives us many examples of missed discoveries; they cannot form any part of the description of the progress of science, but they do have value in enabling us to assess the true worth of a man's intellect and his powers of penetration.

In this paper we see Scoresby and Traill as painstaking experimenters working fruitfully in a field of research on the very edge of scientific endeavour and obtaining useful and pregnant results. Their failure to see the real meaning of the 'irregular motions' and 'sudden variations', and still more, Ampère's failure, make us marvel at the penetration of Michael Faraday. Missed discoveries would form a fascinating and instructive study.

CHAPTER 10

THE LAST TWO VOYAGES

'Great attentions received—I was a sort of lion or Great Whale!'

Despite unctuous letters from Holloway, Scoresby remained loyal to his friend and named a bay after him on the east coast of Greenland. Holloway's stay in Liverpool had been short and he wrote from Shrewsbury shortly after the publication of *Arctic Regions* bemoaning the fact that he had been overcharged by the carriers: 'My furniture filled four carts. The agreement we made was £5 a cart to Chester and double that sum to Edsbaston Wharf. The sum due to Shanklin from me is £5 with £10 to the other party, but I have told them that the 15£ shall be paid to Mr Shanklin in discharge of the whole. Will you be kind enough to call on Shanklin & see him yourself, explain the case and if you have not yet received rents enough from the chapel, tell him as soon as they come in you will settle it. I know that the pew renters are backward in paying their rents—I shall be obliged to you to urge Wilson the clerk the necessity of exerting himself to gather them in. And he ought to for he is paid for it.'

The letter ends with a far from subtle plea for a free copy of Scoresby's book: 'I congratulate you on the favourable reception with which your publication has met. I expect to hear soon that there is another impression on the stocks, which a change in our circumstances will enable us to procure.'

It was on the voyage of 1822 that Scoresby mapped the coastline of Old Greenland. The Spitzbergen area had been over-fished and whales were scarce and so, despite the complete lack of support from the Board of Trade, Scoresby decided to try new fishing grounds and pushed into the north towards Old Greenland. His enterprise was rewarded, for they had a good catch and returned with a full ship, but the cold was intense, and once a drop in temperature from 32° to 2° occurred within sixteen hours. The hardy sailors produced 'an assortment of extraordinary habiliments for defence against cold, and various and grotesque were the costumes to which some of them resorted'.

Even more strange costumes came into evidence on May Day for: 'The 1st day of May is usually ushered in by the Greenland sailors by the suspension in the rigging of a garland of ribbons, attended with grotesque dances and other amusements, and occasionally with ceremonies somewhat similar to those commonly practised in crossing the line. It affords opportunity for the display of feats of activity or strength; for the practice of such kinds of harmless frolic as the circumstances of a whaling voyage will permit, and for the development of that species of original and frequently extraordinary wit peculiar to the sailor.'

Tradition held that the garland was fixed aloft by the most recently married man, and this ceremony was followed by Neptune's appearance—with his wife, of course. Great hilarity is often produced by men dressing up as women, and if the present-day reader would like to witness much the same thing, he should come to Whitby in August and watch the frolics on Regatta Day.

Scoresby, however, had no 'particular taste for witnessing these scenes' and 'did not turn out at the time when the ship's company were all busily engaged in the performance of their various parts of the humours of the day'.

The cold increased as they pushed northwards, and at latitude 80° 34' the thermometer fell to below zero. 'The greatest cold noticed in this situation was $-8°$; which was the extreme of my observations during twenty voyages to the whale-fishery. This intensity of cold, which was rendered excessively penetrating by the strength of the wind, was severely felt. Though we had smooth water, and kept the companion door constantly closed, the cabin became more uncomfortable than the deck. Water spilt on the table, within three feet of a hot air stove, became ice; washed linen became hard and sonorous; and mitts that had been hung to dry exactly in front of the fire (the grate being full of blazing coals), and only thirty inches distant, were partially frozen; and even good ale placed in a mug at the foot of the stove, began to congeal! A damp hand applied to any metallic surface in the open air, stuck to it; and the tongue brought into contact with the same, adhered so firmly, that it could not be removed, without the loss of the skin. Some of the sailors suffered considerably from partial frostbites. The cooper had his nose frozen, and was obliged to submit to a severe friction with snow; and the boatswain almost lost his hearing.'

Scoresby spent many hours at the mast head, scantily protected by the enlarged barrel known as the crow's-nest,—invented by his Father. Of a chain of icebergs he writes: 'Their number was found to be still greater than I had before apprehended. The sea, throughout an area of almost twenty miles in diameter, was almost covered with these prodigious floating bodies. At one time I counted above 500 from the mast-head, of which scarcely any was less than the hull of a ship. About a hundred of them appeared to be as high as our mast-head. Some were certainly twice this height, or 200 feet above the surface of the sea, and several hundred yards in extent. One, which I had a good opportunity of estimating, was at least a mile in circumference, and 100 feet in height; another was about 1000 feet in circumference and 200 feet in height. They assumed a great variety of forms, and some difference of tints, but the prevailing appearance was that of cliffs and islands of chalk. In recent fractures, however, the colour is a fine emerald green; and in cavities, where the light is transmitted through a portion of the ice, it is a brilliant blue.'

When the *Baffin* returned in September and reached the Orme's Head, Scoresby could get no satisfactory answer from the pilot whom they took aboard, 'from real or well-feigned ignorance' respecting his family. They had to wait until the following day for the tide before they could enter the Mersey. Scoresby's account continues:

'Notwithstanding the number of boats that came alongside, no information whatever could be obtained. This surprising ignorance of so many persons, on a subject to which I was so much alive, increased my anxiety. At length, while pacing the deck with an intensity of anxiety, the bare remembrance of which, at the present moment, throws my whole frame into a tremor, I perceived a boat with passengers approaching. As it rapidly advanced before wind and tide, I took the glass, and described the face of a friend. The first emotion in my mind, at this recognition, was that of hope. But on a second inspection of the boat, some peculiarities in the conduct of the passengers checked the transitory joy which this frail hope had created.

'The sail was taken down, and the men lay upon their oars while the boat approached only under the influence of the tide. The kind consideration of my friends had, on former occasions, always relieved my suspense, while yet at a distance, by some token of good news. Now, however, I watched in vain for some encouraging action or word. I supposed they had not seen me. I showed myself at the gangway, but their averted faces and downcast looks too strongly indicated that they were the harbingers of sorrow. I could no longer sustain an agony of feeling which silence and uncertainty rendered intolerable. I called out, "Is all well?" A languid look and an evasive reply confirmed my apprehension and sank me in despair. I could no longer support myself on the deck. I rushed into my cabin. In a few minutes my friend was in my presence. I saw him struggling with himself to break the dreadful tidings. "Let me know," cried I, "the worst—tell it me at once." He grasped my hand with the fervour of friendship while the tear of sympathy gushed from his eyes.—"I am sorry," (my agony obliged him to speak out), "Mrs S— is no more."

'Some of those who glance over these pages, may have been the "sons and daughters of affliction." They may know what it is to suffer. Such will not withhold the sympathetic sigh from one, who, having begun this narrative, in the hope of obtaining some alleviation from the poignancy of sorrow, finds its concluding pages blotted with his tears.'

These are the sad words with which Scoresby ends the *Journal of a Voyage to Greenland*, his second book. He worked on it all that winter, often having little Frederick beside him, for: 'He was fond of being in the room with me, though I might be so engaged as to be able to yield to him but little or no attention. In that case he was willing to amuse himself with such things as might be given him, for long intervals together, seldom breaking in upon me, unless cautiously and gently from any occasional want, and then turning as quietly as before to his employment or amusement.'

The elder boy, William, was sent to boarding school in Cheshire, but Frederick, apart from being too young was also too delicate to leave home. His devoted nurse, Betty, 'a woman homely in her exterior and manners, but sensible and thoughtful in mind, and ardently attached to myself and my children, was his principal guardian and ministering attendant in time of my absence from home'. It was noticed that the little boy's spine had a tendency to curvature and his legs 'became bent'. One wonders if this was rickets, remembering that he was born in November and that sunshine, the great giver of vitamins, was not only absent at that time, but it was deliberately excluded from babies. Also, around the time of Frederick's infancy they were having poor summers, as Sir Joseph Banks had remarked. Be that as it may, his loving guardians obtained 'instruments and stays' for his support, so that after *two or three years* 'of careful application they were enabled to be abandoned altogether, and no deformity whatever, but only the constitutional delicacy of body, and feebleness of growth, remained'.

Manby did his best to pour oil on troubled Admiralty waters and wrote to Barrow praising Scoresby. Barrow's reply was very short:

'I am much obliged by your information respecting Scoresby; he is an enterprising young man, and of very considerable talents and I am glad that he has had an opportunity of applying them to a useful purpose, which that of correcting the geography of our planet certainly is.'

Delighted at having his name on Scoresby's Arctic map, Dawson Turner wrote from Yarmouth:

My dear Sir,

Our mutual friend, Captain Manby, has just put a letter of yours into my hands, at the contents of which it is impossible I should do otherwise than feel myself exceedingly gratified. I cannot indeed tell you how I feel it in you, to have thought of so insignificant a person as myself, when so far removed from home, and to have endeavoured to render the durability of my name coeval with your own discoveries. I use the word *endeavour*, because we both of us know that, whatsoever may be the efforts that are made by the kindness of our friends, there is no arriving at anything like immortality but by our own exertions. Rank and fortune may be hereditary, & talents are the gift of God, but a man must be the artificer of his own fame. Your kindness on this account has been particularly welcome to me. I trust that we may one day or other become better acquainted.

I need not add that I shall be exceedingly obliged by a sight of any of the plants you have collected, or that I shall be particularly happy if my botanical knowledge can in this matter be turned to account towards the furtherance of your proposed publication. I enclose a portrait of Capt. Manby which has been lying many months in my drawer for you. When you come here you shall take as many more impressions as you please for yourself or your friends; & they will not be injured, like this, by folding.

I am with respect and esteem, Dear Sir,
very faithful yours,
DAWSON TURNER

Yarmouth 21st Oct 1822

A kind letter from Jameson enclosed an offer of a hundred pounds from Messrs Constable for Scoresby's new book, the journal of the 1822 voyage.

My dear Sir,

The opposite pages contain Mr Constable's answer. I regret it is not more, but you have another fixed offer in London. As soon as you have made up your mind I beg you will let me hear from you. I think £150 at least ought to be got for the volume, considering that your 'Arctic Regions' is exhausted. Independent of the great interest of your own journal, the publication at the same time as that of Franklin will occasion a great demand & must in a month or two exhaust the impression. These circumstances ought also to be stated to your London publishers—Murray I should think is your best man—Colburn I heard also gives good prices. Do not forget that Parry got £1000 for his 2nd book & thought himself ill-paid.

All my family join in best wishes. We are vexed at the result of my negotiation with Constable as we hoped if more successful that you would have spent your winter in Edinburgh.

I am most faithfully & Sinsy,
Yours
ROBT JAMESON

Scoresby decided to accept both Constable's offer and Jameson's invitation, and he spent much of that winter in Edinburgh. He greatly enjoyed the social life, in which his own attractive personality played no small part. He noted: 'Great attentions received—I was a sort of Lion or Great Whale!' While there, Scoresby made the acquaintance of Sir Walter Scott and through his influence, dedicated his book, *Journal of a Voyage to the Northern Whale Fishery*, to King George IV.

Scoresby was possessed of that extraordinary gift which so often goes with a scientific mind—detachment. Despite his grief, he was able—after the first initial prostration—to switch his mind off, as it were, and concentrate on other things: so it was with this book, the writing of which occupied his mind to the exclusion of all other thoughts, and again, ten years later, when Frederick died, his father was able to write a calmly detached account of his son's life.

There was also an acceptance of the will of God and a deep inner conviction of his working for good. He was a man who depended much upon prayer and spiritual guidance.

The 1823 voyage brought little success and Scoresby made it his last. After more than twenty voyages to 'this inhospitable part of the globe' he decided finally to retire from the sea. For some years he had felt leadings of the spirit. He submitted himself entirely to the will of God and he felt that he was called to minister to mankind in a more direct way than his present life. The inner voice finally made itself heard and Scoresby knew that he must answer the call and enter the Church.

This was no small decision for a man of thirty-three. The years when the habits of study came easily were long past; nevertheless, he started, under the direction of Mr Buddicom, a clergyman in Liverpool, to study Latin and Greek, the first essentials towards ordination.

Scoresby was restless and unable to settle for any length of time in the Liverpool house—so desolate now without his wife—and he spent much of his time travelling. He was in constant demand as a lecturer, and at the beginning of 1824 we find him lecturing in Birmingham and visiting as many factories as possible between whiles. His heart, at this time, was no longer free for there was a lady in the case, unnamed, who 'greatly won my affection and esteem by her elegance, dignity, kindness and accomplishments'. Scoresby had 'some reason given to me to hope that my addresses to her would not be unsuitable'. He only mentions her indirectly in a letter to his friend, Adam Hodgson:

'I have every reason to be most perfectly satisfied with my visit to Birmingham, excepting in one point, namely that I am so involved in engagements and lectures that I have no time for *some object* of much importance. I have met with extraordinary civilities & hospitality &

trust I shall acquire some friendships beyond the ephemeral attachments of a traveller that will be a comfort and advantage to me in future life, if I am spared. I have met with some very estimable people—truly so. And I have also met with some very clever people. Mr Corrie I have not seen much of but like what I have seen—Mrs C. is a charming woman. Please to thank Mr Buddicom when you see him for his introduction. I have been much gratified by the preaching of Mr Burns.

'My lectures have been received with great complacency and civility. The attendance, which far exceeded my expectations, has hitherto (during three lectures) been between 200 and 250. If the attendance continues I shall flatter myself that my magnetism has not been *un-attractive*. It is quite a gay and animating scene, most of the ladies, and these are the most numerous, perhaps, of the audience, appear in full dress.

'Last evening Capt. Ross RN popped in upon us on his way to London. I introduced him to Mrs Corrie, but we could not prevail upon him to remain for a few days, his engagements in London, indeed, preventing.

'I have seen little of the manufactories but design tomorrow, if the weather be suitable, to pay a visit to the large iron works in the neighbourhood. These, I understand, are very interesting. Pins and glass beads was my amusement today! Of the former, in the manufactory I calculated that 10 million of pins were turned out every week, weighing about two or two & a half tons!'

The iron works at Gospel Oak, owned by Mr William Yates, exerted their usual fascination on Scoresby. He watched the methods used, the puddling process, and all the details of the intricate art and carefully noted the amounts and types of fuel used, the output, and the labour involved.

Later visits included a 'lamp manufactory' where, once more, all the processes were duly noted; the making of steel studs was observed, and a visit to 'Mr Boulton'. This might perhaps mean little to us today, but when the entry is followed by reference to Mr Watt, we at once connect the two names:

'Feb 13. Visited Mr Boulton (son of *the Boulton*) at Soho: and Mr Watt at Aston Hall. This hall is a very fine large building of brick of James the 1st time. Contains 94 apartments. The habitable parts furnished with antique tables, chairs and decorations, the furniture of oak & embellished with old paintings.'

And that is all we are told about Boulton and Watt. Only in imagination can we fill in the details of Scoresby's meeting with the sons of these two great men. Nor are we given any details of his next visit, which was to Cambridge to meet Dr Godfrey, the President of

Queens' College, where Scoresby was entered as a 'ten year's man', since he was too old to become an undergraduate. This meant that he would study and work as an ordained Minister for ten years and during the last two years would keep three terms at the university.

A visit to Woolwich followed, where, after watching a display of rocket firing, he fired two himself. The Army Surplus department was busy even in those days, for Scoresby notes:

'There were several thousand pieces of cannon lying in a field in store—and in the store room equipage for 20,000 horses.'

Scoresby's friend Thomas Griffin (whom, incidentally, he had first met on a long coach journey) wrote a tempting letter from Paris, where he was living:

Less than £5 will bring you comfortably to Paris & living here is cheaper than in London. Every branch of science by the first Professors is here free to all persons *for nothing* & continued every day in the year. Gay-Lussac lectures daily.' He proposed going on to Italy and invited Scoresby to join his party. 'Send some clever fisherman to Greenland in your stead this year and come and be a gentleman for a 12 month along with us. There is a good deal to see in Paris and a person may pass a month or two very pleasantly. The sciences in general and particularly Mathematics are certainly more advanced in this country than in England, but the People are at least a Century behind us in civilization, & comfort & from being 4/5ths materialists, they possess no standard of moral obligation & are consequently possessed of the least principles of honour of any Nation in Europe. Lying is no crime whatever with them. But come and see & judge for yourself.'

Tempted by this prospect of the scientific life of Paris, and undeterred by not being able to understand a word of spoken French, Scoresby went to Paris at the beginning of April. He stayed there a month and once again, as had been the case in Edinburgh, he was received as a celebrity and met all the leading men of science. His journal records:

'12 April 1824.　Visited the Institute which meets on Mondays and commences its operation at three o'clock. At the previous request of M. Arago I enquired for him; he introduced me (before the meeting) to Mm Ampère, Cuvier, the comparative anatomist, Capt.——one of the French voyagers round the world, Adml Count Rosily, Baron Humboldt, La Cepede, M. Bricha, Gay-Lussac &ᵗ &c. La Cepede, whose *Histoire des Cetaces* I had criticised in my *Arctic Regions*, was nevertheless very polite & friendly & acknowledged that not having seen whales he had taken everything from research.

'Ampère offered to exhibit to me his electro-magnetic experiments.

Baron Humboldt, who had taken the trouble of twice calling at my lodgings without seeing me, expressed his intention of calling at a still earlier hour until he should find me, a piece of politeness that I requested he would dispense with. He complimented me on the excellent works, as he was pleased to denominate them, which I had given to the world & declared his admiration of the great variety of subjects that I had handled and the manner in which they were treated. It might savour of a too great feeling of self-satisfaction to state all the polite things he said.

'The other gentlemen to whom I was introduced likewise expressed in the most complimentary way their pleasure at seeing me & to make their compliments the more acceptable they had that sort of bearing upon what I had done in a scientific way, to enable me by little self-conceit to receive them with any sort of complacency.

'Four chairs, places of honour, for strangers, are situated near the President; to one of these I was handed by the President, who to my much surprise announced my presence to the Institute to this effect: "I beg leave to inform the meeting that Capt. Scoresby whose works you have seen and read with so much interest, assists at the sitting".

'M. Cuvier handed me a note across the table inviting me to dinner on Saturday & requesting me to go an hour before dinner that he might himself show me the collection of comparative anatomy, which I apprehend is the best in Europe.'

Some parts of Scoresby's Parisian journal have been written out in full and we are given a vivid picture of the Paris of that day; for example, the annual fête of Long Champs, which, he tells us: 'consists of a circuit of carriages in two lines advancing and retreating between the Champs Elysées & the Bois de Boulogne. The object at present seems to be a show off of new dresses & equipages for the spring,— anything new being reserved to be brought out on this occasion. The origin of this fête was an annual pilgrimage to Longchamps shrine of the Virgin Mary, where a vast number of persons resorted to perform the Catholic rites to the Saint. It increased in importance so as to become an object of curiosity, numerous spectators were collected, equipages displayed & dresses exhibited, until, on the suspension of the original rites at the Revolution, the ceremony was continued & modified into its present form.

'Amongst the numerous gay, or splendid, or gingerbread equipages, some were interesting from the public characters who rode in them. Many equestrians exhibited themselves in the course & among these Sir Harry Mildmay & his adulterous wife, late the Lady Roseberry. He is a handsome man & she an elegant horsewoman—but her conduct to her husband and her boldness in thus appearing in so public a manner throws a shade over all her personal as well as moral beauties. As might be expected, the present marriage is said to be very *unhappy*.'

Other events are only recorded in brief jottings in small pocket books and Scoresby never extended them into a longer account, and so the reader has to fill in the blanks from his own imagination. We have to do this in his account of the dinner party at M. Cuvier's. The hour that he spent with his host at his Jardin des Plantes is condensed to a few pencilled lines:

'Jardin des Plantes. Interesting—extensive & complete collection. Cedars of Lebanon—Anatomical—whales—complete skeleton—Cape of Good Hope. Oven—various skulls—Hottentot Venus.

'Cuvier has done everything in the arrangements; it is a beautiful and prodigious work. His library of 6 or 7 or 8 rooms—each room of diff. classes—all zoology in one &c'

The dinner party was likewise condensed, the scientific observer taking careful note of all the dishes and the manner of serving them: 'Dinner about $6\frac{1}{2}$. Soup—fowls—cutlet—egg patty—salmon—roast beef (take little pieces of each). Ham—radishes—salad—potatoes—sweetmeats—preserves. All on the same cloth and served up as quick as may be. No healths. Common wine stood on the table with water—superior wine handed round by the servant. *Strong* coffee without milk. Then the ladies rose and we handed them into the drawing room. M. Arago, Rosily &c dined. Miss —— (Mrs Cuvier's daughter) & her sister speaks English very well. Cuvier very little, but understands it. No carpet on the dining room floor except under table, but one in drawing room.

'Introduced in the evening to several *Barons*, &c and one lady; Madam —— desired to be presented to me. She is a fine looking woman of 25 perhaps, pleasing & speaks English intelligibly. English literature much read. English a part of education in polite society. Young ladies in France do not go out with young gentlemen—but married ladies do. In England it is quite different, the young ladies being more in company than the married. Miss Duvancel very intelligent, frank, affable, full of sprightliness & conversation. Gentlemen in France in conversation not called Count or Baron or Admiral, but Monsieur. (A habit of putting fingers to the nose by ladies and gentlemen.)'

Scoresby and his friend Thomas Griffin were invited by Ampère to witness his 'interesting electro-magnetic experiments'. Scoresby noted that his apparatus was 'very complete and well finished. By means of a plate of brass moving upon an axis he is able to change the direction of the currents through the apparatus in a moment, and he placed a number of pieces of apparatus in the same circuit. He has a vertical multiplier of several coils of copper covered with silk placed vertically, over which a freely suspended wire shows more perceptibly the attraction of similar and the repulsion of dissimilar currents. He makes a copper slip of a circular form revolve by being dipped in dilute acid, and the communication being made to pass through the acid from the poles of the battery. The ring of copper being suspended on a point revolves & much more rapidly when the exterior vessel is encompassed by several turns of a multiplier.'

A visit to St Cloud was followed by a Soiree at the Aragos', where Scoresby 'was introduced to M. Calliot who travelled with the Pascha (or son of the Pascha) to the source of the Nile; M. Simonoff who had visited the Antarctic Circle beyond the ne plus ultra of Cook; General Beary—M. Poisson (Engineer?) &c &c. It was remarkable that the person who had been the nearest to the South Pole—myself nearest the North Pole—Humboldt the highest on a mountain and deep in the earth, the person that had penetrated to the source of the Nile should all be met together in one party.'

This is the most lengthy note of the evening, for the rest we have to make what we can of the following: 'Tea and sweets, lemonade; Billiards with Mad. Arago & Gen. Beary. Mad. Beary handsome. Interesting evening,—*freedom*.'

On Sunday Scoresby was given a ticket to attend Grand Mass at King's Chapel in the Tuileries, where he notes:

'The burning of the incense—the waving of the vessel in which it is held—the bowing of the priests—their various evolutions and performances with the accompanying music are analogous to a pantomime. The file of soldiers who shoulder arms on various occasions and who stand with their hats on in the middle of the chapel are here an important part of the pageant. The ceremony of the cup—the washing of the priests' hands—the kneeling of the assistants—are too usual in these ceremonies to need relation.

'Strange are these pageants to us. If there be any devotion, it is difficult to perceive. Known only to God are his sincere worshippers. God grant that we who profess a more simple form of worship may be found among those who worship him in spirit and in truth.'

A visit to the opera proved disappointing, for though the glittering interior was attractive, the performance was poor and 'very inferior to London'. Scoresby much preferred dinner parties and soirees where he met and talked with distinguished and cultured people, though not always intellectual. He was introduced to the Duke of Somerset, with whom he 'had a good deal of conversation. He was affable and communicative,—but not, I should imagine, greatly scientific'.

At a dinner party at the Aragos' house where 'Baron Humboldt, Admiral Rosily, Mr Griffin and myself dined', Scoresby carefully noted the items on the menu: 'Soup—Bouille—Patties (mushroom

& sweetbread?) chickens—sweetbread and crawfish—Salmon—fine
Capon. Handed roast beef—french beans—spinnage—baked
apples—pears—various cakes—apples—plumbs—jelly—preserved
cherries—baked pears—large ornamental sweet cake with almonds
and raisins—various sweetmeats or bon-bons.'

Once again, the lack of carpets is remarked upon and Scoresby gives
us a vivid picture of his hostess: 'Madame Arago is a charming
woman, with all the gaiety of the French, she is candid, handsome—
kind & obliging. She possesses the vivacity of the French ladies without their frivolity and the intelligence of the English without their
solemn gravity.

'Mad. Arago carved all the dishes & then sent pieces round upon
a plate. She observed on my offering assistance that the French gentlemen left this office to the ladies. Some of the dishes, however, were
handed round by the servants to each of the company. The agreeable
practice in England of drinking wine with each other, which enables
you to notice a friend at a distance in the room, to whom you have
no opportunity of speaking—is not observed in France.

'In the evening M. Arago showed me some curious optical experiments, various rings seen in a telescope looking at a star when out
of the focus & the object glass covered with a metallic plate with a
small hole in the middle gives alternate bright and dark rings.'

Towards the end of his stay in Paris Scoresby was a guest of honour
at the annual meeting of the four Academies of the Institute and
Baron Cuvier 'described the progress of science since the peace, in
which he obligingly took occasion to mention my labours in the Arctic
Seas among the valuable researches of the period to which he confined
himself.'

With these words of praise ringing in his ears, and the memory of
the warmth of his reception by the French scientific world, together
with the kindness of his hosts, Scoresby returned to England in May.

CHAPTER 11

A NEW LIFE IN THE CHURCH

'I experienced a sort of feeling that was quite novel; towards the people a sincere love was felt, even before I knew them. It was sufficient to see them and to know they were of my little parish.'

On his way home, enjoying his year of leisure to the full, Scoresby called at Yarmouth, where he met for the first time Dawson Turner, with whom he stayed. Turner described the visit as 'one of those bright spots in an existence whose colours are for the most part soberly uniform, and to which I look back with constant gratification'. He did not, however, altogether approve of Scoresby's entering the Church: 'As the object is one which you yourself consider desirable (and I know you would not think so without good grounds) I am glad it is in the way of being accomplished. For myself, I still adhere to the opinion that, could you have satisfied yourself to continue in a mercantile career, your sphere of utility wd have been enlarged & you would even have been better able to have performed the great end you have set before you, the spreading of the glory of God upon earth, by religious example & precept.'

Reaching home in June, Scoresby was greeted by a letter announcing his election to the Royal Society, which came as a fitting climax to his reception in Paris and the acclaim of the French scientific world. He immediately answered the letter from Stephen Lee, the Secretary of the Royal Society, and sent him 'the requisite remittance—namely a bill for 50£'.

It was some time before Scoresby was able to go to London to be presented to the Royal Society. On his way there he stayed 'in the house of a most intelligent, venerable and pious friend. My inducement to remain was the proximity of a lady who had greatly won my esteem. I determined on seeking a conversation with the young lady (none having yet passed between us personally on the subject) and receiving from her own mouth her answer and feelings. I called at her home where I had dined two or three days before—her friends left us alone and I opened the business. I told her the causes of my attachment to her, the progress my affection had made. She answered me kindly but repeated her design not to marry. This I took for a denial and in it saw the hand of God. The Lord was merciful to me, for I was won entirely by external appearance and worldly accomplishments and not by her piety—for that was deficient. For many weeks, however, the remembrance of her was attended with painful feelings. I was enabled to see the mercy of God to me in this trial and disappointment, to see that she would not have been a proper helpmeet for me & to hope that God in his mercy has one more suitable, at his good time, in store for me.'

With his affections once more free, Scoresby concentrated on his studies with Mr Buddicom, and early in July 1825 he was ordained at York and appointed to Bessingby as curate under the watchful eye of his friend Archdeacon Wrangham. He had sole charge of the little church of St Magnus, a mile and a half from Bridlington; still, today, very much as it was in his time, it lies off the main road, along a narrow cart track and is surrounded by the same cottages and trees which stood there in his day. To visit it is to take a step back into the past. For this curacy, Scoresby received forty pounds per annum, a rather different sum from the whaling profits which had amounted to about £800 a year.

Of his first service he wrote in a letter to a friend: 'The embarrassment was less than I expected. This was probably owing to the church being a very very small one, the congregation, of course, few, and these almost entire strangers to me. I experienced a sort of feeling that was quite novel; towards the people a sincere love was felt, even before I knew them. It was sufficient to see them and to know they were of my little parish.'

In October he was joined by his two boys and their ever faithful nurse, Betty. Scoresby, who had taken lodgings at Bridlington Quay, had 'not designed to take any servant of my own, but had wished and requested my faithful housekeeper to accept a situation of very ample and superior remuneration which was offered to her in the family of a friend. But she positively refused—with tears in her eyes, requesting only to be permitted to accompany me, and attend upon the children, and she would require no wages; her meat, she said, would be sufficient, and she should be thankful for that! Of course I did not agree to such a proposal; but at the same time could no longer feel justified in leaving behind me one so faithful and so strongly attached.'

Of Bridlington Quay, where they lived, Scoresby wrote: 'The Quay is a most agreeable residence. It juts out in the middle of a most beautiful bay, terminated on the south by a low shore approaching the Spurn, but on the north by the bold white cliffs of Flamborough Head. My small parish has a beautiful little village. The cottages are quite picturesque, the fronts being covered with honeysuckles, monthly roses and jessamine. The neighbourhood is also pleasant and affords some excellent society; while a large number of gay persons flock to the Quay as a summer's residence.'

For the first six months Scoresby taught the two boys himself, but finding that 'this tedious and daily occupation' took too much of his time, young William was 'placed with a clergyman at Driffield' while Frederick remained at home. He was deeply attached to his father, he slept in the same room and was in the habit of climbing into his father's bed 'some little time previous to rising'. They had many talks together and 'wild and giddy as at other times he was, he became grave and sober' when they spoke of religious topics. Though the glimpses of Scoresby's personal life are very few indeed, we are given a vivid picture of the increasingly grave, somewhat humourless, parent and his lively, affectionate son:

'One morning, he had come to my bed as usual and was lying there, whilst I was in progress of dressing. He began of his own accord to speak on the subject of conversion. He expressed his fears that he was not quite ready—he was afraid that he had not got a new heart. After a short interval of apparent thoughtfulness, in which he appeared to have been meditating on his spiritual condition, he said—"Papa, I'm afraid I haven't got a new heart, for I have so many bad tricks yet: but then, I think I'm a little better, for I've got off some of my silly tricks", referring to an occasional giddy habit and making of faces— "and I never forget to pray morning and evening: But, Papa!" he added—looking at me in much earnestness, and in his evident anxiety lifting himself up in the bed—"Papa! Do you think Jesus will let me into heaven *with half a new heart*?"'

Occasionally the little boy went with his father on his parish visits, patiently waiting without any appearance of weariness, while Scoresby talked with the farmers and other parishioners. He was not strong enough to walk very far and sometimes his father took him before him on horseback, at others he rode on a donkey, 'of which he was very fond, though he could by no means manage it without assistance, for the donkey preferred its own way and was wont to assert its power of choice, and sometimes put him into peril by its deviations from the road'.

The parish duties were far from heavy, and Scoresby found time not only to work on the long article on the Polar Regions for the *Edinburgh Encyclopaedia*, but also to deliver a course of lectures on magnetism at York. Through these he met and formed a friendship with William Vernon Harcourt, the son of the Archbishop of York, who later founded the British Association.

Scoresby's saddest duty during his Bessingby curacy was to preach at Whitby Parish Church in 1826 on the occasion of the loss of the last two whaling ships to sail from the port. It was this loss which sounded the knell of Whitby's whaling industry, for no less than sixty-five men were drowned, twenty-one of them from Shetland and the rest from Whitby. The *Lively* was lost with all hands in an Arctic storm and the *Esk* sank off Marske, less than thirty miles from Whitby, within sight of the shore, on her homeward journey.

It was the same *Esk* which Scoresby had saved ten years before almost single-handed and against all advice to abandon her had brought her home with a 22-foot hole in her keel. The interest, therefore, which he felt in the calamity was, he wrote, 'of that peculiar, anxious and painful kind, which it would be difficult for him to describe or others to feel. For a sailor has an attachment even to a ship, and especially to one in which he has safely overcome any uncommon adventures. He regards it with a feeling bordering on affection.'*

There were not enough members of the Marske lifeboat crew to pull the boat through the heavy seas to aid the *Esk*, the coxswain was unable to induce any of the fishermen—who were standing around watching their futile efforts—to volunteer assistance, and so they were obliged to look on helplessly while the gallant ship *Esk* sank before their very eyes and only three men were washed ashore alive.

Almost every member of the drowned sailors' families was present at the service in the ancient and well-loved church of St Mary which clings, limpet-like, to the rocky cliff-top at Whitby. They were a moving reminder to the rest of the three thousand people gathered there that sad day, inducing them to give generously to the collection made for their support during the service.

Even as Scoresby preached, preparations were in hand for his appointment to the chaplaincy of a new venture. This was the Floating Church for seamen in Liverpool, for which the government had given and converted one of its old warships. Scoresby's friend, Adam Hodgson, was one of the newly appointed trustees and it was he who was instrumental in appointing Scoresby as its first Chaplain: thus it came about that he returned to Liverpool in May 1827.

In January of that year he was honoured by being made a Corresponding Member of the Institute of France.

William and Frederick, whose health had now improved, were sent to a nearby school. Frederick was as closely attached to his father as ever and enjoyed accompanying him on pastoral visits whenever he could and showed 'the gladness of his heart by skipping about me, kissing the hand wherewith he was conducted, and by other simple tokens of endearing affection'. He was unhappy at the school for he was a target for bigger boys to bully. He was fond of singing to himself and, being a parson's son, it was usually a hymn; but when he was only ten years old a gang of bullies surrounded him in a back street

---

* Scoresby's last ship, the *Baffin*, was lost at sea in the Arctic during a dreadful storm in 1830, when eighteen other ships shared her fate.

and forced him to sign to them, after which frightening experience, Frederick 'abandoned the practice'.

Though the main body of his Floating Church, which held a thousand people, was occupied by sailors, of necessity a transient congregation, Scoresby's preaching attracted many people from Liverpool itself who became regular attenders and supported him throughout his ministry there. Scoresby was once more in charge of a ship and happy in doing the work to which he felt called. On more than one occasion he refers to the change from being a fisher of whales to a fisher of men. In Liverpool he was undoubtedly the Captain and his willing band of helpers were indeed much more of a 'crew' than the usual 'flock'.

Of this period he wrote: 'The majority of the congregation was composed of those that go down to the sea in ships, and do business in great waters; but the residue was made up of a mixed multitude, gathered, as it were, from "the streets and lanes of the city". The efficacy of the ministrations to the seamen could but seldom be determined, but in due time, incidents of deep and gratifying interest were met with, and cases of warm-hearted experience of the grace of God among the seafaring worshippers became, at length, encouragingly known.' Twenty years after he was to meet one of his transient congregation in America and be gratified to hear how his own preaching had affected the sailor.

Scoresby had many concerns, not the least of which was the heavy drinking habits of sailors, and he felt convinced that a very large proportion of the extremely numerous shipwrecks—in 1829 over 800 ships were lost—was caused through the drunkenness of the master and crew. He therefore preached with great earnestness on the necessity for temperance, especially when at sea. He was also well aware that the cause of these tremendously heavy losses—a much higher proportion than road deaths today—most certainly might be more the fault of a drunken compass than the intemperance of the men; to this end he laboured for many years to produce a more accurate compass needle, as we shall later see.

Another concern, linked with the former, was to prepare the sailors to meet death. If this sounds rather morbid, we must remember that death by drowning was, at that time, if not inevitable certainly a more than likely possibility in the seafaring population, when over two thousand men were lost every year. Since his earliest days, and especially during his Copenhagen adventure, Scoresby had been acutely aware of the indifference of the average seaman towards spiritual matters, travelling thoughtlessly through life with little consciousness of its deeper meanings, and very few of them having any religious feeling or knowledge. To him it seemed a dreadful thing that they should meet death unprepared, and he continually exhorted them to come to God before it was too late. Many of his sermons in the Floating Church were on this same theme.

Funerals, too, came under Scoresby's censure for their display of ostentatious expense—which none of his congregation, being of 'the labouring poor' could really afford—and for their excessive feasting and drinking following the burial.

Scoresby had a deep concern for keeping the Sabbath holy. As early as 1811, on his first voyage as Captain, he had deplored the depravity of other whaling captains who, coming to breakfast with him on an Arctic Sunday, were quite oblivious that the day was different from any other. His veneration for this day was first inculcated by his Father and throughout his life he was scrupulous in keeping the fourth commandment and observing Sunday as a holy day. He once even declined an invitation to dine with Sir Walter Scott on these grounds. Quite apart from any other consideration, he also felt it was essential for a man to have one day a week on which he rested, thus enabling him to return to his labours in the new week refreshed after a quiet day.

This theme also occupied a prominent part in his ministry, so much so as to induce one of his parishioners to 'abandon her practice of selling fruit and confectionery from her cellar door on Sundays' which had been quite profitable. And yet when it came to Scoresby's notice and he asked if they were worse off, the woman told him they were actually better off for the husband, formerly improvident and wasteful, now brought home all his earnings to make his family comfortable.'

Ireland had always held a fascination for Scoresby and it was in this beautiful country that he found his second wife. On holiday there, he met and fell in love with a charming Irish lady, Elizabeth Fitzgerald, of Corkbegg, and in June 1828 they were married.

Very shortly after the wedding Scoresby happened to be in Cork harbour with his brother-in-law, Colonel Fitzgerald, where the brig *Mary Russell* was lying. On her homeward journey her master had gone mad and believing the crew about to mutiny had tied up and murdered seven of them. Scoresby and Colonel Fitzgerald, who was a magistrate, went on board the brig and Scoresby, in the meticulous, detached way of a scientific observer, noted and recorded every detail of the terrible scene of carnage which met their eyes in the cabin where the bodies still lay.

The court brought in a verdict of insanity and the master, Captain Stewart, was committed to a lunatic asylum for the rest of his life, where Scoresby visited him and found him quite lucid and well aware of what he had done. His delusions had been so real that he was convinced of the rightness of his action at the time. Though he was suspicious of Scoresby at first, he came to welcome his visits and corresponded regularly with him. From his letters we see that his madness was safely channelled into a harmless form of religious mania.

The new Mrs Scoresby disliked the quarter in which they lived in Liverpool, for it was in a low part of the town, near the docks, and although it was near the Floating Church and very convenient for her husband, she could not settle there and so in the spring of 1829 they moved to another house near the Botanic Garden. Young William went to Trinity College, Dublin, while Frederick was put to a new school, run by a kindly clergyman, where he was much happier. He drew even closer to his father, jealous of the interloper who claimed his parent's affection. He did his small best to try and like his new mama, but it was a hard struggle for one who had been the sole object of his father's affection for as long as he could remember. He attended almost every service which Scoresby took at the Mariners' Church, rushing through his homework on Wednesdays so that he might accompany him to the mid-week 'prayers and exposition' given to the seaman in the newly established reading room. Seeing that it gave his father pleasure, he also read his Bible frequently and endeavoured to discuss religious points with him, often surprising Scoresby with his original approach:

'He came to me with a grave, but interesting and intelligent expression of countenance, saying:— "Papa! I am afraid I have done wrong."

'"In what, my dear," said I.

'"Because," he answered, "I prayed this morning in my prayers that *everybody* might be converted unto God; and you know," he added, "Christ says that only *a few* find eternal life; and I was afraid I had done wrong in praying contrary to Christ's words"! It was pleasing to unravel to him the little delicate difficulty in which he had got embarrassed.'

During the five years they spent at Liverpool Frederick 'advanced and grew in wisdom. In mere learning he made some progress, but not in like proportion; in stature he made but slow advances, being small and short and child-like for his years.'

The house by the Botanic Garden was also near the railway, which was just in the process of being built. Scoresby had *carte blanche* to wander around and observe all the workings, and very naturally he was given a ticket to attend the opening ceremony in September 1830 and make the first journey from Liverpool to Manchester by train. This important event was attended by a most distinguished gathering, Prince Esterhazy and the Duke of Wellington, no less, gracing the occasion. Also among the party was the city's newly elected Member of Parliament, William Huskisson.

'With a speed as of the swift winged arrow, train after train, to the amount of eight in number, including above 700 passengers, flew along the admirably constructed rails.' When the train stopped for water, Huskisson was foolish enough to leave his carriage, and in trying to get back he was inadvertently knocked down by the oncoming *Rocket* engine. Scoresby the observer was on hand to record in detail the whole event, which he did, meticulously describing the scene, the crowd milling about, the doctor's examination, the wounded man lifted in an improvised litter and being put on the new train which was rushed to Manchester 'at a speed but little short of fifty miles an hour, and in a few moments was out of sight. And now was one of the most splendid pageants ever witnessed, even in this age of wonders, suddenly converted into a grand solemnity, as of a funeral procession.' Which, indeed, it was, for Huskisson died from his wounds, thus making history by being the first man to lose his life in a railway accident.

Two letters of this time give us a fair idea of Scoresby's stature among contemporary men of science. The first is from George Harvey, FRS, who was 'engaged in the composition of a Paper in which the probable Temperature of the Pole' formed a feature of it and he wrote to ask Scoresby as 'the first of all living authorities' his opinions. 'Knowing your eager desire, not only to obtain, but to communicate from the rich stores of your information, everything calculated to enlarge the boundaries of knowledge, I feel no other apology is necessary for the liberty I have taken in soliciting this favour from your hands.'

The letter concludes: 'One of my daughters has just made a copy of your beautiful Crystals of Snow, just published in the Edinburgh Encyclopaedia. Their immense variety is wonderful. Were I a free man I would certainly visit the Polar Regions.'

The second letter, from James D. Forbes, asks for Scoresby's support of his application for the Chair of Natural Philosophy at Edinburgh in succession to Leslie. He earnestly hoped that Scoresby could 'conscientiously speak in my favour, as your character is so well known here as to carry much weight with your good opinion'. Forbes was appointed—the competing candidate being Sir David Brewster. There would, no doubt, be a great deal of activity on both sides to gain support and Scoresby's testimonial would be one of many, but it is unlikely that a man so well connected and with so many influential friends as Forbes should have written to him unless his word carried weight. The request gives us an insight into Scoresby's standing in Scottish scientific circles.

CHAPTER 12

THE BRITISH ASSOCIATION

'Prosperity to Science all over the World'

The year of 1831 was a momentous one for science and for humanity. It was the year James Clerk Maxwell was born; the year Faraday discovered electro-magnetic induction; and the year the British Association first met in York. It was a memorable one for Scoresby too, for he was always proud of his founder-membership of the Association and an enthusiastic and hard-working supporter all his life.

The growth of science had led to the need for a more intimate and personal scientific intercourse between men residing in different parts of the country, more especially in the north, and the coming of the railway made this a practical possibility. Prime movers towards the founding of the British Association for the Advancement of Science were David Brewster, whom Scoresby knew at Edinburgh; John Phillips, Secretary of the Yorkshire Philosophical Society; and Scoresby's friend Vernon Harcourt, son of the Archbishop of York and himself an ordained minister. It was not therefore surprising that the first meeting of the Association should take place in the ancient city of York and that the Philosophical Society should act as hosts to the distinguished visitors. It was certainly the most outstanding event which had taken place in York for many a long year and the editor of the *York Courant* gave full rein to his enthusiastic pen:

'Having last week just introduced our readers to the portico of the Temple and given them a glimpse of the treasures of wisdom within it, we have now to lead them forward to its inner courts and to bring them to a more close acquaintance with the expositors of its mysteries ... these men whose depth of research and whose industrious application are daily and hourly conferring such mighty benefits upon mankind. They labour not for a community, for an empire or a continent, but for the world at large; the blessings they communicate cannot be confined; but free and unconstrained they take flight with the wings of the morning and diffuse themselves to the uttermost parts of the earth. When the scourge of war went forth in all its horrid violence, when cities were laid waste and kingdoms desolated, when commerce was cut off and social intercourse restricted—SCIENCE still retained its freedom, the cannon's roar disturbed not its peaceful pursuits.'

The paper goes on to describe the events of the week in detail, starting with 'the conversazione which formed the prelude to these diversified scientific attractions' held in the 'spacious and elegant theatre of the Museum—brilliantly lighted with gas—thronged till ten o'clock with select company, amongst whom were many ladies, which added much to the brilliance of the scene, and all of whom appeared to enjoy with a high zest the intellectual entertainment provided for them. Tables were placed in the theatre of the Museum at which tea was served about nine o'clock.' The introductory lecture was given 'in his usual style of modest perspicuity' by Mr Phillips, who concluded by extending a hearty welcome to everybody on behalf of the Yorkshire Philosophical Society.

The first meeting for business was held the following day, when Lord Milton took the chair. Vernon Harcourt outlined the aims of the proposed new Association. The resolution to found it was carried unanimously as was the second, 'explanatory of the objects of the Association'; the third resolution, however, which concerned membership, 'occasioned a very long discussion' and the only part of that which the *Courant* thought fit to report was the point made by Scoresby that 'it might be attended with inconvenience to admit all members of Philosophical Societies, as it was certain that all the members of provincial societies were not learned persons, nor were they always admitted to their own society by ballot'. He moved an amendment, which was carried, that the Presidents and office-bearers should be admitted while the other members should be eligible to be proposed as members. Was he thinking back to those early years when he was elected unanimously to the Wernerian Society without the formality of the usual ballot?

The *Courant*'s report of the dinner is here given in full, so that the reader may picture for himself the splendidly august gathering and imagine the dignified solemnity of the occasion. We leave him to observe for himself the ever-increasing warmth with which each succeeding toast was greeted.

THE DINNER

About a hundred of the visitors and residents dined together at five o'clock at the York Tavern. Lord Milton was in the chair, supported on his right by Dr Brewster, Mr Murchison and Mr Robison and on his left by the Rev. W. V. Harcourt and Dr Lloyd. The vice-presidents were Jona.Gray Esq. and Eust.Strickland Esq.

After dinner the toast of the King; the Queen and the rest of the Royal Family; and the Duke of Sussex and the Royal Society were given. Then followed:

Dr Brewster and success to the present and future scientific meetings.

Dr Brewster acknowledged the toast.

Mr Robison and the Royal Society of Edinburgh.

Mr Robison returned thanks.

Mr Murchison and the Geological Society.

Mr Murchison, in acknowledging the honour, said he rejoiced to see before him the father of English geology, (Mr Wm Smith) and the founder of the London Geological Society (Mr Greenough) together with such a sprinkling of geologists as showed that they took a lively interest in these scientific meetings.

Dr Brewster proposed the health of Lord Milton, to whom they were indebted for the distinguished countenance which he had given to the first scientific meeting.

Lord Milton—drank with 3 times 3, and cheers.

The chairman returned thanks.

Dr Pearson and the Astronomical Society.

Dr Pearson, in acknowledging the toast, noticed that in the beautiful building of the YPS there was one defect—a cupola (a laugh); the situation was admirably calculated for astronomical observations, and he should be happy, if a cupola were raised, to put in a few of his own instruments, (loud cheers). He mentioned that Sir Thomas Brisbane (the former President of the Astronomical Society) was present and he had done more than almost any other person to promote astronomical science (Cheers).

Dr Lloyd and the University of Dublin.

Dr Lloyd returned thanks and spoke briefly of the University of Dublin expressing his hopes that the meeting of the Association would be held in that city in their turn.

Dr Daubeny and the University of Oxford.

Dr Daubeny acknowledged the toast.

Mr Murchison, in proposing the health of the Rev. W. V. Harcourt paid a very high compliment to the varied scientific acquirements of that gentleman.

The Rev W. V. Harcourt and the Council of the Yorkshire Society.

Drunk with 3 times 3 and applause.

The Rev W. V. Harcourt returned thanks and said the Council had done nothing more on this great occasion than ring a bell to call other men to church. They were amply rewarded by the assemblage of distinguished men now brought together, and they would be still more so if these meetings were continued. He paid a high tribute to the merit and zeal of Mr Phillips, the scientific secretary of the Society.

The Lord Mayor and Corporation of York.

The University of Cambridge.

Archdeacon Wrangham acknowledged the toast and said he was not
fit to be in the vestibule of the temple they had raised that day. The
cheers of the meeting intimated a different opinion.

The Provincial Philosophical Societies.

This toast was acknowledged by the Rev. Wm Turner, Secretary of
the Newcastle Philosophical Society for thirty-five years, who
regretted the absence of Mr Dalton, the President of the Manchester
Literary and Philosophical Society.* Also by: Mr Frost, Hull; Mr
Dunn, Scarborough; Mr John Phillips, Yorkshire; Dr Booth, Birmingham; Dr Williamson, Leeds; Dr Prichard, Bristol.

Sir George Cayley and Mechanics Institutes.

Sir George expressed his high sense of the utility of Mechanics Institutes, though he thought they could not properly be classed with
Philosophical Societies. He wished that every man in the kingdom
were acquainted with the principles of science, and concluded by proposing:

Mr Macdonald and the Arts.

Mr MacDonald returned thanks.

Prosperity to Science all over the world.

       . . . .

The week went on with demonstrations, business meetings and
lectures on various subjects; although none were outstanding contributions to scientific knowledge of the time, their real significance
lay in the great step forward which had been made in the founding
of such an association and the recognition of science as an activity
of national and international import. Born of the growing complexity
of science and the increasing impact of research on industry and
national concerns, it marked a turning point in the development of
science and of man.

J. H. Abrahams of Sheffield described the dangerous trades of
'needle-pointing and needle-eyeing' and described how magnets could
be used to make it a much safer occupation, for it had been one where
few of the workers survived the age of forty and many did not even
live to the age of twenty-five. Dr Brewster's paper was 'read by Mr
Robison, in the absence of the author, who was indisposed'. By the
following day he was well enough to attend.

On Thursday evening Scoresby 'communicated the results of his
recent researches concerning the law of magnetic induction, the
dimunition of the magnetic force in proportion to the square of the
distance, and the employment of the data for the construction of an
apparatus by which to measure the thickness of walls, the solid inter-

* John Dalton, being a Quaker, would not feel free to attend a gathering
of this sort.

vals between the subterranean tunnels and gangways in mines, collieries &c, and in general to the determination of short distances otherwise immeasurable. These phenomena, with their important applications, were the results of original investigations and discoveries, accomplished for the most part within the last ten months.' Thus we see that Scoresby was by no means merely repeating the lecture which he had given in York five years before.

The following day the entire Association was invited to dine at Bishopthorpe 'to enjoy the cheering and friendly hospitality of the Archbishop, where three delightful hours passed rapidly and then the whole assembly returned to the hall of science'.

A dozen more papers were read before the conclusion of the proceedings, when Lord Morpeth delivered the final address, the words of which remain as vital today as they were in 1831. He said:

'To the character of a man of science I have, unfortunately for myself, no claim whatsoever, but I have the good fortune to be intimately connected with the county and consequently with the city of York, and I feel that they have both received great benefit and additional credit from the meeting which is now brought to a conclusion. I say this both with reference to the positive instruction we have received upon so many interesting and important subjects and also to the circumstances of this town and this edifice, already so much indebted to the zeal, perseverence and ability of our vice-president, having been now selected as the birth place of an association which, I trust, is destined to confer fresh lustre on British science; to give a new motive and a new guarantee to the friendly intercourse and continued concord of nations; to make further inroads into the untravelled realms of discovery, and glean fresh harvests from the unexhausted fields of nature; to promote the comforts and augment the resources of civilised man, and to exalt above and over all the wonder-working hand of heaven. For it will always come out as surely as from the rusty medal we have just heard of: *Benedictum si nomen Dei.*

'Observe well if you wish to appreciate rightly the true value and nobility of science, that while it proposed to itself distinct courses and definite spheres of its own, its general tendencies conduce to peace and minister to piety.'

The *Courier* tells us that Lord Morpeth's speech was received with 'unbounded applause', and the newspaper account ends with a complete list of the names of members.

The thing that strikes us most forcibly about this inaugural meeting is the immense faith in the power of science to benefit human life evinced by the leaders of British science meeting here for the first time.

This faith in the power of the scientific method is needed today. We see in our time a retreat from reason—a fear of science—a taking of refuge in mysticism and obscurities, quite alien to the splendid record of achievement made in science since 1831.

If these men meeting in York and their successors up to and a little beyond 1900 were too optimistic, may not we, perhaps, be too fearful of the future, too timid to forge ahead and take possession of the new worlds opening to Everyman? In a scientific age the finest spiritual values should arise from science, for there is no real conflict between the scientific spirit and the true religious impulse. Peoples who organise themselves scientifically and are prepared to work as national entities without forgetting the general welfare—either of the community or of humanity—will align themselves with the main stream of history and derive therefrom an indestructible faith in the future.

Herein lies the true significance of this first meeting of the British Association. Men of the calibre of David Brewster, Vernon Harcourt, John Dalton, William Scoresby and many more present at that historic York meeting were men of faith and men of intellect and their coming together was a deliberate act—a manifesto of faith in the future of their country and of mankind, nor is it mere coincidence that the main impulse for the founding of the Association came from the north, the seat of the greater part of the nation's work, industry and inventive power. One of the chief aims of the founders of the Association was state aid for science: Science organised by the state, in a democratic community for the benefit of the nation and for the general welfare. As we know, the vision faded; its translation into reality would have required a union of scientists, workers and statesmen beyond anything possible at the time. Only now is it beginning to be seen as an absolute prerequisite for the safety and prosperity both of nations and of mankind.

As far as Scoresby himself was concerned, the Association helped him to continue his scientific interests and enabled him to meet scientists, renew old friendships and make many more friends in the scientific world. He felt great joy at these yearly gatherings and came away from them refreshed in mind and spirit. To one who had pursued scientific research under the Northern Lights and amid falling snow crystals, the chance to exchange mutual scientific enthusiasms came as a most welcome change and stimulating diversion from the arduous duties of a parish priest.

CHAPTER 13

THE BEDFORD CHAPEL, EXETER

'I am thankful in being in any way useful, but much. very much
is yet to be done and great difficulties are in our way.'

The change of residence was still not enough to satisfy Mrs Scoresby.
She complained that Liverpool itself did not agree with her and spent
much of her time at Corkbegg, ultimately remaining there entirely
until her husband should find a new parish. One is tempted to wonder
if Scoresby's parishioners of 'the labouring poor' and seamen played
any part in her dissatisfaction, or perhaps it was that even then she
had a consumptive tendency; we cannot be sure, for there are no clues
at all in the Scoresby papers and we do not know the cause of her
death, twenty years after.

Scoresby hunted for a new appointment, declining an offer from
the Floating Church in London, for that would have been little different from Liverpool; he eventually heard of a fine new chapel being
built in Exeter, which lay as far south of his wife's native Corkbegg
as Liverpool was north of it.

Over the heads of seventy other applicants, he was appointed to
take charge of Bedford Chapel in the centre of Exeter. The chapel
was the central building in an elegant semi-circle of new houses,
named Bedford Circus, which were designed more in the simple, un-
cluttered style of Wren than the elaborate Victorian Gothic which
became very popular only a few years later. The chapel formed a
graceful centrepiece to a crescent of distinguished houses; adjoining
it was the Bedford School, whose primary aim was the training
of girls for domestic service—perhaps in these self-same elegant
houses.

In the spring of 1832 Betty, the 'good and faithful servant' went
ahead to 'receive the little vessel freighted with furniture and to put
the new house in order'. Mrs Scoresby travelled direct from Corkbegg
and Scoresby and Frederick travelled down together. William was
in Dublin, but he very soon joined them, for cholera had broken out
there. The Dean, F. H. Singe, wrote from Trinity College: 'I trust
the good providence of God will prevent you from hearing and seeing
these awful instances of his judgments that are about and around us.
One young man has died in College & if not relaxed before June,
the next examination will in like manner be put off. The violence

of the cholera has, I am told, rather diminished, but still the number of cases is considerable.'

The Bedford Chapel, so named because it was built on land belonging to the Duke of Bedford, was not quite completed when Scoresby first went to Exeter and it was consecrated in August 1832. No sooner was the chapel opened than the city was struck by the cholera epidemic and the new chaplain was plunged into the sea of distress, not least of which was the number of funerals he was obliged to conduct.

In a letter to Mrs Rathbone at Liverpool he writes: 'Our cases of cholera have been fifty daily for above a week, with about one third part of deaths—a quantity which has not been equalled, I believe, in the proportion of population in Britain.

'The means of a remedial nature, under God, are yet very, very imperfect. Being myself a member of the Board of Health, and of two or three committees (for provision for the poor, for disinfection etc) I shall be glad of a few of those hints which, by your experience, you have gained. The best of my time since my appointment to the Board has been spent there. I am thankful in being in any way useful. But much, very much, is yet to be done and great difficulties are in our way.'

At first Frederick was sent to a day school nearby, but at the beginning of 1834 he was sent to stay with the Rev. J. Richey at Culmstock, who took in two or three boys as pupils. In a letter to Scoresby he reports of Frederick's progress:

'He suffers now from past disadvantages & his memory will require great exercise and must gain much strength before it will serve him as it ought. He has evidently been little accustomed to a thoro' preparation of his business and he wants the habit of study. In his conduct I see nothing, taking into consideration his comparatively childish taste in his amusements and the great want of forwardness or maturity of his judgment, to lead me to suspect that his religion will prove the mere consequence of his family circumstances; nor have I seen anything which has called for reprehension. ... In your letter of advice to him I think it would be well to press upon him the consideration of his wants, that he may *think* of *himself* with *humility* and learn to *speak* and *act* with a consciousness of his deficiencies. His temper, of which Mrs Scoresby wrote, I have not had much occasion to correct.'

In this pregnant last sentence we can read much, and one cannot help but wonder if this bad temper was reserved only for his stepmother. To her, Frederick wrote:

'I know that you are very desirous that I should love you; I will now confess my feelings, which change very much. Sometimes I feel myself to be the most ungrateful creature on earth towards you; at other times, I am sorry to say, I feel as if I did not care for you; but I hope I shall not have any more of these ungrateful feelings.'

At this time Scoresby was in Cambridge, at Queens' College, keeping his terms, for it was ten years since he had been ordained. He was awarded his B.D. that summer. During the Easter vacation he returned to Exeter and from there went, with Mrs Scoresby, to visit Frederick at Culmstock, where 'we spent a few hours and returned in the evening. In the interval I walked out with him alone, and had an interesting and endearing conversation with him, whilst he clung about me in the ardency of his affection, and listened with filial reverence and pleasure to whatever advice I offered or injunctions I laid upon him.'

Because of his wife's poor health, Mr Richey was obliged to give up taking pupils, and so Frederick was sent to board at the Grammar School at Bruton under the care of the Rev. J. C. T. Hoskyns Abrahall, where fifty guineas per annum paid for 'Board and Education (Washing and Single Bed included)'. His father took him there in October 1834, and 'having examined the bedrooms and school room, which were unusually airy,—I took my poor anxious boy a walk through the town, returning by a country road. During this memorable walk—the last we ever took together—though no expression of regret or unwillingness to be left escaped Frederick's lips—yet his manner was so modified by feeling and circumstance, as to produce a touching and indelible impression on my mind. It was not that his affection was more manifest than it had been, or his attention more watchful; but instead of the rapturous ardour in which these tokens of his love were wont to be shown, there was an affecting tenderness and subduedness of character in all his endearments. He clung fast to my hand, frequently kissing it, as we proceeded. He listened with watchful attention to every word I uttered; but still, every action, look and expression, evinced a peculiar solemnity of feeling.'

Scoresby was somewhat disturbed to find that there had been fever in the school and urged his son to let him know if there were any more cases. This, however, Frederick neglected to do, for there was another case shortly afterwards.

Once again the dwarfish, almost hunch-backed boy became the butt of bullies, who provoked him on every occasion and Frederick was miserably lonely and unhappy. Even a letter from his stepmother was welcome, and he wrote to her:

'I know you wish me to tell you candidly what my feelings are towards you. I am sorry to say that sometimes I have felt an indifference for you, but I tried to drive it from me, by thinking of your kindness to me and my ungratefulness to you; but when your letter arrived, my indifference went away; and even now while I am writing to you I fancy I feel indifferent, though I am trying to drive it away.'

In the same letter he tells his father: 'The boys began to ask if I thought it was wrong to hunt squirrels—for they had been doing so when we went our walk. I said yes, when it was only for amusement. Then they asked me if it was wrong to hunt whales and I said no, because there was an object in it.'

This is an appropriate place to mention that during Scoresby's time in the whale fisheries the products of the whaling industry formed an important part of the national economy. Whale oil was extensively used in the illumination of houses and streets; it was only towards the end of his seafaring career that gas lighting—using coal gas—was slowly becoming available and gradually superseding other forms of lighting. Even by 1831 at the first meeting of the British Association the 'brilliant illumination by gas light' was thought sufficiently remarkable for special comment.

On p. 428 of *Arctic Regions* Scoresby mentions Mr Gordon's portable oil gas lamp. It is interesting to note in passing that it was in the liquid formed in the condensation vessels in Gordon's process that Faraday discovered benzene. So, in a roundabout way, the whaling industry may claim parentage of the coal tar dyes and the modern chemical industry.

But to return to Frederick. Another letter to his stepmother says: 'I have been a good deal more knocked about than when I first wrote to you. I have tried to bear it as well as I could, though in one instance my feelings overcame me. I begin to feel more used to my situation; though I cannot help feeling lonely sometimes. I passed a very pleasant birthday, especially in the evening, for most of the boys had gone out to spend the afternoon at those houses where they were invited.' Frederick's birthday, we remember, was on the fifth of November, Guy Fawkes night.

Frederick became ill at the beginning of December, but the local doctor described it as 'only a simple fever' and Mr Abrahall decided he was fit enough to be sent for and taken home by 'a trusty servant'.

Scoresby himself was prevented by his church duties from going to fetch his son who was, Mrs Abrahall wrote, 'almost quite well, except that he is weak and also very deaf.' But the illness was far more serious than she realised and on his return home Frederick was put to bed, where the fever took its dreadful course and after two distressing weeks, during which he lost his hearing completely, he died on the last day of the year.

Whilst letters of condolence, rich in conventional clichés, continued to arrive at their house at Mount Radford, Scoresby occupied his mind by writing a biography of the 'dear boy', mourning the 'loss of a singularly endeared child' but at the same time feeling that 'the loss is the departed one's gain' and he was 'supported in his mourning by the animating persuasion that he is not dead but sleepeth'. He comforted himself by the knowledge that 'He who appoints affliction, appoints it for good,—that He who chastises by his rod evinces love in the chastisement—that He who is the author of afflictive dispensations, as well as good, afflicteth not willingly.' The outcome was a book, *Memorial of an Affectionate and Dutiful Son*, which was published by Nisbet in 1835.

Sir John Ross had also published a book that year and he sent a copy to Scoresby:

Portland Place, London.
28th April 1835

My dear Sir,

I send you herewith an early copy of my work of which I beg your acceptance. As I think it probable you may undertake to review it, I have also undertaken to send you some comparative notes, respecting Parry's voyage and my own which in that case would be useful. You will see that I have endeavoured to set the public to rights, in regard to the credit of renewing the search of N.Wt. Passage being due to you—which is indeed only justice.

Owing to my having been my own publisher and thereby displeasing all London booksellers/proprietors of reviews I am to be most severely handled in the Quarterly, Westminster, Monthly Lit. Gazette &c—but how the Edin. will treat me I do not know. You will, however, be glad to learn that I have the consolation that I have 7,000 subscribers amounting to no less than £7,000!—My first object in being my own publisher was to get the book up so as to be a credit to the nation and all concerned, my 2nd object was to give it to the public *cheaper*, and to show thereby how the booksellers impose on both the authors and the public—and lastly that I might keep the property entirely in my own hands.

You will observe that the appendix is not yet published, but I will send you, if not by this coach in a few days, the meteorological journal which is now printed, and which is the most interesting, and if there is any other information you want I shall give it with great pleasure. With my best regards to Mrs Scoresby, I remain ever,

very sincerely yours,
JOHN ROSS

P S   There are only portraits in those I give to my friends.

Ross was an interesting character. He had led the second Arctic expedition in 1819 but had turned back at the sight of a high range of mountains, which he named the Croker Mountains, which appeared to block his way in Lancaster Sound. These must have been cloud formations, but their appearance was so real as to deceive him.

In 1829 he set out on a second, privately financed, expedition in search of the north-west passage and did not return until four years later, arriving in England on a whaler, having had to abandon his ship. The book, *Narrative of a Second Voyage in Search of a North-West Passage*, told of his experiences. But despite his remarks in it about Scoresby being the original instigator of the Arctic expeditions in search of the north-west passage, the credit for it still remains with Barrow and today we read of him called 'the father of Arctic discovery'. If there were any claimant to this title, it should certainly be Scoresby, or even his Father, but not Barrow the landsman. Barrow sat comfortably and safely in the Admiralty while other men went to the Arctic and risked and gave their lives.

Between Barrow and John Ross there was great animosity, and Barrow even went so far as to devote two chapters of his book, *Voyages of Discovery*, to vilifying Ross.

None knew better than Scoresby the deceptive appearance of optical illusions which could blind the onlooker to their reality in the clear Arctic air, and he knew only too well that the Croker Mountains which Ross had seen had undoubtedly been visible. Their firm friendship was based on their mutual knowledge of the Arctic, and this understanding of Ross's error only strengthened it. Ross's mistake had been in not sharing his observations with his junior officers, who were ready enough to declare, on their return, that *they* had not seen the Croker Mountains.

Life at Exeter was by no means confined to pulpit and parish. Scoresby was able to nurture his scientific and intellectual interests. Under the patronage of T. D. Acland, MP for North Devon, he founded the *Exeter Athenaeum*, and delivered the inaugural lecture *On the Influence and Advantage of Scientific Institutions* in October 1835.

He had a growing correspondence and spent a great deal of his time in writing. He was deeply concerned about the Irish problem, not only collecting money for their relief in the famine, but carrying his concern to a personal level by giving orders to an Irish woman for knitting mittens, which he presented to all his friends; he published a pamphlet on the troubles, in which he wrote:

'The sufferings and persecutions of the Protestants in Ireland are not owing to the aversion of the people to a Church Establishment, but are the specific results of the hatred of the Church of Rome to Protestant principles, and evidence of the efforts of the Church of Rome for the extirpating of Protestantism.'

The British Association, now firmly established as an annual event, met that year in Cork, and Scoresby stayed with his friend Dr Singe at Trinity College, Dublin, where young William was studying. The following year, 1836, it was held at Bristol and Scoresby demonstrated his magnetimeter and read a paper on it. He had been much engaged with experiments, painstakingly repeated over and over, upon various kinds of plates and bars of steel, testing the degree of permanence of magnetism in them with reference to the temper of the material—the result of which was a new compass needle, and this he was able to show to the Bristol meeting and he also read a paper on the question of compass deviation in iron ships. The theme was to occupy him, off and on, to the end of his life.

Of William, the elder son of Scoresby, we know very little indeed; from Dublin, he went to Edinburgh University to read medicine, but he was only there little over a month. In the many hundreds of letters in the Scoresby archives, there is but one from William. It is here given in full, for it brings the twenty-five-year-old student to life more than anything else could.

Edinburgh
Novr 6th 1837

My dear Father,
    I arrived here safe on the evening of Wednesday, and found at the College a note waiting for me kindly inviting me to stay at the Traills untill I should be settled in lodgings. I accordingly availed myself of this hospitality, and have received the very greatest kindness and attention. Mrs Traill has been enquiring the price of lodgings and had fixed on some which I have since seen and engaged, they are very comfortable apparently and reasonable, 12 shillings a week including fire. The rooms adjoining mine are occupied by a young man of steady and pious habits, a friend of the Traills and an Englishman, also studying medicine.
    Dr Traill has been very kind indeed to me, having taken the greatest trouble about my classes. I have left everything to his arrangement. He advises me strongly *not* to attend Anatomy or Desections this year, as I shall have them to attend again the last year in Dublin. Neither does he approve of my attending a *grinding* class until the last year. The classes he says I ought to attend besides *Materia Medica* & *Midwifery*, which I must attend as the prescribed course of Dublin, are *Surgery*, *Hospital* and *Clinical* Surgery, making in all four different classes besides hospital attendance. The classes are £4–4–0 on an average & the hospital £7–7–0. The whole expense of the winter course including matriculation fee will be £25–0–0. I have only about £25–0–0, so that I shall have no money for my household expenses, except you are kind enough to send me some. The classes must be paid for within a week or ten days.
    You have no idea how kind the Traills are, I am perfectly at

home with them, they introduce one to all those persons that are worth knowing. They expressed the greatest dissappointment [*sic*] that you did not come to Liverpool, as did all your friends there. They are anxious to know whether there is any probability of your coming into this part of the world. Professor Jameson has been dangerously ill, but is now recovered. I have not yet delivered your letter to him, nor yet to any for whom I have letters.

I had a very severe passage from Liverpool to Glasgow. I never saw it blow harder than it did on our leaving port. During the night the sea broke through the dead light of my cabin where there were four berths & flooded the whole place, soaking my bags, hat box, bed &c &c. I was not quite so sick as I expected, but it was a fearful night.

I saw Mrs and Miss Rathbone, both well, Mary Rathbone was from home, going to be married to Mr Thom, Unitarian Minister. I saw & dined with Mrs & Mr Cooper, both very well, sent their kindest regards to you, showed me a bottle of brandy which you made a present to your *godson* to be opened when he was of age. It was sent before you left the sea. Dr Traill has been very kind to me, went with me to get matriculated, shewed me the college, and the principal lions of the city & got my bill cashed for me at his bank. The 25 £ I said I had included the £1 paid for matriculation. My lodgings are close to the college, those in the new town were more expensive than you would have liked. They are 18 Lothian St, Mrs Guthrie's lodgings. I have a very nice sitting room & a snug little bedroom. The weather here has been very severe, I am labouring under a severe cold and have almost lost my voice. I had almost forgot to say that I was greatly delighted with the *Mariners Church*, which was contrary to my expectations crowded, and numbers of sailors and captains of ships, although the day was particularly unfavourable. Mr Maynard sent his kind regards to you. He was very earnest & devoted apparently to his work, the people seem to like him and listen to him with great attention. Tell Mamma I saw Mrs Hassard, she looks very much worn with mental suffering; Mr Hensman has called on her. Lucy Traill has become I think decidedly pious & Mary Eliza very much disposed to be so. Mrs Traill also has very much altered in that way. They all speak in the warmest manner of you.

Give my best love to dear Mamma, tell her I will write to her the next letter if I am alive. Robert and Thomas Traill have grown up very handsome young men; as tall as I am. Perhaps you would send me some money as soon as you can conveniently.

Believe me, my dearest Father, Your affectionate son,
WILLIAM SCORESBY

28 Lothian Street.
The Traills send their very kindest love to you. We commence
tomorrow. I intend, please God, to work hard.

The poignancy of the words 'if I am alive' is heightened by the
knowledge that the promised letter was never written, for the next
letter which Scoresby received was from Dr Traill, telling him that
William was 'seriously unwell. For some days he had a smart attack
of fever with sore throat for which I have attended him, but did not
think it necessary to send you word, but at 3 this morning I was hastily
summoned to him . . . he is weak, and though I hope the best, I should
not be justified in concealing his illness from you.'
This was followed almost immediately by a second letter telling
of William's death:
'Almighty God give you strength of mind to bear with Christian
fortitude and resignation the afflicting intelligence which I have to
communicate. Your William breathed his last about half an hour
ago.' He went on to assure Scoresby that 'Mrs Traill will see everything done with proper regard to propriety and economy—and recollecting your predilections I shall give orders for the funeral in the
Episcopal burying ground here, should you not have time to come
before it is necessary to bury the body—or should you be unable from
the state of your health.'
Scoresby's health was indeed too poor to allow him to make the
journey—a matter of four or five days—in the severe winter weather
and the Traills arranged everything and saw William taken to 'his
long resting place'. He was laid 'in the West Church New Cemetery
just under the bold front of the Castle Rock at its NW angle'.
The fever, Dr Traill told Scoresby, 'was evidently brought on by
his desire to perform his duty to poor patients whom he was bound
to visit as an accoucheur attached to the lying in hospital. This kindness and laudable zeal had been marked by his superiors, and were
known to Professor Hamilton his preceptor.'
Scoresby's sister, Mary Clark, wrote from her home at Grosmont,
near Whitby:
'Ever since I received your account of the afflictive dispensation
of Providence in the awfully sudden death of my dear nephew I have
been very unhappy about my dear Brother. I greatly fear the shock
will have a bad effect upon his weak constitution. Will you have the
kindness to write again soon (if my Brother cannot) to inform me and
the rest of the family, of the present state of my Brother's health and
that of your own and how you are going on.
'In this sad affair there are some alleviating circumstances to which
I hope my Brother will be able to give their due weight, yet the dear

youth is much to be lamented. He was ingenuous, kind hearted, generous and affectionate and had he been spared, age might have cured his faults.

'Poor Betty bore the news as well as I expected at the first, but I dare say she would feel it more when left to herself. I will look after her and ask her to come to my house occasionally which will make a change for her.'

From this letter it will be seen that the faithful Betty—whose surname we never learn—had returned in her old age to her native Whitby, and it is good to think that Mrs Clark was able to keep a friendly eye on the old servant who had cared for the motherless boys with such devotion.

CHAPTER 14
THE SCORESBY COMPASS NEEDLE

My needles can be magnetised without taking asunder, and
if varnished and placed in pairs, would *never* lose their power!'

The deviation of ships' compasses and more especially in the newer,
iron-built ships, caused grave concern, for many ships, both mercantile and naval, had been wrecked because of compass deviation.
Scoresby was deeply concerned and had done much work on the subject and in 1836 had brought it before the public by his demonstration
before the British Association at Bristol.

The Admiralty formed a Committee for the Improvement of Ships'
Compasses and the chairman, James Clark Ross—nephew of
Scoresby's friend Sir John Ross—wrote: 'The subject of your recent
experiments for making very powerful needles by the combination
of several laminae was mentioned, and the committee being very
desirous to avail themselves of any improvements which you may have
been able to arrive at in the course of your experiments, have desired
me to request that you will have the kindness to allow them the opportunity of comparing needles made according to your plan with those
which the committee have at present under trial, in order that the
best possible kind of needle may be employed in the future construction of all compasses to be used in Her Majesty's Navy. The committee would therefore be glad to receive from you a needle of exactly
6 inches, & another of $7\frac{1}{2}$ inches in length, but in every other respect
than that of length, whatever you consider to be most desirable for
this purpose.' Remembering his previous experience with the Navy,
when he had been summoned to London twenty years before,
Scoresby was encouraged by the final sentence in the letter: 'Any
attendant expenses will be defrayed by the Admiralty.'

The Committee to which James Ross referred had been formed the
previous year and consisted of the following members:

Captain Beaufort, Captain James Ross and Captain E. J. Johnson
of the Royal Navy; Major Sabine of the Royal Artillery; Major J.
B. Jervis of the East India Company Engineers; together with one
specialist from the civilian scene—although the man of their choice
could hardly be said to be strictly non-service, for he was Professor
of Mathematics at Woolwich Military Academy: this was S. H.
Christie (1784–1865), the inventor of the 'Wheatstone bridge' and

co-discoverer with Barlow of the magnetism of a rotating iron sphere.

To find the reason why Scoresby, at that time one of the leading authorities on magnetism—and especially on compasses and their deviation—should not have been asked to join this committee, we need hardly look further than the fact that the original Admiralty letter requesting these men to form the committee was signed by John Barrow, the same John Barrow who had written, twenty years before: 'Mr Scoresby must therefore do the best he can with his private means.'

By return of post, on 26th April 1838, Scoresby wrote to say he would be 'happy to undertake to construct a pair of compass needles on the principle of combining different laminae of tempered steel'. He went on to say: 'The only compass needles I have had the opportunity of comparing with one made of thin plates, are four which I happened to have by me of the ordinary kind used in the Merchant service; the advantage of four plates, in comparison of the directive power of these, was generally, weight for weight from 2 or 1·75 to 1. In a large instrument which I have just completed for Mr Airy— and which I hope to send off to Greenwich early next week—the directive power compared with an instrument of the same length and breadth by M. Gauss is more than double.'

He asked the committee to send him two cards with their needles and caps complete, and ended the lengthy letter: 'When I have completed the needles required I shall be happy to communicate the particulars of the processes employed in the construction, tempering and testing of the plates, or any other information to which my enquiries have led.'

The somewhat stiff, even peremptory, tone of James Ross's letter— do we detect the hand of the Secretary, Barrow, in it?—contrasted strongly with the warm, friendly letters of Captain (later Admiral Sir Francis) Beaufort, whom Scoresby knew personally from meetings at the British Association. Coming, like Scoresby's wife, from the south of Ireland, Beaufort (1774–1857) was a true lover of science. Hydrographer to the Navy and the man after whom the wind scale was named, he prepared an extensive Atlas (incidentally, rising daily between five and six to do this) for which he received no remuneration. With true Irish charm he wrote to say he was 'delighted to find that we are to have the benefit of your magnetic experience and practical ingenuity to help our endeavour. If I can supply you with anything pray command me—but do not sacrifice anything in order to suit the dimensions or form of our present apparatus which must be altogether changed.'

Scoresby asked for some compass needles and Beaufort sent him seven, 'selected for the purpose by Cap^n Johnson. Some of them will probably have lost much of the little power they ever had—and perhaps you will think it right to restore some of it. None of the committee except Johnson and myself are in town, but I know I speak their general feeling when I express the obligation we feel for your prompt and valuable aid in the very important enquiry in which we are engaged.'

Scoresby was not impressed by the needles. He commented: 'I can hardly suppose that these are of average quality, but, I should conceive, a very inferior selection. Compared with these, I find that any of my compound needles are twice as powerful, weight for weight, as the best of the seven, and five or six times as powerful as the weakest, though magnetised to saturation.'

Beaufort hastened to assure him that the needles had not been specially chosen, 'I am afraid that those sent to you were not worse than the average supply from the Dockyards—at least they were not selected for their badness but taken at random'. Once again he thanks Scoresby 'for all the trouble you have so kindly and so zealously taken.

In these early days of the enquiry there was no unpleasantness, nor unwillingness to give freely of his great experience and knowledge of magnetism. All that Scoresby asked was acknowledgement of his invention of the laminated needle:

'I ought perhaps to mention that when I first constructed a needle on this principle above a year ago—I entered a Caveat at the Patent Office, which has been recently renewed. But my purpose in so doing was mainly for verifying the priority of invention, and to prevent, if possible, any other person taking advantage of the invention for a personal monopoly as exclusive manufacturer. But I have no intention of carrying it further if the Admiralty choose to adopt the plan.'

The final paragraph of this same letter is of great interest to us today, for bearing silent witness to Scoresby's claim are the magnets which are now in Whitby Museum, one of which still firmly holds a 14-lb weight suspended from it a hundred years ago.

'Any information I can give on these various matters I shall be glad to submit to the Committee and, if the needles are preferred, all the practical results of a long and laborious inductive investigation of the matter. My needles can be magnetised without taking asunder, and if varnished and placed in pairs, would *never* lose their power!'

Within a fortnight of receiving the needles, Scoresby had completed his experiments and sent four specimen needles, together with a comprehensive report seven pages long, which ended with these words:

Mr Scoresby is fully sensible that the foregoing Results are but propositions—as far as the Committee are concerned—yet unproved; and therefore he cannot expect that they should be unreservedly received on his mere assertion. The proofs, however, are only withheld at present because of the labour which must be requisite before they could be given in detail, and of the delay which must have ensued had he detained the needles or kept back the results of his investigations till the whole were put into form and completed. Mr Scoresby trusts, therefore, that the Committee will acquit him of any desire of concealment as to any of his investigations and discoveries. And should they consider his improvements of such national importance as to be befitting for adoption in the public service, or even to encourage the Committee to recommend the New Needle for this purpose—Mr Scoresby will be ready,—as far as it may please God to enable him by health and opportunity to do so—to exhibit all the practical processes, and to demonstrate by actual Experiment all the foregoing statements.

Exeter. 27th July 1838

Scoresby's sense of urgency was not shared by the Admiralty Committee, for it was quite as leisurely in its affairs as any establishment committee. Formed early in 1837, its members came and went at their own convenience; and long before the Committee had reached any definite decision, its chairman had departed on a voyage of discovery which took four years; a sort of Alice in Wonderland existence. Small wonder, then, that they were tardy in accepting Scoresby's offer to demonstrate his needles, but at long last they did so and this took place at the Admiralty at the beginning of 1839.

Christie, who had already crossed swords with Scoresby when he demonstrated his compass needles to the British Association in 1836, fiercely disputed Scoresby's claims, and the meeting broke up in a state of undecisive dissension. Scoresby was quite unused to have his statements questioned. His long years of sole authority as captain of a ship, his ensuing position of minister at the Seamen's Church, where he was still in effect the 'skipper', and his present position as incumbent in sole charge of the Bedford Chapel had not fitted him for subordination or deferring to another's wishes. Whether Christie was right is a moot point; but that he was unnecessarily curt and abrupt to the point of rudeness is certain.

Scoresby was deeply wounded by this antagonism, and in the heat of his feelings he wrote a letter and addressed it to Sir John Ross, whereas the Chairman was *James* Ross, nephew of Sir John. It is questionable whether this 'mistake' was unintentional, for Scoresby well knew Sir John Ross's feelings towards the Admiralty—and to Barrow in particular.

John Ross, who had been knighted in 1834, was—like Scoresby—

a complete individualist who never took kindly to authority. He had led the 1819 voyage—of Croker Mountain fame—to the Arctic, and it was well known that he had a long-standing quarrel with Barrow, who later devoted two chapters of his book on voyages of discovery to an attack on Ross. He was sent as Consul to Stockholm in March 1839 and Scoresby thereby lost a man who would have been a firm ally, for it was John Ross who gave the credit for originating the Arctic voyages of discovery to him—and not Barrow.

By this time Scoresby was at Queens' College, Cambridge, keeping his terms for his doctorate. Unfortunately for us, there is no record of his stay at the university, but we do know that he was friendly with Whewell,* for they were colleagues at the British Association and Scoresby had given him material on the velocity of waves at sea some years before.

To Whewell therefore, Scoresby submitted his work on the compass needle for an independent opinion, since he had received no reply to his first—misdirected—letter to the Committee. Whewell's opinion, it is almost needless to say, was very favourable. Scoresby told James Ross of this in his next letter.

Exeter 7th March 1839

To Capt. James Ross.

My dear Sir,

It was a great relief to my mind, the receipt of your favour of the 22nd ult., explaining the cause why I had received no reply to my letter to the Committee on Compasses of the 1st ult. For I could not have imagined—even hastily as I wrote—that I could have made such a mistake as that you mention in mis-directing my letter. Not being aware of the cause, however, of no answer being given me, I could not but fear that my request to the Committee was to be understood as negatived by their silence, and I therefore determined to send the results of a part of my investigations to some learned society, and my paper had been already forwarded to Dr Roget with this view when your obliging explanation reached me.

In now addressing you to acknowledge this, and to communicate the accompanying particulars, I do not feel it unfitting to refer to the painful meeting I had with the Committee at the Admiralty, which, the more I have considered it, the more I have felt grieved and surprised; and in speaking of the subject again, I would express

* William Whewell (1794–1866), mathematician and scholar, author of *History of the Inductive Sciences*. Master of Trinity College, Cambridge. As a young man progressive and keen on reform, but in later life became strongly conservative.

the fervent and anxious hope that nothing may appear or occur, with respect to the Report in preparation that may require from me any further, especially any public, reference to the circumstances of that meeting.

Whatever may be the judgement of the Committee as to any claim of mine for discovery and priority of some of the principles and results which I laid before them, which were disputed by Mr Christie—it is but due to myself, I think, to apprise you that certain processes of which Mr Christie's strictures were singularly harsh, have been far differently judged of by another gentleman unquestionably qualified to do so. I refer to my methods of determining the directive powers of needles,—subject, as I said, to an equation, which, if ascertained, as can be most simply done, can in no wise invalidate the principle—and to that of adjusting the mass of the needle to the weight of the card &c to be directed.

Now since I withdrew my paper, I have submitted to one of the *first mathematicians in Cambridge* these two portions of my MS. His judgment I think it but right to communicate to you. But I may first mention that they were sent to him without any reference to the meeting at the Admiralty & with no explanation bearing upon that meeting except this: that one of the methods had been spoken of by a Fellow of Trinity College, Cambridge, as 'beautiful'—and by another gentleman,—'plowing in the same field as having no relation to the object to be accomplished.'

His answer is not only very explicit, but he enters minutely into the subject—and gives his opinion that *the methods are sound in science*, applicable for the objects which I contemplated, and describes them in language *the very reverse* of that by which Mr Christie characterised them.

But I do not wish to pursue the subject further, nor to put you to the trouble of a correspondence on the subject, or I could give you the results of experiments by various methods which prove both the accuracy & the readiness of the method of equated Deviations with singular accordancy.

> I remain, My dear Sir,
> Yours very faithfully,
> W Scoresby

This letter arrived just in time for a meeting of the Committee, where the following Minute was recorded:

> Extract from the Minutes of a meeting of the Committee on Ships' Compasses, held at the Admiralty, March 9th 1839.

> Letters were read from the Rev^d Wm Scoresby addressed to the Chairman date Feby 1 and March 7th 1839. The Chairman was

requested to inform Mr Scoresby that the Committee was appointed for the practical purpose of improving the compasses of the Royal Navy, in the fulfilment of which purpose it is their duty, in addition to the improvements which they may themselves devise, to avail themselves of any suggestions which they may obtain from others: acknowledging of course on their report the quarter from whence they may have received any useful suggestion, but it is not their duty, nor their intention, beyond the acknowledgement, to enter into or decide any questions of priority of discovery or invention.

The Committee having heard that Mr Scoresby considered himself to have made some improvements in the needles of ships' compasses, requested him to furnish them with the needles of his construction for trial.

These when received were submitted to a comparative examination with others which the Committee had also on trial. The results did not prove so favourable as Mr Scoresby had expected. On the particulars of the examination being shown him he said that these needles were not good specimens, as he had not at the time been able to get sufficiently hard steel: and he undertook to furnish others which have not yet been received, and which the Committee will be happy, if he please, to receive from him and to submit to comparative trial with others.

Mr Scoresby requests from the Committee an answer to the following enquiry: 'Whether, in their report, which must be a public and standing document, they intend distinctly to acknowledge the *principle of construction*, supposing these plates to be adopted, as due in regard to its original promulgation to him.' ie Mr Scoresby.

The principle of construction is elsewhere stated to be 'the combining tempered steel plates for compass needles or navigation instruments.'

Assuredly the Committee could not recognise Mr Scoresby as being the first person who made needles on this construction, having abundant evidence that the principle, or these principles, are not new, but that they have been known and applied many years before the period Mr Scoresby names as being that when he first exhibited needles of that construction, viz: at the meeting of the British Association at Bristol in 1836.

The combination of two or more bars of steel in the construction of magnets is of very old date and of very common practice. The application of the same principle of construction to compass needles is neither new nor infrequent.

The committee have now before them a compass needle made by Mr Gilbert of Leadenhall Street, which appears precisely to correspond to Mr Scoresby's specification. It consists of three thin steel plates (clock springs) as nearly as maybe of the same length, breadth and thickness as those of Mr Scoresby's needles and separated by a barrier of brown paper instead of the wood which Mr Scoresby uses. This needle has been in the possession of one of the members of the committee since the year 1823 and must consequently be older than that date.

Mr Scoresby also requests to know whether the Committee 'admits that his method of magnetism, as to its advantages of manipulation, is new'.

Mr Scoresby has justly remarked that from the many subjects discussed in his interview with the Committee, 'it was not possible for him so to communicate them or to render them sufficiently "intelligible".' So far as the Committee understood his method of magnetising, it does not appear to differ in any respect from the method practised by the late Dr Gowan Knight which is described in the article 'Magnetism' in the *Encyclopaedia Metropolitan.*

In regard to the novelty, or value of Mr Scoresby's method of testing the quality and temper of steel for magnets, the Committee beg to be understood as having expressed no opinion whatsoever. From the cause admitted to above the explanation was necessarily too much hurried to be clearly understood, or to justify the expression of any opinion.

The minute is signed by James Clark Ross.

Scoresby had other things to do than beat his head against a stone wall. His thesis had been accepted at Cambridge and he was now a Doctor of Divinity and had been assigned to 'the extensive Vicarage of Bradford'. He concentrated on preparing his sermon—all in Latin, of course—and contented himself with coldly acknowledging the Committee's broadside.

Exeter, 18th April 1839

Mr Scoresby has the honour of acknowledging the reply of the Committee on compasses to his letters of 1st February and 7th March last. He reserves to himself, of course, a right to consider the grounds on which the Committee seems to deny his claim to the invention or priority of publication of the particular needle should the occasion require.

Having tried for two months unprotected, the power of retention of two of his needles, similar but rather inferior to those sent to the Committee, Mr Scoresby is enabled fully to justify the conviction he expressed before the Committee that 'some accidental proximity of similar poles must have occasioned the considerable deterioration observed.'

Mr Scoresby has ordered plates for a superior class of needles—as it seems to have been understood that he should do so—the plates hitherto obtained having proved defective when submitted to the test for hardness as well as, apparently, for quality of steel.

This was Scoresby's final official communication to the Committee, who, after several more years of deliberation, eventually adopted a compass needle exactly similar to those which Scoresby had submitted, and made no acknowledgement whatsoever to him.

CHAPTER 15

VICAR OF BRADFORD

'The immense labour of this parish of 132,000 souls requires all my
time, so that I can do but little in science.'

When Scoresby was first offered the Vicarage of Bradford he declined
it, preferring to remain at the Bedford Chapel at Exeter; but he was
eventually persuaded to accept it. Aaron Chapman, who was a
member of a greatly esteemed shipping family in Whitby, was one
of the first to write and congratulate him:

'I congratulate you & I still more congratulate those to whom I
know you will prove a comfort and a blessing, on the judicious choice
made by the Trustees for the important service required in that district, and for which you are just the individual best qualified to undertake the care of this vast, and I fear unregenerate population.

'Let me as an old friend venture to ask to be allowed to give you
one piece of advice—do not, I entreat you, wear out your constitution
in the exercise of your arduous duties. I passed thro' this district during the last General Election, and at a period of great excitement,
& I found the inhabitants, I thought, very unruly. For this, however,
the circumstances at the time may prove some excuse.'

In July 1839 Scoresby took up his new duties in Bradford. He had
not been there very long before he found Aaron Chapman's words
were all too true. There was no General Election, but the people were
if not 'very unruly', certainly ill-mannered, uncouth and hostile. The
contrast between the gentle, softly spoken, perhaps rather servile, but
certainly deferential, West Country people to whom the Scoresbys
were accustomed and the rough, outspoken and sturdily independent
members of his new parish, with their harsh voices and distorted
vowels, was very marked.

'What does thee do that for?' a man with a pack of wool on his
back roughly asked a woman who had curtseyed to Mrs Scoresby.
'Thee's as good as she. If it had been God Almighty thee couldn't
have done more.' Indeed, the general rudeness of the people, said
Scoresby, was 'gross and painful' and often his wife returned from
her 'visits of philanthropy, deeply depressed by the insults and rudeness to which she had been subjected, and once at least, in grief and
tears from the excess of this painful treatment'.

In Bradford, the established church did not have as firm a hold

on the people as the dissenting churches had. They were a thorn in
Scoresby's flesh, these abhorred 'dissenters'. Ever since his brother-
in-law, George Lockwood—an ardent chapel-goer—had
behaved so badly over the bankruptcy (he repaid only half of what
he borrowed), Scoresby had been antagonistic towards those of the
same persuasion, and throughout his ministry in Bradford he waged
an unceasing war against 'dissenters'.

The gentle Beaufort sent a conciliatory letter, hoping to heal the
breach between the Admiralty and Scoresby the renowned specialist
in magnetism, but it was of no avail. Scoresby had been too deeply
hurt, and the work in his new parish was too demanding. He sent
a short note to Beaufort:

> Vicarage, Bradford,
> Yorkshire. Decr 11th
>
> Dear Sir,
>
> I have considerable doubts whether I could satisfactorily to
> myself undertake the processing of plates and needles such as you
> describe, as I do not myself approve of the particular construction
> & proportions &c. The plates I left, as specimens, could be easily
> compared with what you have of similar lengths; and their respec-
> tive properties, for the purpose designed, accurately determined.
> Had the Committee wished, I would have undertaken the con-
> struction of a needle or two out of such steel on my own plan, or
> on a modification such as that of a greater proximity of poles, to
> which I referred in my memorandum.
>
> I remain, Dear Sir,
> Yours very faithfully,
> WM SCORESBY

Having written this, Scoresby put his mind to tackling the urgent
matters on hand. The parish was disorganised and the voice of the
Vicar ineffectual; its churches were under-staffed; the children were
ignorant and without education. Most of them, from the age of nine
upwards, worked in the factories and mills and—despite the provisions of the Factory Acts, which obliged the mill owners to provide
education for them at least ten hours per week—they were almost
totally illiterate.

There were difficulties on every hand, not the least of which was
the appalling financial situation which meant that the Vicar was responsible for paying his curates and after having done this he was
left with a total income of thirty-nine pounds. This unfair arrangement might not have been so bad if there had been a corresponding
income from the 'dues', that is to say, the fees paid by parishioners
to the incumbents for weddings, burials, baptisms and churchings

(these last two a not inconsiderable amount when we remember that they were almost annual events with most families). But the curates wanted to keep these dues for themselves.

Scoresby was as firmly beset with problems as any ice-bound whaler. As captain of the ship, he set about dealing with them with his characteristic efficiency and within three months he had devised a scheme to overcome the first obstacle. He gathered together as many of the wealthy and influential members of the parish—mill owners, justices of the peace, doctors and other professional men—as he could muster; put the case fairly and squarely before them; told them a hundred pounds was needed every year to make up the curates' stipend and that the collections were inadequate and asked them to guarantee a small annual sum each, in order to bring the collections up to one hundred pounds. It would only be a matter of five or six pounds each at the most, but it would save the ship. At the time, they readily agreed, and fourteen of them signed a Guarantee promising to make up the required amount. One of the signatories was a doctor, John Outhwaite, and it was he who later stirred up the others into a state of dissatisfaction and caused their worthy Vicar a great deal of needless trouble and distress over these paltry annual payments.

Within six months, Scoresby had prepared his next attack on the existing state of muddle. He devised an eleven-part *Plan*, which he submitted to his Bishop at Ripon, who, needless to say, heartily approved of it, for he was ready to agree to anything which would improve the ineffectual management of the most troublesome parish in his see. The Plan proposed a District for each church in the parish of about 3,000 each and while allowing the various incumbents to baptise and bury, it restricted marriages to the Parish Church—that is to say, St Peter's, the present-day Cathedral. At the same time it was made clear that anyone who wished could attend the Parish Church.

It was a Plan to ensure that the Vicar of Bradford had adequate dues and it outlined the Guarantee proposal and laid down the fees payable by the incumbents to their Vicar. It also looked forward, contemplating three new churches in the immediate future and a further six eventually.

It was one thing to devise such a Utopian Plan. It was quite another to implement it. Had Scoresby had the unanimous backing of his churchwardens and curates it might have been easier; but they resented change—the old way had worked, why interfere with it? He was a new broom and he was going to alter their old, comfortable ways: they were afraid of him and what he might do. It could be, too, that there was resentment of him as a scholarly, scientific worker.

'There is no hatred in the world greater than that of ignorance for knowledge': if Galileo's words were true when he wrote them, they were still as applicable in the nineteenth century as they are today.

Though Scoresby had little time and even less inclination to make compass needles after the rebuffs he had received, he did find time—between clerical wrangles—for science, and in 1840 he gave a lecture on Magnetism at the Royal Institution. Faraday wrote: 'It gives me the greatest pleasure to think I shall hear you on such a subject in our house & I long for the evening. The heartiest thanks for your kindness. I will take the greatest care of the things when they arrive. For the discourses you have sent me, accept my thanks. I hope it has been and will be memorable to the poor men to whom you spoke.' Scoresby had sent him a copy of his *Discourses to Seamen* which he had printed when in Liverpool.

After the evening lecture, which was a great success, Scoresby sent Faraday more books, *Sabbaths in the Arctic* being one of them. This is not merely an account of Lord's Day observances, but also includes many exciting and stirring incidents of Arctic voyages. Faraday wrote to acknowledge them:

R. Institution
8 June 1840

My dear Sir,

I am very grateful for your unexpected kindness in having sent certain excellent books. I shall value them most highly both as to the subject & in remembrance of you. Let me also for myself thank you for your admirable evening. It has given me many new thoughts, enlarged many others & has set me & many into a state of thinking which will be some time before it abates.

Mr Anderson will with this note bring the apparatus & I have told him to defray such expenses as you tell him of. I mean those of carriage from Hull here and others that have been incurred for the evening. If you do not know them at present, then whenever you let me know the amount they will be discharged.

Allow me again to thank you most heartily for the evening & when our members meet I am sure they will take the earliest opportunity of giving you their thanks also.

Ever, my dear Sir,
Your obdt Servt,
M. FARADAY

A year later, Scoresby gave two more lectures on the same subject to the Royal Institution. It will be seen from the following synopsis that in 1841 parochial duties had not yet overshadowed his scientific life.

LECTURE I   Tuesday 15th of June 1840

General laws and agencies regulating and upholding the Physical Creation. Sublime exhibitions of the eternal power and Godhead of the Great Creator.

Magnetism.—One of these Mighty Agencies—its relation to other mysterious agencies—essential for conservation of the world—its condition in natural substances—inherent not imparted. Laws and Phenomena in permanent magnets;—*Attraction—Polarity—Directive property—Induction*—with experimental illustrations and applications of their properties. Various means of magnetic development—by electricity—lightning—heat—as well as by ordinary Induction, &c.

LECTURE II—Thursday 17th of June

The results chiefly of Original Investigations:—Principles of Magnetic Induction from the Earth—effects in Catastrophes at Sea—employment for developing the magnetic energy by Percussion.

Improvements in Magnetical Instruments—General principles on which such improvements are founded—Testing the quality and temper of steel and iron—Sea Compasses—Artificial permanent magnets—Powerful compound Magnets—Experimental Results:—Concluding Observations.

Perhaps the most far-reaching and influential friendship which Scoresby made while he was at Bradford was that of Lord Oxmanton, who later became the Earl of Rosse. He first wrote to him about regaining a schoolroom, situated on land belonging to Lord Oxmanton and occupied by those troublesome dissenters. Lord Oxmanton did not at first agree: 'The Westleyans have so long had the use of the schoolroom, and from what I have heard of the former neglected state of the parish were I believe so useful, and considering their friendly feelings towards the Established Church here, and the zealous support they have afforded it in Ireland, I should be very unwilling to deprive them of the schoolroom.'

But Scoresby was not content to let the matter rest, how ever good the 'Westleyans' were in Ireland; this was Bradford and he needed the room which was, after all, the property of the Established Church. He wrote again, and this time he won his case. He would have made a very good lawyer had he decided to enter the law instead of the Church. Lord Oxmanton wrote again and said: 'I have had an opportunity of conferring with Mr Stocks. I find I was under an erroneous impression as to the circumstances attending the transfer of the Westleyans and I do not now think there can be any objection to its being immediately handed over to you for the use of your curate.'

Thus it was that Scoresby became acquainted with William Parsons, third Earl of Rosse (1800–1867). He had married, in 1836, Mary Field, daughter of the wealthy Wilmer Field of Heaton Hall, which was in Scoresby's parish. Scoresby's enthusiasm for the achievements of Lord Rosse gives us an excellent example of his interest in and appreciation of contemporary scientific work.

As early as 1827 Rosse set out to make big reflecting telescopes. William Herschel had made great advances in constructing large telescopes at the end of the eighteenth century, but kept his methods secret. Rosse, who had great skill with his hands, gradually solved the many problems involved and published his results in detail, making them available to everyone. He ultimately succeeded in making a mirror 6 feet in diameter. It was mounted in a tube 58 feet long and was the most powerful telescope in the world.

After the British Association meeting at Cork, and again on several subsequent occasions, Scoresby visited Birr Castle, in central Ireland, the seat of Lord Rosse and the site of the great telescope. He was fascinated by the workshops in which the great mirror had been cast and polished and, of course, by the telescope itself. He saw clearly that the technical information and skills accumulated during the construction of the telescope provided the basis for the further development of astronomical science. He advocated government assistance in a project to construct and erect a great telescope at the Cape of Good Hope and perhaps in other parts of the British Empire where observing conditions would enable maximum use to be made of such instruments.

Scoresby lectured enthusiastically on the telescope and the immense enlargement of our knowledge of the universe made possible by these instruments, laying special stress on their space-penetrating power in light years—'the progress of light in free space', and saw that Rosse's achievement gave Britain an opportunity to lead the world in this great scientific endeavour. But, as only too often, apathy and indifference reigned in ruling circles and the lead passed eventually to the United States.

In his second tour of that great country in 1847–1848, Scoresby lectured extensively on the Rosse Telescope and its revelations, and it is perhaps not too much to say that he may have helped to foster the beginnings of American interest in giant telescopes. However that may be, it is greatly to the credit of American philanthropists and astronomers that they have been able to combine their financial and intellectual capital in the splendid constructions on Mount Wilson and Mount Palomar.

Scoresby's dream of powerful reflecting telescopes in various parts of the British Empire did eventually reach fulfilment owing to the genius and drive of Lord Rosse's youngest son, C. A. Parsons, the famous engineer; he founded the optical and engineering firm of Grubb, Parsons and Company, which has built many famous reflecting telescopes.

As befits a priest of the Church, Scoresby invariably ended his lectures on the great Rosse telescope with these words:

'Animated with the spirit of the Psalmist we shall each one surely be disposed appropriately to join in his emphatic saying: *When I consider the heavens, the work of thy fingers, the moon and the stars, which thou has ordained; what is man that thou art mindful of him or the son of man that thou visitest him?*'

In our own times when scientific advances have brought so much to benefit human life and yet so much that might imperil its future, such a frame of mind would seem appropriate if not altogether indispensable.

Difficulties lay on every hand in Scoresby's new parish. There were several churches still unconsecrated, one of which, St John's, built by a Mr Berthon, gave him much bother. It remained unconsecrated chiefly because Scoresby could not agree with the incumbent of St John's, one Charles Pearson, who had been appointed by the trustees of that church without any reference to the Vicar. Since the church, on the Manchester road, stood in the parish of Bradford, Scoresby naturally regarded its minister as his curate and expected obedience and submission from him. But Pearson, despite being in his very first office, having only taken orders just prior to his appointment— showed little humility or deference to Scoresby, who was his superior and whom he had promised, at his ordination, 'reverently to obey'.

In the Scoresby archives at Whitby there are some hundreds of letters and copies of letters which passed between Scoresby and Pearson. They await the diligence of an otherwise unemployed sorter who may patiently sift through them: even so, from a preliminary sorting it is abundantly clear that Pearson was undoubtedly in the wrong. Among other things, he was in the habit of visiting Scoresby's parishioners without his knowledge. The practice came to light when Scoresby conducted a funeral, and on visiting the bereaved family discovered that Pearson had not only administered the Sacrament to the dying person—an understandable act in an emergency and in the absence of the Vicar—but that he had long been a visitor in the house, and knew full well that the person was dying, yet had never informed Scoresby. Scoresby was hurt when he heard this, but not wishing to make an issue of it, determined to have a quiet word with Pearson. He did so, and requested him, in future, 'where any seat-holder of the Parish Church was concerned' to communicate with

him before 'undertaking the spiritual care of such'. A reasonable
enough request, but Pearson flared up and refused to do this. He had
previously, needless to say, refused to send the Vicar his dues. A sheaf
of letters ensued, and the matter grew to such proportions that an
appeal to the Bishop was made, who came out heavily in favour of
Scoresby. This judgement, however, made little difference to Pearson,
who still refused obedience and threatened to take the case to law:
'It is nothing to me *what* the law of the land might say. My position
before God Almighty is too awful to be shackled by the thin bands
of earth, and by the law of God I claim as my right to have a sphere
wide as my responsibility.'

He refused even to apologise: 'Upon invitation I administered the
Sacrament. You demand an apology or threaten a prosecution. In-
advertence I cannot plead. Satisfaction is not due. I refuse an apology
for none is owed. I express no regrets for soothing affliction. Is the
law then broken? It may or may not be. If it is—to the law will I
give satisfaction.' And so on. Letter after letter passed between them;
Scoresby's letters are always courteous and he is more hurt by the
dissension than angry; but still he was the captain of the ship and
he demanded obedience: 'I cannot but regret the decision you have
come to on the subject of our late painful correspondence, by which
you bring it to a close. My satisfaction is that with all possible careful-
ness, trouble and forebearance I have endeavoured to set the case
before you as, if possible, to show you your true position, my own
integrity of motive, and the necessity of maintaining the respect due
to my position. And my hope was that my appeal to Christian principles and Christian duty would have induced you to have made freely
and fully that recompence for the injury done to my feelings and
rights, which I consider to be your clear duty.'

The trouble with Pearson was never really finally settled. Though
he left Bradford at the end of 1842, he still continued to return every
now and again, visiting his old parishioners, holding meetings and
writing letters defamatory to Scoresby in the local press. These last,
however, Scoresby usually ignored, for Pearson had left his parish and
was no longer under his jurisdiction, and the aim to which Scoresby
worked was clearly to define the position of the Vicar of Bradford
in regard to his curates. He was establishing a precedent and attempting to make the way easier for his successors, and the petty acts of
a former curate bothered him no more than the tavern talk of a dismissed seaman would have done.

St James's Church was not consecrated either. This had been built,
like St John's, by a private individual, a Mr Wood, and he and the
incumbent, G. S. Bull, fiercely resisted Scoresby's *Plan*, refusing to
pay any dues to the Parish Church. No dues, no consecration. The

matter grew to such proportions that Wood went so far as to arrange to close the church completely. The local paper noted:

CLOSING OF ST JAMES'S CHURCH BRADFORD. We regret, as every Churchman must do, the great dissensions which have taken place at Bradford. A complete statement of all that has occurred will, we hope, soon be afforded us, and we shall have much pleasure in publishing it. In the meantime we think it right to record our opinion, after reading attentively all that has been published, that Dr Scoresby has acted throughout with firmness, high principle, and sound judgment, with the courtesy of a gentleman and the forebearance of a Christian. If the Church Building Acts are not modified, they will do more harm than all the Meeting Houses in the United Kingdom.

Yet another church had been built in Bradford by private enterprise. This was another St John's and was built by the Bowling Iron Company in general and a Mr Hardy in particular. He was a fiery defender of the faith, antagonistic to the *Plan*, and letters and still more letters from his London pen appeared in the paper attacking Scoresby's *Plan* and demanding the right of marriage in his new church—and, of course, it almost goes without saying, refusing dues. But this trouble was eventually resolved in February 1842, when St John's, Bowling, was consecrated.

Then there was the trouble with Scoresby's curate Mr Meridyth, who announced he was leaving, allowed his Vicar to appoint a successor, and then turned round and said he was not leaving at all.

Even more complicated was the case of Mr Morgan, the incumbent of Christ Church, who positively refused to keep within the bounds of the new district assigned to him. This was understandable, perhaps, for most of its margin was drawn right down the middle of a street, so that he was supposed only to visit the parishioners living on 'his' side. He too, rushed into print, publishing a booklet, *The Parish Priest Pourtrayed*, purporting to be a memoir of the late Vicar, but in reality a means of venting his spleen against the present one. This obliged Scoresby to remind him: 'Every clergyman when ordained priest is solemnly questioned, as before God, in the following words:

'Will you reverently obey your ordinary, and *other chief minister*, unto whom is committed the charge and government over you: following with a glad mind and will, their godly admonitions and submitting yourselves to their godly judgments?' Answer: 'I will so do, the Lord being my helper".'

There were many times during Scoresby's first year of office when he wondered if he was right to make the stand he did for church dues, and whether he had the support of the people. Doubts on this subject

were resolved at a public meeting held in the Exchange Buildings
in 1840, for he was presented with a Loyal Address, signed by nearly
400 people which read:

'A period of twelve months having elapsed since you were in God's
Providence placed at the head of his church in this important Parish,
we trust that an assurance of your parishioners' regard will not be
deemed unseasonable.

'You entered upon the duties of your high and responsible office
in times of rebuke and blasphemy and under circumstances of no ordinary difficulty and embarrassment. The noble stand you have taken
against the infidel and blasphemer; and the generous effort you have
made to provide for the spiritual destitution of your Parish demand
our most grateful acknowledgements. The dignified determination
you have avowed to maintain your high position as 'Ambassador of
Christ', and in the spirit of the Church Catholic, manfully to correct
abuses and to enforce regularity and discipline when misrule and disorder had unhappily prevailed, demands our respect and confidence.

'Founded as your parochial plans have been, in integrity of principle, and sanctioned by the high authority of your Bishop, we lament
that a spirit of opposition, subversive to your beneficial designs, should
have manifested itself and that false and injurious reports grounded
only on a perversion of facts, should have been disseminated, which
if not firmly withstood, must prove alike painful to our own feelings
and detrimental to your usefulness among us.

'Under a firm conviction that on the maintenance of the rights and
due influence of the Mother Church, the spiritual interests of this vast
Parish greatly depend, we feel it an imperative duty to offer our most
cordial support to the wise and moderate measures you have taken
to preserve the trust committed to your charge.

'Proceed then, Sir, in the path you have taken, secure in conscious
rectitude in the approbation of your Diocesan and in the support and
confidence of your people, rejoicing if at any time you are accounted
worthy to suffer for righteousness sake.

'That the Almighty and Merciful head of the Church may continue
to support and bless you in the arduous work you have undertaken,
is the sincere prayer of your devoted Parishioners.'

The following March there was another meeting in the same building, presided over by the Bishop of Ripon, and the following motion
was carried:

'That a sound religious education is of the first importance, spiritually and temporally to the rising generation, to society at large and
to the welfare of the realm; and that such education is at this time
specially required for the counteracting of the prevalent evils of
ignorance and infidelity, and of systemized efforts to seduce the young

and unguarded. That for the promotion of such sound religious education within this Parish, it is desirable that a vigorous effort should
be made for the extension of Parochial Schools, especially for the
children of the working classes and the poor.'

This was the springboard from which Scoresby started his vast
scheme for education in Bradford. The very next month the first
school was opened. It was the Parish Church Factory School and it
was held in the church room at Stothill under the able guidance of
Mr William Ross and one assistant, who very soon had nearly four
hundred pupils, mostly children drawn from the nearby factory.

Almost immediately after this public meeting the building of an
altogether new school, as distinct from using an existing room, was
started at Eccleshill, and it was completed, at a cost of £628, before
the year ended. The money came from three sources: a grant from
the Committee of the Privy Council for Education of £150; special
subscriptions collected by Mrs Scoresby and the Curate of Eccleshill,
the Rev. J. Atkins; and the remainder being taken from the Parochial
Fund. It had an average of a hundred and fifty pupils and 'teachers
of very respectable acquirements and efficiency were prevalently
employed'. The fees at these schools, the children's pence, were: 'two-
pence per week for reading, threepence for writing on slates and fourpence for writing in copybooks, with arithmatic [sic] &c. Girls, fourpence in any class, one penny additional for sewing, but not to exceed
fourpence per week.' Lower terms were arranged for a second or third
child from the same house.

The teachers were set on their way by the invaluable Mr Ross and
when he had trained them he was ready to go on to the next school.
Many of them were, of course, 'pupil teachers', that is to say, older
children who hoped to become teachers themselves when they left
school and were intelligent enough to teach the infants the rudiments
of reading and writing.

The next school was the Model School, opened on 19th October
1842, in the 'presence of the Lord Bishop of Ripon, when the large
number of children, healthful in appearance and animated by the
novelty of their position presented an interesting scene'. This school
took 480 children and was later enlarged and admitted nearly six
hundred pupils.

After the pack ice of the Dues and Districts dissension, Scoresby
found it much easier to navigate his Church Schools programme, for
though uncharted, it was open water: he and his workers had a
unity of purpose and a great end towards which to steer.

CHAPTER 16

SCORESBY THE SOCIAL WORKER

'This determination has ever been the principle upon which I act:
"I will do what I can".'

The trouble with Mr Hardy was finally and happily resolved in
February 1842, when St John's Church, Bowling, was consecrated.
The *Bradford Herald* gave a very full report of the impressive ceremony:
  'The day was peculiarly auspicious, and although the service was
advertised to commence at eleven o'clock, long before that hour the
beautiful structure was crowded in every part. The church is built
upon an elevated plot of ground and its towering spire forms a pleasing
object for many miles round. The simple and chaste style in which
the interior of the church is finished is highly befitting and appropriate.'
  The account named all the twenty-six clergy present, who, led by
their Bishop, formed a procession and walked all round the new
church. Scoresby then read the Morning Prayer service and the
Bishop followed with Communion and also preached. 'The whole of
these imposing services', continues the report, 'were not concluded
until half-past two, and not one among the highly respectable and
crowded congregation could have left the newly consecrated walls
without admiration at the unostentatious munificence of the gentlemen who erected and brought to completion at their own cost so commodious a church.'
  But this was by no means the end of the ceremony. There was 'an
elegant *déjeune* at the neighbouring school room, and to which those
who had attended the service at the church were freely invited. The
room was tastefully decorated for the occasion. Every delicacy of the
season was provided, and when we mention the name of Mr Wade,
of the New Inn, in connection with the *déjeune*, not another word need
be added.'
  There were toasts, there were speeches. The *Herald* reporter faithfully recorded all that was said:
  'Dr Scoresby in responding to the toast said that he returned his
sincere thanks for the honour done him. The event which they had
witnessed that day was one of great importance to their poorer fellow
creatures. As for himself, he felt placed in the position of one who

saw so much before him that he could scarcely do anything. When he remembered the vast extent of the parish, its immense population and that he had only some fifteen or sixteen fellow labourers, he was ready to exclaim,—what are these among so many? (Hear, hear.) At the same time there was this consolation to support their over-whelming amount of labour, that they were not accountable to their Maker for what they could not do, but for what they had done. He felt that when they had done all they were still unprofitable servants. He did not say this from affected humility. They saw around them myriads of their fellow creatures sunk by reason of ignorance into degradation for want of that spiritual instruction which the church provides. The poor were not to blame for this. They could not teach themselves.

'Though he felt the deep responsibility of his situation, this determi-nation had ever been the principle upon which he had acted—"I will do what I can". (Applause.) He would say to his parishioners whom he saw before him—"You must come to the help of the Church". (Enthusiastic cheers.) It was the duty of those to whom God had given the power, to come forward as one man to the help of the Lord. There was a need that the church should be as one man,—that there should be one mind and one spirit pervading the whole. (Applause.) The enemies of the church had rallied their forces and there was a unity in their purposes. (Hear, hear.) There ought to be the same unity in the church. The worthy Vicar resumed his seat amid loud applause.'

Nor was this all. 'In the evening 500 scholars and 140 teachers par-took of tea &c, in the School-room, which was also liberally provided by the Bowling Iron Company. The evening was spent in the most pleasant manner possible. Thus ended a day long to be remembered by the population in this district; a day the remembrance of which will be precious to those privileged to take part in its religious services; a day the real effects of which will only be unravelled in eternity.'

The work in and on the schools was proceeding apace, and in this context it is interesting to quote from a letter received from Scoresby's friend, the Rev. W. R. Lythe, who had been Rector of Hadleigh, where they had pioneered a new scheme. Not a factory school but a factory, no less, built expressly by the parishioners, to employ 400 children. It was opened in 1834 and the good result was immediately apparent by a four-fifths reduction in the rates. The care and superin-tendence of the children 'devolved entirely upon the rector and his curate only'. The regulations were strict: 'Any young woman having a child was dismissed and never re-admitted under any circumstances. Neither was any young person admitted who had ever had a child. A report was brought to me every morning containing the names of any who had been seen walking in the streets at improper hours or in improper company, or found in any house of public entertainment. Those from the country were only allowed to lodge in houses approved by me, under pain of being suspended from their work or dismissed. Any superintendent or mechanic employed about the premises, either male or female, behaving immorally, was liable to be removed.' The writer of the letter says nothing about the children's education except: 'a certain weekly sum was retained out of their wages for the payment of a school mistress'. He suggests a similar scheme being tried in Bradford for, 'if any mill owner were to make the experiment, it would be found that his mill would always have the children of the most respectable parents in the place, in preference to any other, and be managed both cheaper and better'.

The foundation stone of the next Church School, at Daisy Hill, was laid by Scoresby himself in June 1843. He wrote a succinct little cameo, which brings the scene on that summer day very vividly to life:

> Vicar: On this good work, here to be done, we seek the Divine blessing, for we are divinely instructed to do all to the glory of God.
> Psalms—sung by the children.
> Psalm, read by the Vicar and the children in alternate verses.
> Prayers: 'Prevent me O Lord' &c with the Lord's Prayer.
> The Stone Laid: The Vicar, spreading some mortar on the place designed for the reception of the stone and the stone being duly lodged there and necessarily adjusted in the designed position, said:
> 'This *foundation stone*, designed for a *school* for affording a sound, useful and religious education to the children of this village and district, I now lay *thus*, and *thus*, and *thus* (using the mallet), and may the blessing of Almighty God, whose glory we desire to promote, rest upon it *for ever*!'
> Vicar's address.
> Psalm C sung by the children and others.
> Benediction.
> After the ceremonial, all the children, headed by their teacher, walked in procession to the Vicar's residence, where they were amply regaled with buns.

The distance from the school site to Scoresby's home was quite considerable, but Walks were a feature of church life in the West Riding of Yorkshire. The culminating event of the Sunday School year was the Whitsuntide Walk, and we may be sure that these children were certainly ready to be 'regaled with buns' at the end of their long walk after the Vicar had laid the foundation stone of Daisy Hill Church School.

We find a very vivid description of one Whit Walk in Charlotte Brontë's *Shirley* which ends thus:

'The broad white road unrolled before the long procession, the sun and sky surveyed it cloudless, the wind tossed the tree boughs above it, and the twelve hundred children and one hundred and forty adults, of which it was composed trod on in time and tune, with gay faces and glad hearts. It was a joyous scene and a scene to do good: it was a day of happiness for rich and poor; the work, first of God and then of the clergy. Let England's priests have their due; they are a faulty set in some respects, being only of common flesh and blood, like us all; but the land would be badly off without them: Britain would miss her Church if that Church fell. God save it! God also reform it!'

Of all people, Charlotte Brontë was indeed qualified to write such words. As a daughter of the parsonage, she knew the faults and foibles of the Church's ministers only too well. But it is good to note that of all the districts under Scoresby's care, Haworth gave the least trouble. In his time it was only a chapelry, and it was Scoresby who recommended that it should be made a parish in its own right. He always agreed with its charming, scholarly incumbent, the Rev. Patrick Brontë, coming as he did from the same part of the world as Scoresby's wife. At this time none of the daughters' works had been published and they were known solely as the parson's daughters. Scoresby mentions 'Miss Bronte' in a letter to the curate, the Rev. J. B. Grant, about a teacher for the Grammar School: 'Should they approve of my suggestion, I would come out, God willing, with Mr and Mrs Cranmer on the day of the election & I should be glad, in such case, if the trustees would take dinner with me at the principal Inn at Haworth, where they would make their acquaintance with the parties. Perhaps Mr Bronte, if well enough, would join us, or Miss Bronte, to keep company with Mrs Cranmer. I think some of their friends would also like to come, and make a pleasant social party for the occasion, yourself joining us, of course.'

The luncheon party must have been a success, for Scoresby's candidate, Mr Cranmer, was appointed to the Grammar School.

Another interesting document refers to the non-payment of dues from Haworth to the Parish Church owing to the very hard times— there had been a depression in the mills—and the plea of poverty is actually drawn up by Scoresby himself, who was in complete agreement with the Haworth parishioners' action. The only part he wished to be made quite clear was their obligation to pay the dues on future occasions, thus making the position straightforward for his successor. He never was bothered about the actual money, but merely the legal rights of the Vicar of Bradford.

As each school went up, the planning of the next one grew more difficult, more hedged about with petty objections, the source of more squabbles. Difficulties of obtaining funds prevented progress and Scoresby's dozens of letters on the subject of education grew into hundreds; building costs increased; the architect became awkward; the committee could not agree—Scoresby was never a committee man, he was always the captain in sole command of the ship. He firmly fixed his sights on the pole star of his ultimate ideal and continued to write letter after letter, using whatever influence he could and enlisting support from all quarters—the more influential the better. He wrote to T. D. Acland, the son of his old patron at Exeter Sir Thomas Acland, and now in Parliament, who said Scoresby's letter was a very important document: 'I thought that the best way to do justice to it was to put it into my father's hands who is more in favour of the Bill than I am. I confess I do not wish the Bill to pass in its present shape ... I think that if it were now to be passed through Parliament it might do more harm in the way of withdrawing dissenting children from such schools as yours than the good done by setting up the new State schools. I own the effect of the year's agitation on my mind is to make me think any good Bill for State education hopeless; and to look with hope only to an extension of voluntary schools where what is taught may issue from love and faith. The prevailing opinion is that the Government will not press the Education Clause further; it is much to be feared that they withdraw also the rest of the Bill.'

It was another quarter of a century before the British Government passed an effective Education Act.

In the meantime Scoresby continued with his Church Schools programme, raising money for them by lecturing on magnetism in places as far apart as Cheltenham, Torquay, London and Whitby. The scientific observer's eye was as keen as ever: it happened to snow at the time he was in Cheltenham. Out came his hand lens and on a scrap of paper Scoresby, man of the Arctic, carefully drew the beautiful pattern of the snowflakes which settled on the black sleeve of his coat.

The final church school in Bradford at New Leeds was the most ambitious building of all, for it included a Master's residence. The architect was given free rein—or rather he thought he had been—and he let himself go with pinnacles, elaborate chimney pots, gables and mullioned windows (letting in very little light, the one thing most needful). When it came to settling his account there was trouble, occasioning many, many more letters to be written. But even before the architect had seen one brick laid there was more trouble. The conveyancing was not straightforward and the lawyers argued over the purchase of the land; there was much delay and meanwhile building costs increased, but as the estimates had been given at a time when

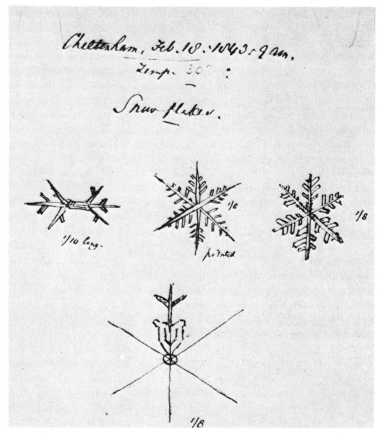

Four snow flakes

wages and materials were cheap, the builders were powerless to charge more. Scoresby wrote: 'It was to myself a source of much pain, the loss which I believe ensued to some of the contractors, especially to Mr Benwell, the mason, by the delays with the building, and the advance of prices in materials and labour, during its erection. This loss was the more to be regretted as the work was well done and the result so fine and excellent a schoolhouse. But I had no means of compensating them, unless by personal sacrifice, which was already far greater than due to my position.'

The school committee were not concerned about the increase in costs; they had contracted for the original price and they stuck firmly to it; it was the builders who had to bear the extra cost.

The kindly President of the Council for Education, Lord Wharncliffe, supported Scoresby in all his claims for financial assistance. 'The general rule,' he wrote early in 1843, 'is to grant towards the building of a school, 10/– per head for each child which it will accommodate, at 6 square feet per child. Under this rule the grant to Daisy Hill would probably be 174£, and that to New Leeds, £72:10:0. But this rule has, under certain circumstances, such for instance as Spitalfields and other places of extreme poverty and dense population, been extended to 20/– per head, but never more.' Scoresby's plea of extreme poverty in Bradford was effective, for a grant of no less than £300 was awarded and in December 1844, the Daisy Hill school was officially opened.

'The building is an ornament to the place', the *Halifax Guardian* wrote, 'and we may say creditable to the parish. The painting of the desks, pulpit and furniture, with the partition of the room, which lets down to one half its full height, so as not to interfere with the clear view of the whole room from the pulpit, is grained oak varnished. The whole is uncommonly church like, when arranged for divine service, and handsome. On Sunday afternoon last the schoolroom was opened for divine service by the Vicar who officiated to a large and very attentive congregation. The choir of the parish church attended for this occasion which was one of much solemnity and interest. This school house, which is very near the Vicar's residence, Dr and Mrs Scoresby, we understand, have made great efforts to get erected.... What adds to the importance of this erection is the peculiarly destitute state of the neighbourhood as to any effective means of instruction for their children, and the consequent results of ignorance and rudeness which so extensively prevail there.'

The New Leeds School was fated. The lawyers and the architect squabbled on. Lord Wharncliffe, Scoresby's staunch ally at the Council for Education, died suddenly and the grant for New Leeds was not as great as Scoresby had hoped. The whole business, he wrote, 'occasioned a degree of trouble, anxiety and responsibility which I should have hardly ventured to have encountered could it have been anticipated', It was not until June 1846 that the school was finally opened. Even then their efforts were hardly crowned with success, for in a very short time another school 'under other auspices' was opened in the immediate neighbourhood. We are not told just who the 'other auspices' were, but one suspects they must have been the dreaded 'dissenters'.

Nevertheless, quarrels and dissensions subside, the begging for funds is forgotten, but this great fact remains; that in Scoresby's seven years at Bradford, over six thousand children received an education at his church schools. When he first came to Bradford there were no church schools of any description and the total number of scholars in the whole of the town was just over four hundred attending private schools: when he left, the church schools had a total of 1,500 daily and 1,200 Sunday pupils. The words of the chairman of the Oddfellows, who made him a presentation when he retired, were indeed prophetic when he said:

'When we remember the period of your first coming among us, a peculiar period in the history of the Church in Bradford,—when we remember the great exertions you have made for extending the boundaries of your Master's kingdom—when we remember the great personal sacrifices you have been called upon to make, and all this too, in the midst of trials and difficulties of no ordinary character,—we feel that the seed you have thus sown, although you may not be permitted to see the result, will be like bread upon the waters, which shall be found after many days.'

In Bradford today, who can say, or who can know that their present happiness and success may not have been owing, in the very first instance, to this supreme act of William Scoresby towards their great- and great-great-grandparents?

There may be many who think pollution is a twentieth-century word. It was, however, very familiar to Scoresby, who wrote:

'The mills are well adapted for their object—most of them large, lofty and well built and thickly set with corresponding tiers of windows—which give to the town, after the period of lighting up, the effect of an extensive illumination. But with all the advantages derived from excellence and cheapness of building materials, Bradford is a smoky, I might justly say, dirty-looking town!

'Its forest of tall chimneys pour out their dark produce of imperfect combustion of the inferior coal in unrestrained plenitude. The chemical source of power and prosperity has ample indulgence to smoke its utmost. Here is the region of smoke-liberty. The whole population as a body, are interested in the results, and no class takes effective steps to abate, much less to destroy, this great disfigurement and public nuisance. Nay, science has been questioned in aid of its toleration— as to whether fully decarbonised vapours are not more injurious to the health and fitness of the district than the ample rich rolling volumes of the prevalent smoke?

'This indifference to atmospheric pollution arising from the employment of steam power in the working of machinery, is so prevalent a characteristic of our manufacturing towns that, except as to *excessive indulgence* in the general apathy, Bradford but follows the common rule. Nothing, indeed, but the most stringent, authoritative regulations with a watchful attention to their isolation and a rigid punishment of offences against them, will ever overcome the selfish indifference of man, as a class or a species, to the inconvenience or injury he may inflict upon others in operations in which he seeks to gain personal wealth, or realize personal pleasure.'

Nor was this just useless criticism, for Scoresby went on to suggest the adoption of methods, already patented, to alleviate the smoke nuisance.

The chimneys were not the only source of pollution. 'There is a *canal* at Bradford,' he wrote, 'which is a stagnant reservoir of filthy water, an unqualified pest and nuisance. Such is the condition of the water there that the surface is all over disturbed by bubbles of inflammable gases, generated in surprising quantities by the decomposition of the defiling elements suspended in the water.' In addition to the canal, there ran 'along and near it, the polluted waters of the once clear trout-stream of Bradford Beck, conveying down its open bed the washings and refuse of dye-works and additional defiling elements from other sources'. Why not, he asks, fill in the canal and cover up the beck in its progress through the town?

'The prevalent inconsideration of remote or consequential evils is one of the defects of the human character, which, in respect of circumstances bearing so painfully on personal well-being, is most surprising. Of the importance of circumstances immediately affecting human life, we are sufficiently sensible. When life is violently cut off, whether by accident or design a strong sensation is produced among the population. But when the springs of life are merely acted upon by unseen agencies, or by influences not distinctly evident to the careless and unobservant, it is surprising how much will be contentedly risked and relatively suffered.'

The Government Commissioner visited Bradford in 1843 and his report on the town is even more horrifying than Scoresby's remarks:

'A stream, called Bradford Beck, intersects the town; and from the obstruction to the free flow of the water in its natural channel, by the erection of mill dams and the encroachment of houses, it frequently overflows the lower part of the town, causing much havoc in the cellars and lower floors of shops and dwellings. There is sufficient fall for the natural drainage if it was not so obstructed. Some of the smaller cross streets are extremely steep, so that in many places the moisture from the dung-steads of the upper houses drains into the cellars of the houses beneath. The main sewerage of the town has been very defective; the chief sewerage, if sewerage it can be called, of the inferior streets and of the courts, is in open channels; and from the rough and unequal surface of the streets the flow is tardy and the whole soil is saturated with sewerage water. The main sewers are discharged either into the brook or into the terminus or basin of a canal which runs into the lower part of the town. The stench is very strong and fevers prevail much all around.

'Taking the general condition of Bradford, I am obliged to pronounce it the most filthy town I visited; and I could see no symptom of any improvement in the more recent arrangements for the abodes of the working classes. The scavenging of the streets is but indifferently done. The chief slaughter house is in the middle of the town, and forming a most decided nuisance to its immediate neighbourhood. The sewerage is defective and the supply of water for the inhabitants is very limited. At present a great part of the town is supplied by water carriers, who bring the water upon carts and upon donkeys, and charge a halfpenny for three gallons, which forces an economy in the use of this important element, highly injurious to health, cleanliness and comfort.'

And then there were the woolcombers. There were upwards of ten thousand of these home-workers. The same report says of them:

'Woolcombing is admitted to be a very unhealthy employment. The woolcombers assort the wool chiefly in an apartment of their own dwelling. The work is done over a fire of charcoal, which sends forth volumes of carbonic acid gas, and the workpeople are obliged to keep their windows open in all weathers, to prevent, or to mitigate, the evil effects of the gas. They are roasted to perspiration on one side, and have often a current of cold air rushing upon them from the window. They look pale and cadaverous, and are short lived, few reaching fifty years of age (the average age of death among woolcombers and their families is 16 years). Their roasting employment and exposure to the carbonic acid gas, gives them a desire for spirits and opiates, and it is probable that the free use of them may have some considerable share in shortening their lives.'

As always, Scoresby asked what could be done to help. He and a few others called a public meeting in the Exchange Buildings and a 'Sanatory' Committee was formed which included the name of every prominent person in the town, to the number of eighty, with Scoresby as its Chairman. The work which this committee did would form the subject of another book and it is good to know that William Scoresby was one of its primary instigators.

The 'Sanatory' Committee recommended the following action:

1. Since Bradford Beck is the main natural channel for carrying off the drainage of the town, all further encroachment on its bed should be energetically prevented, and any necessary alteration and improvements of that stream be made.

2. The abatement of the nuisance caused by the filthy and pestilential state of the Canal.

3. The thorough and effectual drainage, sewerage, paving, and

scavenging of the town, and the frequent and efficient removal of offensive deposits.

4. No houses shall be suffered to be erected nor streets laid out, which will not admit of thorough ventilation, and which are not provided with drains into the main sewers.

5. The abatement of the smoke nuisance.

6. The establishment of public cemeteries outside of the town.

7. The supply of water at a cheap rate to the poorer classes.

8. The establishment of public hot and cold water baths, and wash houses for the poor.

9. The registration and due visitation of lodging and boarding houses for those of the poor who come from a distance into the town.

10. The provision of public walks, and spaces for due exercise, recreation, and healthy games.

Scoresby the whaling captain, who had never had a case of scurvy in his ships, and who had always kept them clean, scrubbed and aired, and his crew healthy, was the man who suggested this last item. But the whole plan was a Utopian dream and more than a century later item 5. had still not been attended to.

Shortly after Scoresby came to Bradford he was asked to become the official Chaplain to the Workhouse. This he gladly did, neither expecting nor receiving any remuneration whatever for the work which he and his curates undertook; that is to say, regular visiting of the inmates and two services weekly. All ran smoothly until one day in 1843 when, with not more than a couple of days' notice, the committee arranged for a dissenting preacher to hold services in the workhouse.

Scoresby was incensed. His position was the stronger because he had never received any money from the Board of Guardians of the Workhouse, yet he was their sole official Chaplain. Sparks and letters flew back and forth and unpleasant and unkind things were said about him. There was much distress, but the 'Establishment' won the day and the dissenters were finally excluded from the workhouse.

But the toll on Scoresby's health, and especially his nervous system, was very great and by 1844 it became necessary for him to have a complete break from all these distressing scenes. The Bishop of Ripon gave him six months' leave of absence and at the end of April he embarked on the sailing ship *Patrick Henry* for a tour of America. The ship sailed from Liverpool, and before it left, Scoresby visited his old Floating Church, where he had spent so many happy years at the beginning of his ministry. He was 'greatly gratified with the characteristically pious aspect of the congregation and serious performance of the service'. Prayers were offered for a blessing on his forthcoming voyage, and the following day he sailed.

CHAPTER 17

AN AMERICAN TOUR

'The President shook hands, was courteous and friendly. Happy
to make my acquaintance. We conversed on general and
miscellaneous topics for half an hour.'

There were no fewer than 335 emigrants on board the *Patrick Henry*
and they were mustered, shortly after sailing, on the poop deck. 'Only
one outlet, forward, being left for them, they descended to the main
deck as their names were called over and their tickets examined and
their several family parties enumerated. They consisted of a great
variety of classes, many of them, apparently, very respectable. About
one fourth were females. Their destinations were very various. Many
were from Halifax and were bound to the westward of America. Their
payments were £5 : 10 : 0 to £4 : 10 : 0 for adults according to their
quarters, and the children half price for the earlier applicants. When
the ship began to fill, children were charged as adults, because they
occupied the place of adults in limitation of numbers. They find their
own provisions, except bread and water, the ship being bound, by
legislative enactment, to provide a pound of bread or its equivalent
in some other form of food, and 70 gallons of water for each passenger.
The legislative has also wisely regulated the number of passengers to
the proportion of tonnage. The British rate is, not exceeding 3 passengers to 5 tons burden; the United States allows only 2 passengers to
5 tons. Proper officers are appointed to oversee these provisions.'

The first-class passengers fared rather better than the emigrants,
for, although there was room for thirty-six there were only eleven
travelling, which meant they each had 'an entire cabin, which
rendered the arrangements peculiarly comfortable, and, the contrivances for ventilation being very complete, the condition of the air
was more agreeable than I ever remember to have experienced in
any packet in which I ever sailed.'

The captain was 'highly respectable,—an active, efficient seaman,
a gentlemanly person, and possessing much variety of scientific knowledge, and a taste for meteorological observations which he attends
to regularly—the thermometer, barometer and dew-point being
observed every four hours'. Scoresby's journal contains about a dozen
pages of these readings, covering several years before the voyage,

which he carefully copied from the captain's records. Needless to say, he also noted the state of the weather daily, with thermometer and barometer readings, for the entire voyage of five weeks.

On Sunday Scoresby was asked, both by the captain and the emigrant passengers, to take divine service. 'The day being fine the *Church* was "rigged out" on the poop deck. The cabin passengers for the most part, if not all, attended; and nearly the whole of the emigrants and other passengers. The females, amongst whom were many respectable persons, were accommodated with seats on a range of elevated boards; the men for the most part stood. Having put into the hands of a pious man from below the hymns from the Mariners Church Hymn Book which I proposed to be sung, they were got up very well by a party of serious persons, and sung with a pleasing and devotional effect.

'The service was solemn and the attention and feeling manifested by some of the congregation, interesting and encouraging. I humbly hope and believe that He who preached to the people out of a ship was graciously present with us in our humble services.'

Among the emigrants, Scoresby 'found a party of about 80 from the Parish of Halifax and about 30 from that of Sheffield—destined, mainly, for settlement in the territory of Wisconsin, lying to the west of the lake Michigan. They are all members of a society: "The British Temperance Emigration Society", established at Liverpool in 1842. By weekly contributions from the members, a fund is raised so as to purchase 80 acres of good land, to build on each lot a house, and to supply goods altogether to the value of £40 for each member emigrating. An estate steward resides in the place of emigration and a "conductor" is appointed to meet the emigrants at New York and conduct them in the most economical manner to their destination. Land is purchased in Wisconsin for them and the members are appointed to shares therein by ballot.'

'Several families were discovered from time to time on the passage whose information and experience in manufactures or mechanism must render them very beneficial to the country into which they are emigrating. One individual, Greaves, with his wife and family, has been the principal artisan in a Chronometer maker's establishment in Liverpool. He had left a situation of 3½ guineas a week (with Messrs Frodsham) on account of the occupation being too sedentary for his health. He was designing to settle in Wisconsin. In the project and prospects of another individual (Mr Crowther), who had had charge of the blast furnaces of a large iron-works at Wolverhampton—I felt greatly interested, and the more so from his being a God-fearing man and otherwise a person of much apparent intelligence and solidity of character; a loss to our country and, with the party he takes with him, no small boon to the United States. His destination is to a property which he has purchased in the neighbourhood of Morgantown, Virginia. The property consists of an estate of 1900 acres of land of which 600 are in cultivation. Mines of iron ore and coal run through the whole and are worked by drifts in the side of the hill. On the property are some houses, a water wheel of 40 horse power, with abundance of additional water power; and a blast furnace capable of smelting 35 tons of iron in a week. The whole purchase money was 8000$. His own family, including a son-in-law, comprises most of the principal managers and workmen—and what was deficient he has engaged and taken along with him.

'An Englishman naturally regrets to see so many industrious and respectable persons becoming colonists *out* of our own colonies in Canada, which present many advantages—and for accessibility, much economy.'

Scoresby's scientific eye took note of everything on the passage. He noted the 'striking change' in the colour of the sea. It had been generally blue, but by 6th May it had 'changed to an olive green. It was an indication, as I believe, of an abundance of coloured animalcules. The examination of the water, however, with a common lens, detected some living minute creatures, but no such aggregation of them as might account for the colouring effect. Probably they were too minute to be detected by such a low magnifying power. The supposition, however, of the existence in the water of myriads of medusae or other animalcules, was fully confirmed in the night by the brilliant phosphorescence of the water. The swell being considerable and the ship plunging against a head sea, the broken water about the bows became splendidly luminous. Even at a distance the little curl of the waves exhibited the like peculiarity. Alongside the water was partially phosphorescent—presenting an interesting variety in this beautiful phenomena. The disturbed water as it passed by the side of the ship appeared studded with brilliant points, and discs of light like that of a small firework exploding below, were seen beneath the surface. The effect was most beautiful and attractive. The variety in the phenomena seemed to arise from the variety in the size and form of the phosphorescent animals. The minute kind, no doubt, were crowded in the water; the kinds producing bright specks and discs were scattered and larger; and those producing flashes of light were probably of still greater magnitude.'

He goes on to describe and draw, in great detail, specimens of all the floating marine organisms which he found. Two years later, in December 1846, a young naval surgeon, T. H. Huxley, began a voyage which was to lead him to new fundamental knowledge of the same medusae and allied organisms—the beginnings of our modern knowledge of surface sea life; and here was Scoresby once again on board ship, once again linking up the threads of scientific observation and investigation; the whaling captain—the man of the sea, the explorer and investigator working in his own element and true to his inner gift and compulsion.

The ship's compass, too, came under his notice, and he persuaded the captain to rig up a stage, clear of the mast and compare 'a compass thereon, assumed to be true, with the indications of that in the binnacle'.

On the 21st May Scoresby notes: 'An interesting incident occurred this afternoon in the baptism of an infant born on board on the 14th of May. It was the child of William and Mary Thompson, Agent, emigrants destined for Wisconsin. It was named Patrick Henry, after the ship. I officiated.'

We wonder how little Patrick Henry survived and whether any of his descendants still have the certificate which Scoresby wrote:

Baptized on board the Packet Ship Patrick Henry, according to the form of the Church of England, *Patrick Henry*, son of William and Mary Thompson, agent, May 21st 1844, an infant child, born at sea in the said ship.

WILLIAM SCORESBY D.D.
Vicar of Bradford, Yorkshire.

Land was sighted on 24th May and the following day they came in sight of Long Island. The final entry in the journal of the voyage reads: 'Long Island as seen from the sea is very uninteresting, presenting to the eye a tame and continuous bank of sand surmounted with but a faint appearance of verdure.'

The tour which Scoresby made of the States was enough to daunt the strongest of young men. He was neither young nor strong and the heat, oppressive and extremely tiring to any ordinary person, was all the more so to an Arctic man. The pages of this book do not permit a greatly detailed description of his tour. In the notes which he made during and after his journey there is almost enough material for another book. With time and care they could well be studied as the basis of a most interesting story of a visit to America long before the Civil War. Many of the notes, alas, are only in faint pencil and at times rather cryptic, thus:

'Sherry cobbler—refreshing drink with a vulgar name.'

'Philadelphia 31 May. Black servants and porters. Gentlemen rude to porters.'

'Passed some fine fields of maize. Cows with bells on neck in case of wandering.'

'Coffin merchants or store rooms. Handsome mahogany cases in French polish of different series arranged on end. Some with *windows* for viewing the face of the dead.'

Fortunately, much of what he saw and jotted down he later put into lecture form. For instance:

'Women. New York. Pretty. Early brought forward & married at 17. Not so clear complexions. Few with good busts—flat generally. Children not plump like ours. Ladies, pretty, neat figures not good busts. Take no exercise walking.'

Later becomes:

'In personal appearance the American women are generally admired. In the principal cities they dress fashionably and expensively. The style of it is French, generally in good taste; but the fault into which it runs is the being dressed ordinarily too well and too expensively—and the carrying of fashion into extremes.

'In person the American ladies are generally slight; in complexion pallid with much feminine delicacy of appearance, both in figure and in countenance. An appearance of high health and vigour is rarely to be seen among this class, for the nature of the climate, the mode of living, and the want of regular walking exercise present physical conditions unfavourable to the acquirement of the clear, blooming health of many ladies in our own country. For the coldness of the American winter, and the fervent heat of the sun in summer prove hindrances to exercise in walking and lead to sedentary habits. The use of close stoves and the spending of so much time in warm rooms so heated, contribute, it is considered, to the prevalent delicacy of appearance, if not of constitution, among the American ladies.'

'A stranger is struck with the numerous handsomely dressed, interesting looking and very pretty women. In ladies of majestic figure and mein, and of extreme beauty, however, and in the prevalence of women of clear, healthful complexions and fine busts,—our own country is generally allowed, I think, to have the advantage.'

Armed with letters of introduction, Scoresby visited several prominent people in New York, which he describes as 'a mixture of Liverpool and Paris—public offices fine—Exchange noble building' but also notes: 'Streets wretchedly paved & filthy.' They in their turn gave him other letters of introduction to use on his tour. He went to Washington by way of Philadelphia and Baltimore. The first attempt to visit the President,* who 'receives all who call at certain times, when all shake hands.—Has been known to have the arm temporarily paralysed with the exertion'—was unsuccessful for he was 'not at home' though 'expected in a few minutes'. Scoresby and his friend Mr Pakenham 'walked through the house to the front and

* John Tyler—President 1841–1845.

about the gardens for near $\frac{1}{2}$ an hour, but the President not arriving we retired. The entrance soiled with *tobacco spitting* against the walls— untidy entrance—worn, much-faded curtains.'

The second visit to the White House was more successful for 'the President was fortunately within and received us. Mr Pakenham, leaving me in the reception room, went into the President's private room, into which I was soon invited. The President shook hands, was courteous and friendly—happy to make my acquaintance. Conversed on general & miscellaneous topics for $\frac{1}{2}$ an hour or 20'. He attends St John's Church, where I was invited to preach. Entrance door, marble doorway, greatly stained with *tobacco spitting!*'

This habit of spitting, already noted with disgust by Charles Dickens, who had visited America two years before, was a nation-wide abomination, tolerated by Americans with indifference. Scoresby was quite shattered by the practice and devoted a great deal of space to abhoring the filthy habit, prevalent everywhere, ships, streets, hotels, dining rooms or wherever the tobacco-chewing men happened to be—and on the carpets too, they indulged themselves unrestrained by anyone. Though there were spittoons about, they were seldom used. 'The practice of smoking or chewing is prevalent & every public resort and hotel indicates its disgusting consequence.'

Scoresby duly preached at St John's Church, which was attended by 'the British Minister & suite—John Q Adams, ex-President and family, and many of the chief officers of the State'. The congregation numbered about six hundred and Scoresby 'had greatest liberty and comfort through the Divine mercy'.

While in Washington, he visited the brand new Telegraph Office where Professor Morse's electric telegraph had just been set up between there and Baltimore. Scoresby notes: '70 cells or electric jars on Grove's principle with concentrate acid and porous earthenware cylindrical septum. Two wires on poles by railway: but only one in action at either end—the circuit *being completed by the earth*! Message communicated—"Dr Scoresby is here"—reply: "S-c-o-r-e-s-b-y 1:50"! I then requested to ask, (having a letter to him) "Is the Bishop of Maryland at Baltimore?" Answer: "I don't know". "Will you send and enquire". "I have no runner".'

From Washington, Scoresby went to Louisville by way of Charleston, Cincinatti and White Springs. The heat was oppressive all the way and at Cairo he notes:

'Waiting here, in this sickly-feeling, hot, depressing, close atmosphere, waiting for the chance of a steamboat to St Louis —the Providence, I should say—I felt greatly depressed and anxious, especially in the still disordered state of the system. After prayer for the Divine guidance and support, I comforted myself by reading one of the loving letters of my dear wife. Its affectionate, hearty expressions of love were again and again cheering. The Lord bring us safely and happily together again in his own good time.'

Nor was the night any better, for: 'The heat in bed within the mosquito bar was oppressive. The door of my room and windows were both wide open, but not a breath of air penetrated to me. The mosquitos were swarming and I had a choice betwixt being made the prey of these distressing creatures, or suffering under the oppression of a still, closer atmosphere than I might otherwise have had. Without any clothes on me I was in a state of solution most of the night. Towards morning it was a little cooler.'

Eventually a steamer did come and he was able to go on to St Louis and thence to Chicago, 'a remarkable place, a city sprung out of an Indian village in 10 or 12 years and now numbering 8 to 10000 inhabitants with the prospect of a large increase. The majority of houses wood, but there are some good homes of brick & some good villa residences—generally with an observatory at the top. It is formed into a port by means of a small river, protected and extended into deep water by two wooden piers of considerable length.'

At an evening party at Mr and Mrs Butterfield's, Scoresby had 'an opportunity of seeing the society of the place, of which I was pleased to avail myself. I understand 200 invitations had been sent out—there might be 120–130 persons present,—evidently the elite of the place. Several very pleasing young persons—well looking girls—were present and a goodly number of professional men. Miss Whiting, Miss Butterfield struck me as particularly pleasing & pretty; Mrs Ogden (jnr) a pleasing conversational person. The flower garden, (the house being on the outskirts of the city) was lighted up and a band of music engaged, so that most of the party from time to time retreated from the warmth of the entertaining room into the cooler air without. Within the house two or three ladies played on the piano, in very fair style, one with a rather painful touch, but the instrument (a New York made one), though quite as handsome in appearance as those of our best makers, and with a great extent of scale,—was not equal to the English, there was a want of tone and richness. The refreshments were lemonade, ice cream and cakes—no wine or liquors. On the whole I was much pleased with the party. The style was unostentatious, but very respectable. The conversation was much of the English style. The ladies were not so dressed as at New York—generally in white muslin dresses; several of the ladies spoke with very little of peculiar accent—I should say in a pleasing manner. I left about 11 pm along with a good many others; but many of the younger faction remained for social dancing.'

After Chicago Scoresby went northwards into Canada, by way of

Lake St Clair, Detroit and, of course, Buffalo from where he visited
Niagara. By 20th July he had reached Toronto, where he was invited
to dine with the Bishop, Dr Strachan, and the following Sunday he
preached in the Cathedral where the congregation was 'rather thin—
there might be 500 or less present. I had much comfort in preaching.'
He dined with the Bishop and noted: 'Dinner handsome & in the
English style.'

The following day he visited the University site and grounds, which
was in the process of being built—one wing only had been completed.
And then, quite by chance, he found there was a Magnetic Observatory in the grounds, so—naturally—he visited it and found the assistant observer, Mr Younghusband, who showed him round and then—
let Scoresby himself take the narrative up:

'On going into Mr Younghusband's house to see a pair of powerful
compound bar magnets which he had incidentally mentioned—what
was my surprise to find that these were composed of hand made plates,
and were literally and strictly on my principle and construction! Yet
Mr Younghusband was not aware of the fact—nor knew whose construction they were. It appears that they were forwarded by Col Sabine
(or Prof. Lloyd) probably the former gentleman. Why did Col Sabine
adopt my principle of construction, & send out such an instrument
as being most effective and powerful and yet neglect to intimate in
any way whose instrument or construction it was? And why did Col
Sabine, a public officer & one of the Cttee of the Navy for the improvement of Sea Compasses—adopt this construction, privately, and withdraw himself from the section of the British Assn in which I was on
two diff: occasions explaining the principle of instruments & construction of compass needles, for the improvement of which the cttee
was appointed? Why did he attend all the sittings (for the most part)
of the British Assn at *Manchester* & at *Cork*, & when my papers came
on, walk out? Was it that he wished to make use of what he could
learn or hear or obtain elsewhere & surreptitiously? I will not suppose
it. Yet why did he so act—& in this case too?

'(I apprehend these compound magnets had been made by my
friend Rev T Dury: but neither his labour nor my principle had any
acknowledgement).'

After Toronto Scoresby went on to Montreal, where he met and
dined with the Governor-General and then to Quebec, preaching
there on Sunday. He next went on to Saratoga Springs—'the Harro-
gate of America'—with 'a train of three heavily loaded, clumsy
coaches'. Though the distance was only twenty-five miles it took them
six hours, 'but the road, mainly deep with sand and dust, could not
be traversed very rapidly'. The street was 'crowded with hotels,
which—though but frame buildings—became important because of

the magnitude of some of them'. He was not able to get in at the
largest of these, the *United States Hotel* so he went on to the next
one, the *Union Hall*. 'This house was also "full", but when the
"cars left in the afternoon," I was told, "they would see what could
be done." The result was that I got a small, but clean and comfortable
bedroom.'

Here Scoresby observed and noted that particular form of American 'hustle' which Dickens depicts so well in *Martin Chuzzlewit* when
young Martin, hearing a bell, thinks there must be a fire as the guests
push past him and rush into the dining room. 'The dining room',
writes Scoresby, 'has two long rows of tables. No places are definitely
numbered, yet each guest has his or her particular chair—which is
pointed out and brought from the side of the table by the waiters,
each waiter being responsible for a particular number of guests. The
guests are summoned by the ringing of a bell (a preparatory bell having been rung half an hour before) and in three or four minutes the
400 are seated and the clattering of spoons or knives and forks, general.
The courses are removed by signal—here a small bell—and everything is very orderly: but rapid—though not by any means so rapid
as I have witnessed elsewhere, for other places are places of business:
this of recreation and pleasure.

'All *seem* to be tee-totallers; all, therefore, rise as soon as the dinner
is done. The bell rings at 2 o'clock, in 5 minutes all are seated and
the soup is over; in about 40' the dinner is finished and in 50' 400
persons have dined, "desserted", and left the room.'

The saloons of the hotels, especially in the evenings 'present a very
animated and interesting scene. You here see "life in America" concentrated. Persons of all grades, from the senators and judges, merchants and manufacturers, clergy and other professions down to comparatively humble tradesmen and clerks, and even artisans—are
found in the same house; and leading about their wives and daughters
or female friends, mingling together, eating together and perambulat-
ing in the same saloon. Anyone who is willing and able to pay ten
dollars can associate for a week with the first people of the country.'

The visitors took their water drinking very seriously. 'So popular
is the water of the Congress Spring that from the hour of 6 to 8 in
the morning I generally found from 50 to 200 persons surrounding
the well—drinking or waiting their turn. Four boys were most actively
engaged in dipping it up out of a tube sunk in the ground. The proprietor of this spring liberally allows the free use of the water to the
public—the boys who dip being paid only by the gratuities they
receive from the visitors. But as an article of merchandise the water
yields a magnificent return. So great is the demand for "Congress
Water"—so called from the discovery of the spring by a party of

gentlemen, one of whom, John Taylor Gilman, was a member of Congress—that the bottling on the spot, which is carried on from breakfast time till evening, does not suffice, at times, to fulfil the orders received. Dr Clarke, the proprietor, who purchased the spring and a farm betwixt 200 and 300 acres for 6000 dollars,—now receives about 25000 dollars annually for the mineral waters he supplies from this one spring.'

Albany and New York were next on Scoresby's itinerary and then he made his way to Boston, preparatory to sailing from there. He visited the Perkins School for the Blind near Boston, and there he met Dr Howe's star pupil, Laura Bridgman, who, though deaf and blind had been taught by him to communicate and write. He was away in Europe at the time and Scoresby's 'communication with her was through the medium of an intelligent young person, Mary Swift, one of the teachers to whom Laura is evidently greatly attached— evincing that attachment by frequent endearments. The mode of communication is by a finger alphabet—it is sufficiently rapid not to be tedious.

'She was first informed, at my request, that a gentleman from England had come to see her—an intimation which she perfectly understood and asked the name, which being given her as *Doctor* Scoresby, asked "whether I gave people medicine". She was then informed I was a clergyman, whereon she laughed as if amused with her mistake. Thinking it would interest her, she was informed that I had been near the North Pole. She said—she should not like that, was it not very cold? It being intimated that I had seen and killed whales and bears— she seemed interested about the white bears—but suddenly asked whether I was an Esquimaux? On being told that I was an Englishman, she then proceeded with the subject of bears, asking how many I had killed. I told her perhaps 10 or 12. "Were you not afraid?" she said. I replied that I was more afraid of the mosquitoes on the Ohio. "You should not mind trifles!" was her remark.

'The instructor said that I had a large number of people to preach to, there being 120,000 in the Parish from whence I came. She naively and playfully replied: "Oh, I am glad there are so many out of the way of the bears!"

'Great and commendable care, I observed, is exercised to prevent Laura from feeling or knowing that she was an object of peculiar interest. Hence, when I requested her to be told—"that I was much pleased in having seen *her* and that I should remember *her* in England", Miss Swift declined putting the observation on these terms, substituting "The Institution" for the personal pronoun. This I thought very judicious.'

It is strange to think that the very part of Scoresby's American tour which had the most enduring and lasting effect took place almost by chance in the last days of his visit to that remarkable country. This was his visit to Lowell, the busy cotton manufacturing town in Massachusetts, then in its early days, for it had only been established about twenty years. Despite its youth it boasted a population of 25,000 which included nearly 7000 factory girls. Remembering Bradford and its problems, Scoresby was immensely interested in their conditions and toured the mills and factories and visited their lodging houses, asking questions and noting down facts, many of which were self-evident: 'The mills are ornamented, in the windows, with plants in flower pots the property of the girls, and factories are kept remarkably clean and neat, the floors and the staircases beautifully clean and the steps painted, except a space as if *meant* for a stair carpet. The mills are smaller than ours in England, but better kept. Nice tastefully laid out gardens or plots of grass and trees adorn the enclosures of many of them and everything is strikingly fair and clean—both in and about the mills and the city. Here we mark the striking advantage of a *water power*, the whole of the machinery being driven by the water of the river, dammed up above the town and brought in by a canal to the respective mills. Altogether it is a fair town, beautiful to look upon. Rows of trees adorn many of the streets.' But it was the girls themselves and their conditions which impressed Scoresby so much; with astonishment he notes their wages: 'The girls in the cotton factories work chiefly by the piece or quantity. On average they can earn about 2 $ per week in *addition* to the charge in the boarding house. In the carpet manufacture they can earn about 1 $ a day! These high wages are necessary to get the hands, which are at present scarce.

'The effect of employing so many young women of a respectable class has been to abridge very greatly, the sources for domestic servants. Before the commencement of manufacture, the wages of a domestic servant were £5 to £7 a year: but now, Mr Appleton told me that his six female servants have 20 to 30 guineas per year!' Great emphasis was laid on 'respectability'—any girl becoming 'disreputable' was 'not associated with, but obliged to leave'. But not only the factory workers, but the keepers of the boarding houses must have impeccable characters: a new one was about to be appointed to one of them and there was a 'stain on her character'—the girls banded together and threatened to leave if she was appointed and so the managers had to look elsewhere for their housekeeper.

Armed with all the salient facts about the wonderful system at Lowell Scoresby returned to Boston and 'the limits to which I could extend my visit to the United States having arrived, I prepared to embark in the British steamer, the *Acadia*'. 'As the hour of sailing was 1½ hours after noon, I agreed to preach at Grace Church—the Rev

C. M. Butler, Rector—, and had the comfort, therefore, of attending Divine Service immediately before my departure, and once more bearing my testimony to the grand truths of the Gospel, and their practical obligations. A carriage was at the door of the Church at 12: so that immediately at the conclusion of the sermon, not being able to unite with the communicants in the celebration of the Lord's Supper, I was driven to the steamship—arriving in sufficient time for a satisfactory embarkation.'

But his holiday was not quite over. The ship called at Halifax and Scoresby was able to go on shore and visit some of his wife's relatives of the family of Uniacke, one of whom was a judge and another had been Solicitor General and a third, The Rev Fitzgerald Uniake, was Rector of a Halifax Church.

The voyage home was a new experience for Scoresby the sailing ship captain, for it was his first long voyage in a steamer, although he had crossed to Ireland in' a small paddle steamer. It was certainly much faster, for the homeward journey took only two weeks, whereas the outward passage had occupied the best part of a month. 'Notwithstanding the sea, the motion of the ship was remarkably easy—and her steering so perfect that she was constantly leaving a "wake" as straight as a railway.'

The account of the journey might almost be called a ship's log, for Scoresby duly noted the daily temperature, wind force, and position of the ship. It need hardly be said that he got on well with the master, Captain Harrison, who lent him compasses in order that he might make detailed observations, and on Sunday asked him to take Divine Service, which was held in the saloon: 'The seamen, being previously mustered, a fine set of stout and sailor-like fellows, were present, together with most of the passengers—all of whom seemed very serious and attentive.'

'Sept 7. During the day's run we had a surprising number of porpoises playing about us. At one time they appeared in large shoals. One shoal, or *regiment*, comprised several hundreds (I could count nearly 200) formed in an oblique line and going rapidly to windward leaping clean out of the water in succession. The line extended for more than a quarter of a mile in very close order. They presently came close to the ship and seemed to change their course near us as if coming down to view us and sport about the ship.'

'Sept 12. Being within 190′ of Cape Clear at noon, the passengers became animated by the prospect of a speedy arrival—so that the dinner was followed by toasts and speeches & songs & mirth. Unfortunately it was followed, as it had been for several days, with card playing and gambling for such sums, that, I was told, £20 or £30 was sometimes won or lost by one individual in one evening. The playing was continued, I believe, on different evenings, much beyond the time for putting out the lights in the saloon.

'Sept 13—Friday. I was asleep when loud clapping of hands of persons in the saloon awoke me, followed by cheers and then the cry of "Cape Clear, Cape Clear". This was about 3 am when the light on that headland was descried, and the passengers who had been sitting up, playing, and some drinking, made the noises referred to.

'At 10 am we passed Cork Harbour, where, though the weather was hazy, it was pleasant to observe the lighthouse—Camden Fort—Trabalgen &c, places of interest by their association with domestic relations.'

On landing, Scoresby noted: 'In America the houses look white and smart and showy, the fields of a dingy green in summer. Here, the houses look dingy and the fields *green*, even near Liverpool.' The final entry in the journal ends with praise to God:

'Several waiting for me & Mrs Scoresby expecting me at the arrival of the Railway auxiliary at Bradford at 6 pm. Arr^d at home at 7½ pm & found all well.—*D.L.*'

CHAPTER 18

JAMES PRESCOTT JOULE

'As for any trouble I may be at, I can assure you that the pleasure
I take in magneto-electricity is an ample compensation for that.'

It was at the Manchester meeting of the British Association in 1842
that Scoresby first met J. P. Joule, who was then twenty-three. The
young man was fascinated by the gifted parson who was so very
different from the great majority of clergymen he had met. He had
probably heard of him from his father or from other members of the
Manchester Literary and Philosophical Society. The celebrated John
Dalton, who had been Joule's boyhood mentor in science, would be
well aware of the achievements of Scoresby, whose reputation stood
high among the older generation of scientists.

For his part, Scoresby was immediately interested in Joule's ideas
regarding heat and other forms of energy and in his attempt to
measure the efficiency of the electro-magnetic engine, and much
desired to collaborate with Joule in these researches. But there were
many difficulties in the way. Scientific research requires, if it is to
be successfully prosecuted, freedom from material care and anxieties,
and ample leisure to devise and perform experiments and calculations. Joule's father, with admirable foresight, had provided the
means to make these conditions available to his son, but Scoresby was
in the middle of his most difficult and exhausting period as a minister
of the church and his sense of duty and responsibility was such that
he would not—even if he could—have abandoned his parochial work.

We might pause here a moment to consider the relationship
between these two men. Joule was at this period almost unknown to
the wider scientific world. His friends in Manchester knew and
esteemed him, but he was not a university man, nor was he attached
to any institution which might have lent him support and encouragement; he was a lone worker in the scientific world, and his ideas were
original and profound. The scientific worker who is in process of
incubating new ideas and concepts is of necessity a very lonely man.
This young Manchester man from whose private laboratory emerged
the universal Law of the Conservation of Energy and the experimental
determination of the Mechanical Equivalent of Heat was such a
worker.

Joule visited Bradford and stayed with the Scoresbys shortly after the Manchester meeting. We may well imagine the lively discussions between the two men, and there can be no doubt Joule was much encouraged by Scoresby's interest and enthusiasm. The following year he sent a paper to Scoresby:

> New Bailey St, Salford.
> March 30 1843

Dear Sir,

   I beg your acceptance of the enclosed Paper extracted from the forthcoming part of the 'Manchester Memoirs' in hope that you may feel interested with it. You will observe a note at p. 19 respecting new experiments. I may state that these, as far as I have carried them, go against the 5th proposition and tend to establish the 3rd more generally by showing the *non* interference of magnetic reaction with the quantity of heat due to chemical changes.*

   With kindest regards to Mrs Scoresby and yourself, in which my Father and Brother desire to join, Believe me, dear Sir,

> Very respectfully yours,
> JAMES P. JOULE

The next letter is of great interest, for it records a turning point in Joule's researches.

> New Bailey St, Salford.
> April 24 1843

Dear Sir,

   I believe that in the note accompanying my papers I said that recent experiments had militated against proposition 5. I must now beg to retract that statement which was founded on 5 or 6 experiments in which the errors happened to be all on one side while the caloric† to be measured was too small to be appreciated.

   My last experiments with a better contrived apparatus have clearly demonstrated that heat *is* evolved by the coils of the magnetic electrical machine, proving the generation of heat by mechanical action & the prop^n of the paper at the same time.

> With kind regards to Mrs Scoresby,
> Believe me, dear Sir,
> With the greatest respect, Sincerely yours,
> JAMES P. JOULE

By following the important clues presented by the experiments mentioned in the letter, he was led to the statement:

---

   * The fifth proposition states: 'The magnetic electrical machine enables us to convert mechanical power into heat by means of the currents which are induced in it.'

   † Heat.

'The quantity of heat capable of increasing the temperature of a pound of water one degree of Fahrenheit's scale is equal to and may be converted into a mechanical force capable of raising 838 lbs to a perpendicular height of one foot.'

Professor Osborne Reynolds in his classic memoir of Joule says: 'This result is the climax of Joule's research. For though he was immediately able, by using simple means, to obtain greater accuracy in the determination of the mechanical equivalent of heat, this was of small importance compared with the philosophical insight which resulted from the comprehensiveness and sequence of this investigation.'

Between January and early August of 1843, Joule was engaged in the completion and presentation of the most important, and in many ways the most significant, of his early researches which culminated in the reading, before the Chemical Section of the British Association meeting in Cork (21st August) of his now famous paper *On the Calorific Effects of Magneto-Electricity and the Mechanical Value of Heat*.

During the months that Joule was working so well and so fruitfully, Scoresby was driven almost to distraction by the problems and personalities of his parish, so it is not surprising that there is a blank period of some two years in their correspondence. During this time the matter of the guarantees remained unresolved; there were committees and parish work; there was trouble over the workhouse chaplaincy. Though Pearson had left the district, he had not obtained another curacy and he kept returning to visit his ex-parishioners and he continued to assail Scoresby with long letters in the press, abounding with slanderous allegations that were simply not true and involved Scoresby in so much writing that his eyesight gave cause for concern. There was unpleasantness about yet another unconsecrated church, this time at Bowling; he was unjustly criticised and, hating injustice, had to make his defence. He was deeply involved with his schools programme; and there were a hundred and one calls upon his time. All these took such a toll of his strength that it is small wonder he was obliged to take a complete break and visit America in order to have a change of scene and thought. Thus, his scientific interests were overlaid by a great weight of other matters, but we can be sure that young Joule and his researches were never far from his thoughts, and shortly after he returned from his holiday he invited Joule to Bradford to see his 'stupendous magnet'. Joule replies:

New Bailey St, Salford.
May 20th 1845

Dear Sir,
    I received your letter this morning and shall be most happy to

avail myself of the opportunity of witnessing the performance of the stupendous magnet you describe. The machine I had when the British Association met in Manchester had for a long time been buried under hop bags in one of the rooms of our brewery. I have just now, however, got it out and will immediately set about putting it in order for your experiments in which I shall take great pleasure in assisting you to the utmost of my power.

Perhaps you recollect that in my machine there are two revolving armatures, which will render it necessary to use 4 straight magnets in order to the proper excitation of the coils.

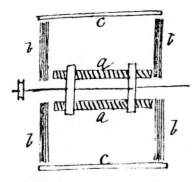

aa being the armatures, it will be best to dispose the magnetic force in four separate parts, bbbb, and to unite the spare poles with a couple of iron bars cc which should be 3 feet or 3 feet 4 in long in order to correspond with the size of my armatures, which are 30 inches long.

If you would be kind enough to write a line per return of post to let me know whether you can divide your magnet into four parts without inconvenience, and what is the size of the magnet in length, breadth and thickness, I might be able to provide accordingly and thus save you some trouble.

I anticipate the pleasure of seeing you at Bradford on Tuesday next if that day suit your convenience.

My Father & Brother (Mary is at present in London) desire to unite with me in kind respects to Mrs Scoresby and yourself, and believe me, Dear Sir,

Ever yours most truly,
JAMES P. JOULE

We have felt it right to quote all the letters from Joule to Scoresby in entirety, since they have never been published before. Unfortunately the story is not quite complete, for Scoresby's replies have not yet been discovered, but the letters printed here give a fairly comprehensive picture of their work together; and since Manchester was so comparatively near, Joule was able to visit Bradford frequently, so much of their communication would be verbal in any case and not in the form of letters.

New Bailey St, Salford
May 23rd 1845

Dear Sir,

I find that my armatures will not suit your magnets, and have therefore according to your wish, arranged for new ones. You will 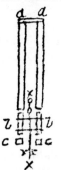 understand the plan I propose from the adjoining sketch. aa are your magnets. xx is a spindle carrying two electro-magnets bb each 15 inches long and 3 in diameter. The iron to be insulated portions to prevent loss of power. There is room left at cc for an armature to join the spare poles of the electro-magnet or for the poles of another system of magnets placed perpendicularly. This arrangement will allow you to change the electro magnetic coils with facility in order to have quantity or intensity. I hope we shall be able to furnish you with the quantity arrangement in a week or ten days when I expect the pleasure of seeing the experiments with it. When we see how the quantity coils work we shall have a guide for the construction of the rest.

The experiments I would suggest with the quantity arrangement are decomposition of water, electrotype and heating of platinum wire. I will bring the material for these experiments with me. I shall attend to what you say about the expenses. As for any trouble I may be at, I can assure you that the pleasure I take in magneto-electricity is an ample compensation for that.

In haste to save the post, believe me, Dear Sir, with kind regards to Mrs Scoresby,

Yours Ever Truly,

JAMES P. JOULE

During these weeks of preparation and construction of apparatus much thought and discussion of experiments would ensue. There would be meetings to work out problems of design and delighted and enthusiastic acceptance on both sides when a new idea facilitating progress came into view. This working together on scientific problems by kindred spirits is an experience of unalloyed pleasure. We can be sure that Scoresby no less than Joule would look back at these weeks of endeavour with delight, tinged perhaps on Scoresby's side with not a little sadness at the thought of so much he wanted to do and so little leisure time for it. He was concerned at all the trouble Joule had been put to and had expressed that concern to the young man. Joule's reply heads this chapter and needs no comment.

New Bailey St, Salford,
May 30th 1845

Dear Sir,

In reply to yours of yesterday I would observe that the plan of having the wheel at one end of the magnets, and the commutator at the other end, would require an axis of great length and at the same time would add very little to the facility of experimenting. In devising the apparatus you wish, I have thought it very desirable to secure *portability* as far as practicable, well knowing by experience the trouble incident to large and heavy machinery. At the same time I have done my best to reduce the expense, well knowing that experiments may very probably point out a better arrangement, *and then* it will be time enough to make a more showy apparatus: what I shall send will, however, be perfect in all essential points.

The coils will be wound on a series of concentric iron tubing insulated from each other and divided longitudinally to cut off mischievous currents.

I will bring along with me the steel wire No 4 which is easily obtained in this town. As for the gun barrels, they are not very readily met with, particularly rifle barrels and sell at 2/6 bad or good. Would not the wrought iron tubing do as well? which can be got in lengths of 4 or 6 feet, 1 inch in diameter, $\frac{1}{8}$ thick in metal, at the price of 6d a foot. These have the advantage of being uniform in thickness, but the bore inside is not so true. The wrought iron tubes can be got from one inch up to about 3 inches in diameter, the thickness remaining about $\frac{1}{8}$ inch. Perhaps you will write to say what sizes would suit best.

I am pushing the work on as fast as possible and hope to be ready about the middle of next week.

Believe me, Dear Sir, Yours Ever Truly,
James P Joule

The following letter* from Scoresby to Joule is of great interest for it shows us Scoresby actively engaged constructing the electro-magnetic apparatus and devising ingenious ways of obtaining maximum magnetic power. Although the experiments and calculations were performed by Joule and the all important theoretic concepts underlying the investigation were his, yet Scoresby—despite the many distractions—was able to do some useful work getting the apparatus into good working condition with maximum magnetic power.

* Quoted by kind permission of Professor D. S. L. Cardwell, University of Manchester Institute of Science and Technology.

Field House, June 2nd

My Dear Sir,

I find that by a new mode of sustaining the power of my magnets during the progress of construction I can *almost double* the ultimate power. This is so important that I have just commenced taking down the whole concern. I hope, however, by the facilities afforded by practice to be able to get the whole replaced and ready in the course of the week, possibly if all is well, by Friday morning or Thurs. ev. If you could kindly come to us, therefore, on Thursday (we shall dine at 5) at any part of the day suitable for yourself, the whole machine would I hope be sufficiently advanced for the commencement of the department you have so kindly undertaken. I now *hope* to get a power equal to my fullest expectations.

Yours (in haste) ever faithfully,

W. Scoresby

Our united kind compts to your Father and brother.

The next letter is written six weeks later, which is not surprising, for Joule visited Bradford frequently and he and Scoresby could discuss their problems *vis-à-vis*.

New Bailey St, Salford.

July 26 1845

Dear Sir,

In my last letter I quite forgot to ask what is the distance between the axle and the base board of the revolting apparatus; viz,

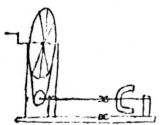

the distance xx in the adjoining sketch, which limits the size of the revolving armature to about 15 inches (I think) between the extremities of the poles. Would you favour me with a line stating the exact distance?

I have ordered 8 lengths of 1/10 inch copper wire each 80 yds long, to be covered with cotton. This is a little more than half the length mentioned in your note. But I found it impossible to procure a greater length of 1/10 in wire in one piece, and I thought it very inadvisable to send it in soldered pieces to be covered. Had I done so the soldering might have been loosened in the covering process, and the injury concealed: besides by putting on the wire in lengths of 80 yds we shall have the advantage of being able to vary the arrangements in intensity and quantity.

I hope Mrs Scoresby is enjoying better health. With kind regards to her and Miss Fitzgerald, believe me, Dear Sir,

Respectfully and Truly Yours

James P Joule

The result of their combined work appeared the following year, 1846, in a paper which appeared in the *Philosophical Magazine* under the title:

Experiments and Observations on the Mechanical Powers of Electro-magnetism, Steam and Horses. By the Rev. William Scoresby, D.D., F.R.S. L and E., Corr. Mem. Inst. Fr. &c., and James P. Joule, Secretary of the Literary and Philosophical Society of Manchester, Mem. Chem. Soc. &c.

In his splendid memoir of Joule, Professor Osborne Reynolds says of this paper: 'The final results of this investigation, which are of great interest, may be shortly summarised as follows: The duty of an electro-magnetic engine per grain of zinc consumed in a Daniell's battery, is 80 lb raised one foot high, about half the theoretical maximum duty. The duty of a Cornish engine at that time, per grain of coal, is 143 lb raised one foot high, or one tenth the *vis viva* due to the combustion of coal.

'The duty of a horse per grain of food is 143 lb raised one foot high or one quarter of the *vis viva* resulting from the combustion of the food.'

In the reprint of the paper given in the 1884 edition of Joule's collected papers we find the following interesting note by Joule:

'On the occasion of the meeting of the British Association for the Advancement of Science, at Manchester, in the year 1842, I had the happiness of forming the acquaintance of Dr Scoresby, eminent for qualities seldom united in one man. At once an experienced seaman, a successful geographical discoverer, a hard working and eloquent clergyman, he was also a zealous student of nature and a scientific investigator. Dr Scoresby became greatly interested in the view I was at that time beginning to take of the relation between heat and other forms of force, and in response to my express wish to work with a powerful arrangement of magnets, he kindly invited me to Bradford, of which town he was at the time Vicar, in order to pursue an enquiry with him. The duties of the parish were, however, so onerous and pressing, that the production of our paper devolved almost entirely upon myself, so that it was not without great objection on his part that Dr Scoresby allowed his name to appear with mine. Inasmuch, however, as the facilities for the experiments were afforded by him, as well as the great magnetic battery, I felt that I could not, in justice, allow it to appear other than as a joint paper.'

So it was that Joule and Scoresby came together, the young man of rare gifts and great promise and the older man of experience and rich achievement. Such a relationship is often a fruitful one—especially when the younger man has intellect and delicacy of feeling and the older man a rare understanding combined with real experience. But the scientific union never developed, beset as Scoresby was with ecclesiastic troubles, and soon Joule was to meet William Thomson, the future Lord Kelvin; this was at the British Association meeting at Oxford in 1847. Despite Thomson's great interest in and sympathy for Joule, three years were to elapse before he finally accepted Joule's ideas regarding the nature of heat and the inter-relationship between heat and other forms of energy.

Scoresby almost alone among the older generation of scientists appreciated Joule and saw the significance of his work. This is greatly to his credit and is all the more remarkable in so far as his deepest interests lay outside the field of Joule's endeavour. Perhaps the key to Scoresby's enthusiasm for Joule lay in his great concern for the serious impact of the new coal-fired industrialism on the human being. He describes the 'dark clouds of air-defiling smoke pouring out of the numerous lofty chimneys' and deplores the 'indifference to atmospheric pollution arising from the employment of steam-power in the working of machinery'. Nothing, he says, 'but the most stringent authoritative regulations will ever overcome the selfish indifference of man, as a class or a species, to the inconvenience or injury he may inflict upon others in operations in which he seeks to gain personal wealth, or realize personal pleasure'. It seems probable, after his visit to Lowell, that the vision of an electrically powered industrialism had touched Scoresby's imagination and led him to view Joule as the prophet of a new age.

We must remember that Joule was not an academic scientist—no university or institution supported him; his work was so novel and so original that it met at first with almost total silence. Scoresby's interest and friendship provided valuable encouragement and support, and though he was unable to assist Joule to anything like the extent he would have wished, the very fact of his interest helped the young man. Joule, like most men of genius, was upheld by an inner certainty of truth and insight, but he must at times have felt very lonely in his quest.

One may well imagine Scoresby and Joule after exchanges on points arising from their mutual scientific interests moving on to discuss wider issues. Joule was a reserved, quiet man, but in the company of such a choice spirit as Scoresby's, conversation would readily turn to deeper matters,—the true aims of science, the proper use of discoveries and inventions, the application of science to the welfare of humanity, and the 'enhancement and betterment of human life'. In our account of the friendship of Scoresby and Joule, we have stressed mainly the scientific aspect, but it is also evident that they held similar views as to the proper aims and objects of scientific research, as we can clearly see from the following extracts of a paper which Joule wrote some twenty-five years later,* and which are reproduced here by kind permission of Manchester University.

'The admiration of the works of the Almighty is a source of pure delight to every man whose mind has not been debased. He loves to behold the beauty and order of nature and his intellectual faculties are occupied by an endeavour to obtain a more intimate acquaintance with the wonders of the creation. In this view natural philosophy may be considered second in importance to religion only.'

'The study of nature and her laws is essentially a holy undertaking.'

'The state of mind of a proud man is wholly inimical to success in the pursuit of truth.'

'The great object which natural science has in view is to elevate man in the scale of intellectual creatures by the exercise of the highest faculties of his nature in developing the wonders of the glorious creation. The second is to promote the well-being and comfort of mankind. The first object is therefore at least as much more important than the second as the intellect is more noble than the body.'

'Such then are the legitimate objects of science. It is deeply to be regretted that another and most unworthy object has been introduced and has gradually and alarmingly increased in prominence. This is the improvement of the art of war and the implements for mutual destruction. I know there are those who think that these improvements will tend to put an end to war by making it more destructive. I cannot think that such an opinion is based on common sense.'

'We must also deplore the prostitution of science for the aggrandisement of individuals and nations, the result being that the weaker is destroyed and the stronger race is established on its ruins.'

We may suppose such ideas to have passed readily between Scoresby and Joule and though Scoresby never saw these words, which were written in or about 1872, nothing can be more certain than that he would have given unqualified approval to them.

* * *

The ideas, so admirably expressed by Joule, have a more profound depth and greater urgency in our own time than ever before; they

* J. G. Crowther thinks it probable that this paper was to have been Joule's Presidential address at the British Association. He was prevented from taking office by illness.

express modes of thought and depths of feeling so often and so tragic-
ally overlooked and neglected since his time.

We can only hope that the awareness of these deeper issues so clear
and so insistent in the minds of Scoresby and Joule and very real and
vital to them, will come to guide and direct the true spirit of research
for the welfare of humanity.

The achievements of men of science, important and far-reaching
as they may be, are of less significance for humanity than the cultural
values of discovery. The mastery of machines by knowing all about
them does not ennoble humanity, but joy at newly found insight lifts
us up when understanding for it has been cultivated.

Scoresby's early interest in and appreciation of Joule's ideas is
surely one of his finest achievements and makes more poignant the
failure of a scientific union of such promise. But in these mature
thoughts of Joule wherein he moves away from the problems of the
laboratory into the wider world of aims and ideals, we see his mind
and the mind of Scoresby as one, and the intellectual outcome of their
union manifest in profound and elevating thoughts.

CHAPTER 19

THE FACTORY OPERATIVES SCHEME

'Let us unite together in such a noble enterprise.'

The good effect on Scoresby of his holiday in the States did not last for long. The guarantee business was no nearer settlement than it had been before he left. It will be remembered that the original agreement was that the fifteen signatories would make up the deficit for the extra curate's stipend to the amount of £100—after collections, which meant that no one guarantor would be asked to pay more than six pounds a year at the very most, probably only a trifling amount, which Scoresby might have paid himself, just for the sake of peace; but this was not his way—Right was Right. One or two of the original guarantors stirred up the others into a state of rebellion and more unpleasant things were said—among them that the Vicar had misappropriated the fund to his own use. Scoresby battled on.

The work in his church schools was continuing well, but the building of New Leeds School was still not finished. There were many delays and letter after letter to be written. But the last straw came when he discovered that in his absence the Ecclesiastical Committee had approved a new District plan, quite different from the one he had made, and this had been submitted to the Bishop of Ripon. This had been done quite deliberately behind his back, and when he found out about it he immediately sent in his resignation to the Bishop. We quote the greater part of his long letter of resignation, despite the fact that he was persuaded to withdraw it, and did not actually leave Bradford for another year, for it gives an extensive account of the work done by Scoresby in Bradford and all the troubles he had to suffer, which is far more telling than any words of ours.

Bradford, Dec 13 1844

My dear Lord,

It has long been a matter of deep and prayerful enquiry with myself whether it was my duty, at such a sacrifice of peace, health and property as has been required of me, to continue in a parish where trials and difficulties seem to be interminable.

Yet, though unsupported, in most cases, in my heaviest difficulties, except by the full consciousness that integrity and upright-

ness of purpose would ultimately sustain me; though left to fight
battles for the church and the parish against spoliation and wrong
single handed, though made to bear the burden of almost every
good work I attempted on my personal responsibilities; though
opposed by those who ought to have rejoiced in my labour; alone
and unaided where I looked for support or protection elsewhere,—
I yet continued to labour and contend, spending and being spent,
from the encouragements which a gracious God from time to time
yielded me, in seeing great and substantial work effected, which,
however little regarded now, must be permanent blessings to be
realised and appreciated in after times.

This may not be apprehended by some, or as to the magnitude
of the things, I may possibly over-rate them, but they are referred
to as cheering, and encouraging results and fruits which others
must reap.

And besides these things, the state of the Parish Church with its
large and attentive congregation; the schools with their numerous
and well instructed civilised and christianised children; the Church
Institution, with its prosperity and important influence on the development of church feeling and instruction in church principles;
the various services in school rooms for the benefit of the children,
the teachers and residents near them; the relieving of the Parish
Church and churchwardens from £140 annually of the charges for
divine service and by a successful arrangement for a rate. The building of school houses, four in number, at a cost of between £3000
and £4000, with the appointment and putting of such existing
buildings, and the rescuing of an endowed Grammar School at
Haworth out of the hands of Dissenters and placing it, according
to the trust, under church influence and with a clergyman as the
Master; the raising of funds for building a church at Eccleshill:
the formation of several ecclesiastical Districts under, for the most
part, efficient clergymen and the appointment of several additional
curates for the benefit of the parishioners;—These attainments, to
which I hoped to have added the grand one of bringing the whole
of the parish of 120,000 souls under pastoral and effective church
superintendence, encouraged and cheered me in the grateful hope
that, however others might oppose, my labours were not in vain
in the Lord. And thus encouraged, I have been induced to retain
a position up to this time, the trials and discouragements and persecutions of which, would otherwise have been unsupportable.

Now, however, I feel it due to myself and I trust that herein my
duty to Him whom I would humbly desire to serve and glorify for-
bids not, to resign into your Lordship's hands the vicarage and
charge which I have held since the year 1839.

Model School

Eccleshill School

The four Church Schools at Bradford

Daisy Hill School

New Leeds School

The letter, eleven pages long, goes on to complain bitterly at the rearrangement of Districts which had been made 'in violation of good faith with the Vicar of the parish'. Much of this had been during Scoresby's absence in America. It goes on:

As for the case of Denholme, however, ill as the managers of that church had treated me, not merely by breaking faith with me, but by printing and circulating within and without the parish a painful document in order to bring a clamour against me—I should have been willing to submit. It is an utterly destitute region ...

But as to Manningham, the circumstances are altogether different. Here was no poor population which, without the proposed church might have perished for lack of knowledge. The population (mainly) within the district assigned and granted lies within 200 yards of the large fine church of St Jude, not, at present, half filled. The population of the new district residing at a greater distance is but few and many of them of the wealthiest class, keeping carriages. . . .

But whilst I supposed everything was in abeyance—I am incidentally informed that a District has been arranged, and, under your Lordship's setting forth thereof, 'approved'. . . .

I have thus stated, my dear Lord, freely and frankly, as I have ever done, my views of the matter referred to. And on these views my decision has been arrived at, of tendering my resignation to your Lordship with the full and most decided intention of abiding by it. I have prayed for the resignation to take effect on the day when I received Institution from your Lordship's hands, and this delay I have thought necessary for the winding up of my business affairs about schools—and endeavouring to release myself from my *heavy responsibilities* that if possible I may leave to my successor a clear and unembarrassed field.

The contents of New Leeds School will rest on my personal responsibility till the school is completed. The debts of several schools to their treasurer on account of building funds rest on me. The architect of Eccleshill Church *demands* of *me*, personally, the cost of work done for the late Vicar and some done out of his own head, to the amount of £80 (only a small part being done under my orders).

Praying your Lordship's forebearance if I have said one word unfitting my position on so painful an occasion—and begging you to understand that this course I pursue in preference to seeking elsewhere for remedy in deference to your Lordship—I remain,
My dear Lord,
Your faithful and obedient Servant,
W. Scoresby.

The one word which recurs over and over again in all Scoresby's letters and accounts of this time is 'painful'. The troubles did indeed cause him much pain, but there are times when one feels it is hardly a strong enough word for what he endured.

To his friend the Vicar of Leeds he is able to express himself freely:

26 Feb 1845

My Dear Dr Hook,

The very kind invitation and arrangement for my preaching in your parish *cathedral*—for such in character it is—I feel much obliged by; and, God willing, I will endeavour to undertake the duty you assign to me. It will give me much pleasure to become your guest for the occasion—though I regret that Mrs Scoresby—who desires her kind regards and best thanks to Mrs Hook for the invitation to her—will not, I fear, be able to accompany me. For nearly two months she has not been able to go to church on account of delicacy of health and great debility. . . .

I feel much obliged by your kind interest about my remaining at Bradford. My position has for a long time been so exceedingly painful—by reason of opposition of the most ungenerous and cruel kind—misrepresentation and want of support from churchmen—that I had long doubted whether it was my duty, at such a sacrifice to health and peace of mind to remain. And when, without any intimation to me, or even any communication whatever, the abstraction of the *very best section* of the whole parish was promoted before the Ecc^l Ctt^c, and of course sanctioned by the Bishop, my duty appeared quite plain. What his Lordship designs to do I know not, but the District, comprising the principal villa residences of the parish and a portion I had designed to reserve to the parish church has been 'approved generally' by the Ecc. Ctte. Besides, whilst several of the extremely destitute country townships *without church or clergyman*, are postponed for want of funds, here is a District assented to and all but fixed where there is no need of a church at all! The proposed new church (a small one) is to be within 120 yards of a fine recently built church, at present but half filled; and within a mile, on the other side, of a licensed school room, like a chapel fit to hold 400 or 500, with a concert hall attached!

To build a church, no doubt a good thing, is *here* in Bradford, made the infliction of every kind of grievance and injury, instead of a real benefaction.

Unhappily, I find, the Bishop 'had suggested' the *whole* residue of Manningham township being a portion in an E^{cc} District of 1000 to 1200 acres and a population of 6 or 7 times the capacity of the church and taking in my house, so as to drive me from my own parish.

Happily, the parishioners, as a body, and indeed all, I believe, of the Church, except those who have done the wrong (and those not being Christian men of course hate the individual they have injured) appear now to have arrived at a better knowledge of my actual endeavours for their benefit, and the kingdom of Christ being promoted amongst them. It is a great consolation to learn that the poor, to whom the gospel is preached are (I am told) with me.

Only a few days after this letter was written, Scoresby was asked to attend a meeting at the Church Institute in order to receive two addresses. The first, which bore over three thousand signatures, was from his parishioners and read as follows:

> To the Reverend William Scoresby, D.D., F.R.S., &c.,
> Vicar of Bradford.
>
> Reverend Sir,   We the undersigned Lay Parishioners of Bradford, desire to express towards you our respectful esteem, and our regret at hearing of your intention to retire from your important position as the Vicar of this parish.
>
> This feeling of regret is increased by the knowledge that the extensive plans which you have formed for the interests and benefit of the Church generally—particularly those for providing the Children of the Poor with a sound and cheap Education (some of which you have so perseveringly and successfully carried out) are not yet fulfilled.
>
> And we would express our earnest hope that your determination to leave us is not so fixed as to prevent your reconsidering your purpose—and that by the blessing of the Almighty you may long continue your valuable labours among us.

The second address was signed by every teacher in the Sunday schools connected with the parish church. It read:

> Rev and dear Sir,   As the Teachers of the Sunday Schools in connection with the parish church, and as unworthy labourers in assisting you to execute our Redeemer's command, 'Feed my lambs', we venture to convey to you our deep sorrow and regret at your resignation as vicar of this parish.
>
> You have been connected with us for several years and we can assure you that we have become warmly attached to you for the benefits which our schools and the children taught in them have received at your hands; and there is engrafted in our minds the highest sense of admiration of the school discipline you have

established among us, and it is our ardent wish that you would still cooperate with us in carrying out the same. It has been your constant study to promote the education of our youth and a source of the greatest pleasure to us to know that you have so manfully advocated a reduction in the hours of labour for factory children, in order that better opportunities might be afforded them for the cultivating of religious knowledge, and making them better subjects for both their earthly and heavenly Sovereign.

As dutiful children would not attempt to dictate to a parent, so we will not presume to dictate to you our spiritual father; yet we feel assured you will pardon us for calling to your remembrance Abraham's prayer for Sodom and Gomorrah, and the answer to that prayer; we trust you will, even for the sake of ten lambs, continue with us; and we pray that while you exercise your sacred office in future, that the Giver of all good gifts may defend you from all your enemies, that you may pass your time in rest and quietness, and that He will pour upon you the continual dew of His blessing.

In conclusion, rev. and dear Sir, we shall ever be grateful for the inestimable services you have already rendered this our parish, and with the greatest regard for your orthodox principles, you have our best wishes and most earnest prayers for the happiness of yourself, and that of her whose lot in life is linked with yours.

The newspaper report of Scoresby's reply to these addresses occupies the whole of one page. He clearly stated each fact which had led to his final decision and concluded:

'In making these remarks in reference to those circumstances that have given me so much pain, it is but fitting that I should say that I believe they now apply to but a small body of my parishioners. I am unconscious of having done an act of unkindness or wrong to them, and I would further say that they who have erred and done an injury to another, will ever seek occasion of offence against the man they have injured. But I pass from these things, having, I hope, laid before you distinctly the position in which I feel myself to be at the present time, with reference to my continuance among you. I must speak something, before I conclude, as to one or two other subjects with which I have been much connected. The schools I feel to be measures of philanthropy towards our working population and their children so important, it will be my endeavour to place them in a more satisfactory position than they can be under my personal responsibility alone, as at present. Having sustained this responsibility now for four years almost alone, it is time that you should share the burden of the management of the schools. And that which one has sustained alone, cannot be very heavy for so many.

'I have another point on which I would address you in conclusion, with respect to my anxiety to do something among the factory population of this manufacturing town. My anxiety to see some plan in active operation for the improvement of their condition ... is an object in which I believe Churchmen and Dissenters may most cordially unite.

'In referring to Dissenters I feel it right to express the satisfaction I experience on learning that there are the names of a very considerable number of my Dissenting parishioners attached to this memorial; and in rendering thanks to the Dissenters it is due to myself to say that I feel gratified in this act of kind consideration. They will bear me testimony that I have never, as a Churchman, opposed or interfered with or censured, my brethren who are Dissenters from the Church.

'My Brethren—I speak to you who are Dissenters—let us unite together in such a noble enterprise; let us see if something cannot be done to consecrate the wealth and property of this large town and parish, and bring out some memorial of loving-kindness on the part of the employers with reference to those employed. (cheers). There is a noble enterprise before us, and if all unite, if the minister and his people go hand in hand and heart with heart, impressed with a sense of their responsibility to God for the talents committed to their charge, the result will be the benefit of their fellow men and the glory of God. (Loud cheers).'

The following week the Bradford Operative Conservative Association gave Scoresby yet another address. 'Delusion has triumphed for a time, but virtue and truth, we ardently hope, will yet reign triumphant. With all gratitude for your truly faithful and zealous, but ill-requited services, with the most profound respect, we most earnestly implore you still to continue among us.'

These loyal addresses played no small part in influencing Scoresby to remain in Bradford, certainly until he had launched his 'factory operatives' scheme. His appeal to the Dissenters was not altogether successful, for we find that they did their utmost to draw the children away from the church schools. In September 1845 Scoresby writes in a letter: 'There is a regular system of attack being made on our schools in various quarters—as it appears to me—by the dissenters, every occasion for fault is pushed forth and every means adopted to get the children from our schools.

'A large number of factory children have been removed by dissenting millowners from the State Hill school, and many against the will of the children, who have earnestly besought the chaplain, Mr Tomlin, to try to have them restored.

'In Horton, the Rev. Mr Glyde and other gentlemen have been

urging a mill owner there to "let the children go where they please, who now attend the church school", in other words "to have them at the dissenting school". This system, one would suppose, has been tried elsewhere.

'At Daisy Hill (no factory children) every effort is made to get the children away—Sunday School teachers (Baptists) go about from house to house telling the people "that these children, if they go to the church school, will go to Hell" and a minister or preacher has been at the cottages (I have been informed) telling the people that "every word they hear at the church at Daisy Hill is a lie"!!

'In regard to your enquiry about my remaining here, I am not yet able to answer quite decidedly; it depends on the frail arrangement of the District, on the grounds of which I tendered my resignation. This matter has been painfully delayed, but I am now in strong hope of a satisfactory arrangement.'

Scoresby was a realist and no idle dreamer. He accepted the fact of children working in the mills as a part of the existing social system, and his crusade was not so much to try to abolish the practice as to see what could be done to help those children, as well as the mill hands. With his usual facility of finding the longest possible, all-embracing descriptive word, he called them 'factory operatives', that is to say, not only the mill girls but also the children, girls and boys, who worked in the Bradford mills and factories.

For these factory operatives he proposed—at yet another Public Meeting—setting up a committee to try and improve their conditions, much on the lines which he had seen at Lowell. This was done and the committee came up with a comprehensive report proposing various measures, including properly supervised boarding houses, a ladies' visiting committee, evening schools ('for general instruction including Needlework and other domestic attainments'), a sick club and a savings bank to encourage thrift. No mention was made of how these impoverished workers might manage to save anything out of their pitifully small wage, a mere fraction of that paid to their sisters at Lowell. The report ended with these words:

'Such plans as are here suggested can scarcely fail to result in the improved order and respectability of a class of persons worthy of attention and consideration on many accounts, by aiding them to economise their earnings, providing them with better and cheaper modes of living, preserving them from many temptations, providing against times of sickness and need, probably supplying them with medical attendance, and giving them such useful instruction as will enable them in after years the better to discharge their social and relative duties.

'We may add that the Vicar stated in the Committee his readiness to build or purchase a house for the purpose of forming a Boarding or Lodging House, on a suitable plan, by way of an experiment, and as an expression of his conviction that there would be little risk of loss in similar undertakings.'

It is interesting to note that among the names of the many people who attended this important meeting was that of Titus Salt, who later did so much for the town of Bradford.

It was in 1845 that the ill-fated Franklin expedition set off in the two ships, *Erebus* and *Terror*, to search for the north-west passage. As far back as 1818 Scoresby had conjectured that although there most probably was a north-west passage it would almost certainly be blocked with ice and therefore of little use. The following letter, in reply to one from Captain Manby—now in his eighties—is interesting for in it we read the views of Scoresby—man of the Arctic—regarding the success of the expedition.

Bradford, Yorkshire,
May 17 1845

My dear Friend,

It was quite cheering and interesting to me to recognise again, after the lapse of some years, the characteristic tracing of your hand. And after a life of so much adventure and public enterprise—it was gratifying to find you still enjoying the blessings of health and energy....

But to the subject of your letter. And here, I fear, I shall not be able to write with any advantage to your object, nor to afford any information not already in your hands. The matters connected with my Arctic researches and inquiries have been long estranged from my mind by reason of the various heavy duties of my present official position—which I find so trying to my health as to contemplate, if it please God so to appoint for me, a removal to a place of less labour and responsibility.

Unfortunately I have not seen the account of Capt. Graff's voyage, and therefore cannot judge how far the researches of that navigator might be considered as conclusive. As to anything I have yet seen—the impressions I early received about the site of the ancient Icelandic colony ... have not been changed.

Sir John Barrow is no doubt as familiar with these matters* by reading and research as almost anyone, but, unfortunately, if his theory becomes fixed in his mind, the matter as to the government or admiralty research becomes fixed also. Yet he is by no means always correct—his 'polar basin' for example! Nor do I think he has been correct in delaying the present exploring expedition till

* In early youth Barrow made one journey to the Arctic.

about the 20th May, which, I understand, was the result of his
opinion and advice. My opinion is that the ships ought to have sailed
three weeks earlier, so as to have had more time to renew their
stores and prepare for their exploration after their arrival in Davis
Strait and especially to have had the chance of embracing the first
opportunity of making progress to the north and westward. They
may yet be early enough, no doubt, but if they should have a long
passage they may miss their earliest chance of progress to the westward, and the loss of one day's favourable progress might make
a serious difference in the passage—if the passage should be
effected. The steam apparatus is of the first importance, I consider,
to the success of the expedition; but I have no idea myself of such
a succession of favourable circumstances occurring as to enable Sir
J. Franklin to complete the Arctic portion of the enterprise in one
summer. The enterprise I do think to be probably practicable, but
not probably practicable in any one year. The season the most
favourable for clearing off the ice from one side of the jutting points
of land about which it is wont to cling, would, probably be the
most unfavourable for clearing the other side. . . .

Pray give my kindest regards to Mr Dawson Turner & any of
his family with whom he may yet be surrounded. I wish I could
get a day or two to run over from the meeting of the British Assn
at Cambridge, which assembles about a month hence, and where,
please God, I hope to be.

I remain, my Dear Friend,
Yours ever faithfully,
Wm Scoresby

One cannot help but wonder if the Franklin expedition might have
been successful had they left earlier, as Scoresby here suggested.

Very soon, Scoresby saw all too clearly that it had been a mistake
to withdraw his resignation. Bradford remained much as it always
had been. In a letter to a well-loved parishioner of his earlier days
he paints a sad picture of his 'painful labours':

20 Jan 1846

My very dear friend,

Your affectionate, warm hearted letters are so like your hospitality that one can imagine oneself present with you. At all events
they urge to an immediate reply, *except* when the table happens
to be loaded with business letters that must be attended to.

I do now feel, dear Mrs West, that the work here is perfectly
incessant, laborious and interminable; and worst of all, so much
of it is painful to the feelings and secularising in its tendency.
Greatly do I feel the lack of sweet Christian communion with the

spiritually minded children of God. Here, the work is mainly hewing wood or laying it for the temple. Here at Bradford has been my *only* painful labours. Everywhere else, at Bridlington and neighbourhood—at Liverpool, at Exeter—I experienced complete satisfaction and all but complete peace. Here has been all but general contention *till of late*. But from what has been effected, I think the Lord sent me here for a great, though painful, work. All has turned to account. And a great work is going on, now arranged for, or will be, God willing, shortly, which a person of more youth and strength may manage, *better then myself.*

God be with you and yours and guide us all in all our ways for his glory! With affectionate remembrances to your sister,

I remain my Dear Friend, Yours ever afftly,

W Scoresby.

Once again, Scoresby sent his resignation to the Bishop and this time determined to leave Bradford once and for all. The last of his church schools was finally opened in 1846, but it had cost him dear.

Almost the last sermon he preached was to a congregation of two thousand 'factory operatives'—the forgotten people of Bradford, on whose work the town depended for its prosperity; or rather they had been forgotten until Scoresby came their way. There were many people who had tried to discourage him in the very first instance, saying that you could do nothing for the factory girls without a Ten Hours Bill; that they would resent interference; and that even if you built lodging houses for them they still would not go to them. To all these Job's comforters Scoresby's reply was the same, 'let us try'. He was still true to the principle he had spoken of three years before: 'I will do what I can.'

The very fact of two thousand mill girls attending the Parish Church spoke for the success of the scheme, which was well under way and had an active ladies' committee, already harassing the mill owners, with a good deal of success. The sermon was listened to with great attention; the text was 'Come with us and we will do thee good' and on this theme the Vicar expounded, not in pompous empty platitudes, not talking down to his congregation, but eloquently, in language they understood.

'As our hearts, in this matter, are right towards you, let your confidence be right towards us. You may be sure we have no motive whatever but what is consistent with what we profess—that is, to do you good.... The leading principle in the plan is *to help you to help yourselves.*' He then went on to tell the girls of the plan for them; lodging houses, evening schools, a sick club and a savings scheme together with a ladies' committee. 'These designs, we hope, will shew you how anxious we are to do you good. Yes, dear friends of the factories, we earnestly desire that *you should feel* that we do care for you; and that others of *our* class in society should feel that it is a duty, and will be a privilege to join us in this friendly Christian care. For if those whose wealth and prosperity are derived from your labours shall be engaged in the promotion of your welfare,—then not only shall be wiped away the reproach so long deserved by us all for our neglects; but a blessing from heaven descend upon our manufacturing undertakings. The wealth gained by means of your toil must, in the course of time, pass away from the present possessors unto others; but any Christian effort to do you good would produce an ample reward....'

Scoresby went on to refer to the Lowell system and his lectures on it which he had given when he returned from America. 'It has indeed been objected by some of our countrymen that the American mill-girls are of a different class from ours. But is that any reason why ours should not aspire to an equality of character? Is there any rational reason why the young women of England should not be as intelligent, as respectable, as chaste, as religious as those of the United States? I should be sorry if there were any substantial reason, why you might not emulate, to the fullest extent, the high character of the Lowell factory girls.

'Come with us, then, dear young friends, that we may help you towards this great good. And happy will it be for you and your parents; happy will it be when you become wives and mothers; happy will it be for the town in which you labour, and for the people with whom you may associate—when your zeal for improvement shall successfully urge you to emulate, by self-consideration, by religious attainment, and by intellectual cultivation, what strangers have looked on with so much admiration among the factory girls at Lowell!'

He then offered them practical ways in which they could help themselves; by their personal behaviour, their choice of associates and their use of leisure; he urged them to make use of the evening schools; he advised them to choose most carefully their lodgings and the factories in which they worked, and to follow the example set by the Lowell girls in shunning 'those of ill-repute'. He ended by gently reminding them that the Church was there to help and watch over them.

CHAPTER 20

A SECOND VISIT TO AMERICA

'On his return to England he laboured with great assiduity to introduce into the manufacturing population of Bradford some of the
reforms which he found existed here.'

Though overshadowed by the Bradford clouds, science was still all-
important to Scoresby. Despite the parish work, he never failed to
attend the meetings of the British Association for the Advancement
of Science which he had helped to form. But even there he found dissension and favouritism. He had become acutely sensitive to animosity
in his Bradford years and perhaps took offence more easily than most,
but it does seem in the following letter to the 1846 President, Sir
Roderick Murchison, that he had been rather slighted.

2 Sept 1846

Dear Sir Roderick,
    I have made the preparation for a lecture in my official com-
munication to you, addressed to Southampton, with a good deal
of hesitation, from the painful knowledge of the assiduity with
which one of the members of the permanent staff of the British
Association has discouraged (or if I be not misguided, *prevented*)
any prominent place or part in the public proceedings of the Assn
being taken by myself.* No doubt it is fitting that those best qualified should be so brought forward; but it is not fitting nor right
that any individual should be systematically and by private design
or feeling kept back.
    That I speak advisedly hereon, I might appeal to facts of which
you yourself can hardly be unconscious when they may be pointed
out. At *Cork*, for instance, when you yourself kindly proposed that
Labould hold the office of a vice president of Section A,—this was
corrected at the suggestion of an individual. At *Liverpool,* when a
grant was applied for for aiding my magnetical investigations,
(which I hope have not been useless or unimportant) this was upset.
At *York* when I was a local secretary, and the senior man in the
list of secretaries, I was not asked nor apprised of any arrangements,
and the acknowledgement of the thanks to the secretaries was
appointed, unknown to me, to the junior secretary.

* Almost certainly Sabine.

Scoresby goes on to cite other occasions. 'These things *should not be*.' He blames it on 'the virtual management by 3 or 4 individuals, who are able both to put the matter forward or to keep back or throw aside others who might be as useful in the Institution'.

'The proper correction, as it appears to me, would be the annual election of all officers except an Assistant Stipendiary Secretary.' For this post, Scoresby recommends Professor John Phillips, who was already assistant general secretary to the Association. He became its President in 1865.

He ends the lengthy letter by saying his experience of the world, 'both as a man of the world in early life and a Christian Minister in later life, has shown me something of human character and of the circumstances which may generate an ungenerous line of conduct. This experience, did the present occasion require it, I could abundantly illustrate and extensively develop.'

Although we have not found Sir Roderick's reply to this letter, after Scoresby's appeal matters undoubtedly improved in the British Association and Scoresby was once more able to make his voice heard.

When the time came finally to leave Bradford Scoresby and his wife decided to settle in the Isle of Wight until such time as he might find a less arduous situation.

Friends all over the country wrote giving helpful suggestions, but Scoresby was not in any hurry; first, he intended travelling about Britain visiting these many friends. Mrs Scoresby's health was too poor to allow much travelling so Scoresby left her in the Isle of Wight and set off on his tour. He got no farther than Liverpool, however, where— at the home of his friends the Rathbones—he was taken ill and had a breakdown which lasted several months.

By the summer he had sufficiently recovered to take his wife back to her native Cork, where they stayed with her widowed sister. It was a small house and there was barely room for one extra person, let alone two. The doctor assured Scoresby that her health was much improved and there was no cause for alarm. Reassured by this statement, Scoresby decided to take a sea voyage and visit the States once more.

There was difficulty in securing a passage at short notice and so Scoresby obtained a government order on the grounds that he 'contemplated researches in scientific, philanthropic and religious objects' and he was given a berth on the *Cambria*, a 'strong, powerful, wood built steam ship of 1500 tons burden and 500 horsepower of engine. The ship was crowded with passengers—the amount being around 130 in number. All the circumstances of confusion and perplexity usually attendant on an embarkation of this kind were aggravated by reason of this unusual body of passengers, and by the setting in of continual rain. It required some time, more than one night's endurance, before people and chattels were shaken into any kind of order.'

Scoresby's berth was not a very good one for he was closeted with 'a sea-sick gentleman who occupied the sofa' for the greater part of the voyage. He notes: 'As I always suffered by close air, I sought during the day the free though wetting exposure of the main or saloon deck. Under the lee of the funnel I contrived to shelter from the heaviest sprays and to obtain a cool and rather wetting refreshment in this elevated exposure.'

At first Scoresby, travelling as he was on a government order, was not exactly popular with the ship's officers. On Sunday there were no morning prayers—'which I much regretted. In the afternoon the Captain performed Divine Service and read a sermon of, I believe, Mr Blunt's.' But by the following Sunday matters had changed and Captain Judkins asked Scoresby to conduct a service—'a duty which I readily undertook. I had no sermon at hand which I thought exactly suitable to the case of such a curious admixture of creeds and characters. We had ministers of the Episcopal Church of America, Roman Catholic priest, a minister of the Free Scotch Church, an Unitarian min. and people of still further variation of views—Quakers and avowed sceptics. The passage John VII. 17 occurred to me as suitable and I ventured to adapt it for a hastily studied and extemporaneous discourse. The Lord, I trust, was present with us. I was enabled to speak freely, affectionately and, I hope, scripturally. The attention was marked and interesting. About 100 passengers or more attended besides officers and sailors.'

Twelve days after leaving England they sighted land. 'We dined early, at 2 instead of 4, and just as we finished the ship entered the bay of Halifax. It was a fine picturesque sight—the varied character of the land on either side—the ample channel—the residences and hamlets to the eastward—and at length the city, so finely situated, with its wharfes and shipping.

'I was on shore by 3½ pm. Having just heard the cheering sound of the church-going bell—I proceeded first of all to the Lord's house, there to offer my thanksgiving for mercies experienced on our voyage across the Atlantic. I enquired for the church of the Revd Fitzgerald Uniacke, a relation of my wife's, and found it so conveniently near that I reached it during the reading of the Psalms.' Scoresby was impressed by Mr Uniacke's 'manly person, ample forehead, good countenance and good reading' though he was not able to hear him preach for a visitor was in the pulpit. They went after to the parsonage, 'a commodious good house close by, and made the acquaintance of Mrs U., a very interesting and pleasing person'.

There was just time to send a letter back to England by the out-ward-bound packet, and to see Mr James Uniacke, the late Solicitor-General, and the ship sailed again in the evening. 'Having a fine, still night, with smooth sea we made the speed of about 11 knots. The morning was again fine—beautifully fine—and weather calm.'

Scoresby's arrival in the States was noted in the *Boston Atlas* of 20th October 1847:

'*Rev Dr Scoresby*. We notice among the list of passengers the name of this worthy gentleman. Dr Scoresby has visited our country before. When here a few years ago he gave great attention to the social condi-tions of our female factory population and was highly interested in the so wholesome regulations for the moral and social well being of this important and interesting class of citizens, with which he became acquainted in Lowell. Dr Scoresby was the Vicar of Bradford in York-shire. On his return to England, he laboured with great assiduity to introduce into the manufacturing population of Bradford some of the reforms which he found existed here. If he was not successful in all his plans of improvement the fault was not with him. When we were in Bradford about 14 months ago, we were an eye witness to this gentleman's labour on behalf of the factory population. He was uni-versally loved and respected as a Christian Minister, a philanthropist, and man of science. We are glad to welcome him again to our shores.'

The tour which Scoresby made on his second visit was mainly a re-visiting of many of the places which he had been to three years before, though this time he went no further south than Washington and now it was winter and he was no longer oppressed by the heat and humidity, but much more at home in a climate more nearly approaching the Arctic summer; he was a man of the north, well used to a frigid climate and he seldom comments on the discomforts of cold weather, though at Montreal on the 22nd October he notes: 'The rain turned to sleet and snow. Very uncomfortable.' Here, at the start of his tour, Scoresby made a most interesting discovery:

'In the bar of Tetus's hotel I saw a large, 4 sheets (?) Map of the World in which my researches in Greenland were specially mentioned by the general title in large capitals SCORESBY'S LAND. The map is published by —— of Philadelphia. Thus researches which Sir John Barrow tries to hide and never notices in his modern Arctic disco-veries, America acknowledges and gives to the author.'

Thus, at last, light is thrown on the mystery of why Scoresby's discoveries in the 1820's were not accepted. It was Barrow who was responsible: Barrow, who had an unexplained animosity towards Scoresby and who stood in his way whenever possible: Barrow who had said Mr Scoresby must do the best he can with his own means, when he had asked for the loan of instruments. The reason for the attitude can only be a matter of conjecture at this distance of time. Was he jealous of Scoresby? Resentful of his relationship with Sir Joseph Banks? Was it conscience that made him a coward, knowing as he did that the original suggestion for a voyage of Arctic discovery had come in the first instance from Scoresby and not Barrow himself? Had he suppressed Scoresby's letter wilfully and ever afterwards been fearful of discovery? We shall never know, but certain it is that up to this day the myth is perpetuated that the voyages were made at Barrow's suggestion.

In Montreal Scoresby was welcomed by the Rev. W. Adamson and preached in his church, where prayers were offered 'for help in time of plague'. This, he notes, was 'on account of the prevalence and mortality of the emigrant fever in this diocese of Quebec. 5 valuable clergymen had died of this fever, one, Mr Willoughby, of Montreal.'

On his tour, Scoresby lectured on Lord Rosse's giant telescope; at the same time he preached wherever he went and one could say that it was as much a preaching tour as a lecture tour. The clergy almost always gave him hospitality, one of the kindest being Bishop Duane of Burlington, for when Scoresby was taken ill with 'spasms in the left breast, very violent—followed by pain in the legs' the Bishop 'attended me most kindly and tenderly most of the night'.

In Boston, Scoresby had a list of no fewer than twenty-six people to call upon. In the last week of November he notes that he was nursing a bad cold and fever, but he did not let this stop him from visiting Dr Warren, the senior physician at the 'fine institution' the Massachusetts Hospital, where he was invited to witness surgical operations taking place under the wonderful new 'ether vapour'. This he did, and recorded every detail with his usual scientific accuracy. He was a man who was able to observe everything in a completely detached manner and did not appear to be nauseated or affected by what he saw. 'A French apparatus for inhaling (a new and clever invention) was here used for the first time. The nose of the patient was stopped by a brass pinching spring and a mouthpiece pressed close on the mouth. A great sense of suffocation appeared to ensue and it was long before the vapour took proper effect. The test was to tell the patient to open his eyes—when he could no longer do so—or when the eyes appeared like those of one mesmerised and the countenance became calm, consciousness to pain had ceased and the operation commenced. One physician held his hand. The pulse got high but the face became calm—like one asleep. I touched it and examined it carefully. The operation was effected without return of sensation.' There was no cleaning up between patients, and Scoresby next observed the removal of a woman's breast, followed by a tumour on a man's neck where 'red hot irons were used to destroy the cancer'.

After this Scoresby toured the hospital: 'The wards, high, lofty—beautifully commodious and clean and every appendage of the best kind and convenience. The superintendent recognised me at once. He had been a sailor & often attended my ministry at the Mariners' Church.'

The list of names to visit in New York, where Scoresby spent Christmas and New Year, was twice as long as that of Boston. Dining at the home of R. B. Minturn he met Washington Irving who, he notes, 'had rather a heavy manner and appearance—voice not musical'. Scoresby thought him rather retiring, for he did not talk much; the only time he came to life was in a discussion about mental illness, when he vividly described 'a moving panorama of figures climbing the bedpost'.

Christmas Day was naturally spent in attending church and in the evening he dined with Dr Hosack and Mrs Harvey, Dr Hosack entertaining them with story after story. On Boxing Day Scoresby preached at Grace Church where the congregation was 'the elite of the City—all wealthy, or at least of the wealthier class. There are no pews for the poor and none attends.' Concerned at this, Scoresby asked why it was so; he was told in all earnestness that, 'being strangers, they would not be given seats'.

Scoresby was particularly impressed with the New Year's Day custom of visiting from house to house without previous invitation; a sort of daylight extension of 'first footing'. There were no women to be seen outside on that day, for they were all in their homes receiving the peripatetic gentlemen.

He stayed in New York almost a month and visited every place which his friends thought would interest him, the schools of the School Society; the House of Refuge; the Deaf and Dumb Institute and a Day School for the Poor, where the children were taught and clothed gratuitously. He attended meetings of the Historical Society and dined at most of the leading citizens' houses. He was shown over the Naval Yard and made copious notes of his visit. He was particularly interested in a steamer which they had made there for the 'Sovereign people'. He noted that it had berths for 600 persons, but what really impressed him were the staterooms, and more especially, the Bridal state room, which had 'a superb bed-stead, a sort of triumphal car shape, wheels in front and robed canopy—all full gilded! Drapery beautiful silk damask—room white and gold moulding, furniture rosewood and silk damask—curtains of same material. . . . Two others with a four poster and 2 berths.'

From here Scoresby went on to Burlington and stayed with Bishop Duane, where he gave a lecture on Lord Rosse's Telescope at the College there. 'The room was full, all the college and professors were present—the Bishop and family. It lasted $2\frac{1}{4}$ hrs with fixedness of attention and I received the kindest and most general expressions of pleasure and interest. Being under circumstances where I was wholly at liberty on religious subjects, I was able to speak with much comfort on the consecration of our talents and acquirements for the glory of God—& on the instruction derivable from astronomical research as to eternal power and Godhead of the great Creator, and in contemplation of the vast and immeasurable expanse of the sidereal system, for the humiliation of man. "When I remember the heavens, the work of thy fingers ..." &c.'

It was shortly after this lecture that Scoresby was taken ill and Bishop Duane was so kind. He recovered after a few days and then went on to Philadelphia, where he stayed with Bishop Potter. Here the English mail reached him and he learnt that his wife had died at the beginning of December. Although he had half expected this news for some time, it need hardly be said that he was distressed; but his scientific detachment came to his aid and he was able to sit down and calmly write about her:

'In this great bereavement of our Heavenly Father there is much to consider. Her uncommon and most intelligent piety; her delicate conscientiousness without morbidness of conscience; her intense truthfulness—deep humility—feminine delicacy; her purity of mind and integrity & holiness of life were such as I had not elsewhere known. As a wife she was devotedly attached—ardently loving and child-like in her expressions of affection: wise and considerate & prudent, had an extraordinary cleverness and tact in household affairs and the obtaining of a well ordered establishment, was wise in council as well as in acting, her advice being always characterised by the highest principles of honour and piety & by sound wisdom and common sense—a helpmeet indeed!

'But she had for some time been in a state of health and under disease which did not, in her case, render life desirable. She only would have lived, indeed, *for me*. Her sufferings for many months (acute neuralgic) were exceedingly severe and they admitted of no alleviation. For her to live was Christ, but to die, *gain*. Her present felicity, doubtless, *is perfect*: and if in our Father's House be many mansions differing in degrees of glory, as I believe there are, she, I feel assured, enjoys a very exalted place there. May a gracious God fit me for a like position—& qualify me, as her anxious desire was, for reunion again, in participation of the same felicity.

'Always cherishing domestic life—happy in an affectionate, devoted wife's constant companionship almost whenever I could,— I feel to be a *lone* being. I love to think of her now happy spirit in the joyous occupation of a ministering angel (a condition she used to delight in contemplation).'

Mrs Scoresby had died six weeks before, thus there was no point in abruptly terminating his stay in the States and so Scoresby continued his holiday, preaching and lecturing as he went. After Philadelphia he went to Washington, where his list of visits to be made had swelled to the number of sixty-three names. He found 'the rapidity with which the Americans dispatch their meals at public tables' was the same as it had been when he last visited the country. If the stranger 'knows no one, he speaks to no one, unless incidentally he may converse with his neighbour at the table. But conversation is not the business. The business is "to take in wood and water" to keep up the steam, and this, generally, is done in silence and as quickly as possible.

'But the *eating in the steam boats*, especially when crowded with passengers, is the most remarkable, and, to an Englishman, the most disagreeable, and, shall I say? disgusting. Just conceive, gentle reader, a parcel of decently trained gentlemanly dogs accustomed to be fed together at a certain hour;—imagine them to be so well trained, or so well kept back that, till the provision is cast down and duly spread, none are permitted to approach. Imagine the intensity of their look— all eyes fixed on the provision and all eager to pounce upon it, and then when liberated and free to attack it, what a fine scramble there is for the self-supply. Such a picture will represent, not inaptly, what takes place at a meal on board of an American steam boat. All is heat—rattle—scramble—selfishness. A fork darts across the table and striking, like the harpoon into the desired article of refreshment, carries it off to the plate of the harpooner. Right and left, across each other's plates and shoulders, instruments and hands are perpetually being stretched, making prey of such things as may be wished for within reach. In like manner the knife, that has been used for the ordinary purpose of cutting and carrying, covered as it may be with the gravy or sauce, is thrust forth into the steak or cutlet, or butter or viand, so as to secure and bear away, like the trowel of the brick-layer, the portion of the article desired by the gastronomic artificer,— or rather "bolting artificer" for gastronomy is an art not practised in steam boats.'

Towards the end of February Scoresby made his way to New York, where he found two steamers about to sail for England. 'The *Hibernia* on Saturday, and the *Sarah Sand*, iron screw vessel, on Monday. I de-cided on the former, not liking the risk of the uncertainty of the com-passes.' They left New York on 26th February, 'The day was beautiful and calm, but the air very sharp. We sailed promptly at 12, the hour appointed, with only 18 passengers. A fine breeze came on from the

SWd—and we set head square sails and all fore and aft sails.' Once more, Scoresby the sailor was in his natural element.

Daily, he noted the temperature, state of the wind and sea. From his notes of the journey, it would seem that he spent the greater part of his time on deck, either on the cuddy roof or the larboard paddle box, for he was interested in ascertaining the height of the waves:

March 5th ... Heavy sea. In the afternoon I stood some time on the saloon deck, or cuddy roof, watching the sublime and terrific spectacle presented by the sea. I do not remember to have ever seen the sea more terribly magnificent. I was anxious to ascertain the height of the waves but found almost everywhere rising high above the level of the eye. I therefore went upon the top of the larboard paddle box. Here I found the waves were far above this level.

'Illumined, as the general gloom frequently was, by the sunbeams breaking through the heavy masses of cloud—and yielding a partial glare, rolling and foaming as the monster waves pursued us, whilst the gallant, buoyant ship—a charming sea bird—rose as she scudded along, as by anticipation of their attack so that their fierce strength passed away harmlessly beneath her—altogether presented a grand example of "the works of the Lord and their wonders in the deep". Oh, that man would praise the Lord for his goodness and for his sparing, preserving mercies, "His wonderful works to the children of men". We had Divine Service at 10½ am. I gave an extempore discourse on God's covenant with Noah, and its beautiful token in the clouds.'

The journey passed without incident, and for the second time in his life Scoresby sailed into Liverpool a newly bereaved husband. At the end of his first American tour he had come home to Mrs Scoresby and found 'all well', ending his account with the significant letters D.L.—Praise God. This time he was utterly alone and he closed the second journal with these words:

'At 9 am in my hotel, safe and well—thanks be to God for all His mercies.'

CHAPTER 21

THE FRANKLIN SEARCH

'It would be appropriate and becoming if it originated with us
Arctic Men.'

Scoresby was now rootless and a wanderer over the face of the earth.
But he was not without friends. Invitations to stay came from all over
Britain. He made his base at the home of his sister, Mary Clark,
at Grosmont, near Whitby, and from there he went to his friend Dr
Hook, Vicar of Leeds, the nearest town to Bradford. He then settled
his home affairs, and arranged for the furniture and his organ to be
stored.

Among the many letters he received was the following from Lady
Franklin, the wife of Sir John Franklin who had, at the age of fifty-
eight, set off three years before in search of the north-west passage.
The two ships, the *Erebus* and the *Terror* (commanded by Francis
Crozier), with their hand-picked crews of officers and men to the
number of 130, had been seen in the summer of 1845 by a whaling
captain in latitude 74° 48′ and since then nothing at all had been
heard of them. Unlike many of Lady Franklin's letters, this one is
dated, 25th February 1848:

> 21, Bedford Place,
> Russell Square.

Sir,

I beg to apologise for the liberty I am taking in addressing you.
You are of course aware of the steps which the Admiralty have
taken to search after the Arctic Discovery ships under the command
of my husband & of Captain Crozier. I am deeply grateful for the
interest thus exhibited in their safety, but still am under great uneasiness lest the efforts made by the united expedition of Sir James
Ross & Sir John Richardson fail of success considering that the
reason for search must be confined to one short summer. To look
to a second seems to me altogether hopeless—I am therefore most
anxious to see multiplied the efforts & resources of the first. It
appears to me my private resources might be made available for
this purpose—I venture to ask of you who have so much knowledge
in these matters how I could best employ a couple of thousand
pounds or more, if necessary, to the relief or rescue of the missing

ships or any portion of their crews. Is there any scale of rewards that could be offered with advantage to the Captains, Crews or Owners of whaling vessels?

I am well aware of the many difficulties which beset every view of this question & it is these very difficulties which I wish to meet in the best way possible. You would be doing me a great favour if you would turn the whole matter over in your mind and give me every reasonable encouragement you can for the accomplishment of my purpose.

If you are not already aware of the intended course of my husband & the ships going in search of him, I shall have great pleasure in telling you all I know about it. It appears to me that what they are going to do ought to be distinctly known to any other parties engaged in a similar pursuit.

I am Sir, your obdt servt, JANE FRANKLIN

Thus it was that Scoresby became involved in the great Franklin search which lasted for almost another ten years and was not finally resolved until long after Scoresby's death. He was quick to reassure Lady Franklin that it was more than likely the men were still alive. They had, after all, taken supplies with them to last three years, and even if they were beset, it would be possible to catch food after the manner of the Eskimos in order at least to keep alive. And had not John Ross, sailing in the *Victory*, a vessel of only 150 tons, been in the polar regions for four and a quarter years, from 1829 to 1833 without being heard of, yet returned safely with almost all his crew?

But Scoresby's experience in the Arctic had always been with whalers, whose sailors were the toughest in the world; well trained in the ways of living in that all but lifeless, stark, icy wilderness. He did not reckon with an ageing commander and crews, who—if not of the softer type of man—were certainly not all experienced Arctic sailors. He had already remarked that the ships had made too late a start in 1845. These facts, small in themselves, all contributed to a wholly large inadequacy.

Today, with hindsight, it is sad to reflect that even as Lady Franklin wrote this letter to Scoresby to enlist his aid, her husband was already dead. There is an ominously sad tale told of Lady Franklin, sewing the Union Jack which her husband was to take to the Arctic and playfully throwing it over him as he sat opposite her. He, recoiling in horror, pulled it off and exclaimed, 'Don't do that. They cover the dead with a flag.'

Later that year Scoresby went to stay with Lady Franklin and a sincere friendship grew between them, and on Lady Franklin's part a deep affection—'he was always my hero'; of Scoresby's feelings we are not sure, for he did not so readily commit his feelings to paper. The visit was followed by a letter from Sir John Franklin's daughter, Eleanor, who asked, among other things, if he could do anything about the 'vile French novels sold on railway stations'. She said that Lady Franklin thought 'the license they give to the circulation of bad books one of the most crying evils they are guilty of; the books I especially allude to are cheap translations of the vilest French novels, such as those of George Sand, Dumas, De Balzac &c &c. It is possible you may be ignorant of the vast numbers of these publications which are for sale at each station of the railways, for to my surprise in talking to our Rector yesterday, he was quite ignorant of these vile books being translated into English at all. Can you not use your influence to get this *increasing* evil stopped?'

For Scoresby 1848 was a year of wandering. His home was broken up and his furniture in store. Much of the time he was in poor health, for he had not properly recovered from an attack of erysipelas he had while at Bradford. In Ireland he stayed with Lord Rosse and in Scotland he was the guest of Sir John and Lady Maxwell: no visit north of the border was complete without calling to see his Edinburgh friends, Dr Traill and Professor Jameson foremost among them. Mary wrote from Whitby: 'If you can now descend to me and my plain face I shall be very happy to see you.' She was now a widow and intended leaving all she had to her brother, but this was not to be, for she outlived him by many years. Wherever Scoresby went he was made welcome, but Exeter had an especially warm place in his affections. And Torquay too.

He still had found no church or clerical post; there was a great deal of correspondence about an appointment to the chaplaincy of Hampton Court and just when it seemed that Scoresby might be appointed, the office was withdrawn. One appointment in which he had success, however, was in being elected to the exclusive Athenaeum Club in London, which was arranged by his friend Theo Dury. In the letter announcing the proposal, Dury also mentions a new phenomenon: 'Last night I was amused with the exhibition of the Electrical light on the porch of the National Gallery which illuminated the steeple of St Martins Church, the Nelson Column, & enabled me to read small print in Parliament Street. They placed a reflector behind & a lens before the light. Tomorrow it is to be exhibited at the top of the Duke of York's column.'

Did Scoresby, we wonder, remember his experiments with Traill all those years before and the unexplained 'variations and irregularities' in that small brass tube? They were the very beginnings of this new 'electrical light', but it took a Faraday to interpret them.

Scoresby spent more and more time in the South, and especially in the Torquay district. Mary Clark was hurt that he did not write more often and she assured him once more that he was welcome at the Hollins, her Grosmont home: 'It gives me pain when I think you hesitate to make this place your home, for I beg to assure you that as long as you need one, *or you feel contented here*, it will give me the greatest satisfaction for my house to be your home. All the household will be happy to see you return'.

Her brother replied at once:

My dearest Mary,

Before I do any one thing this morning (excepting breakfast)— I feel called upon to acknowledge your kind letter recd last night— and to express my deep concern that you had felt at all anxious or hurt about my silence. If I wrote but seldom to *you*, it was because I was writing almost every week to Whitby about my letters & I thought you would hear; but I did not think seldom of you, but *often* & always with affection.

Thank you, my dear Mary, for your very kind offer of hospitality for the winter—which I feel to be most kind. If I should not avail myself of it—as to which my plans are not quite arranged yet— it will be for reasons which you will quite approve: viz—the consideration that whilst without a church or place, whether I am not in a more likely way, under a gracious Providence, whilst either moving about or residing in or near some large or genteel town, to be at once useful & have the hope of an appointment &c? With you I have *every comfort* & in many respects can do more than elsewhere in my writings &c, but the other contingencies for which I am naturally and prayerfully anxious deserve consideration.

I was rather anxious about my face a fortnight ago, as it had become susceptible & more scaly, but, thank God, I was induced to try my own remedies, as usual, and it went away in three days! I am now, through the Divine mercy, quite comfortable in feelings—the people here say, looking well. It is cheering the *warmth* of affection of *all* my old friends—my dear young friends to whom it had pleased God to make me useful, as well as others, are full of affection.

I begin to have still stronger impressions that our suffering niece might yet survive—her case seems so like Mrs Bird's; but Mrs Bird was cured by mesmerism! & is now a wonder here, walking miles!

I think of remaining here, DV, 2 or 3 weeks at Mrs Haynes, who makes me *most comfortable*—giving me an excellent bedroom, a parlour to myself, a carriage when I need, &c, and actually orders her household for me, almost like yourself.

St James Chapel, Ryde, is about to be sold—the place where

Mr Sibthorpe used to preach—a genteel congregation. I have written about it, but find Mr Hewitt asked, I think, far too large a price, viz: £4400, whilst the income is little above £500 a year from seat rents. I am doubtful whether I ought to take a place of this kind or wait till it may please God to open my way.

Remember me kindly to Mr Brewster & accept the kindest love for yourself, of your ever affectionate brother,

W. Scoresby

Scoresby's enquiring mind could not help but wonder about Mrs Bird's recovery and the powers of mesmerism. He wondered if it bore any relation to magnetic force and he made a few experiments with some of his interested friends. Rather to his astonishment, he found he could mesmerise subjects very easily; he undoubtedly had hypnotic powers. He gave this power the unwieldy term of *Zoistic Magnetism*; though it did describe what he was doing, still, it is an awkward name and animal magnetism is a better one.

He believed that the position of the subject in relation to the magnetic force was of first importance and usually placed them—having experimented with other directions—with their head towards the magnetic north; he paid great attention to polarities and always held their left hand with his right or made his left-handed passes on their right side. The fact that all his subjects were female was only coincidence, the ladies were always willing to offer their services in the cause of his investigation—or the services of their maid-servants. He firmly believed that the magnetic force played the greatest part in the experiment and carefully placed magnets to attract and repel as he thought fit.

What had at first been a small matter of curiosity developed into an absorbing occupation and he went into the subject very thoroughly, eventually publishing a book on it. He carefully allowed for every contingency—he investigated 'clairvoyance' and named it Deceptive Clairvoyance*—always excepting the one great fact of his own personal 'magnetic' attraction.

Under hypnosis his subjects could hear his voice only and not any other in the same room:

'In about half an hour the patient was quite asleep. She replied to my questions, but not promptly, not always quite distinctly. The ladies present, at my request, spoke to her, but there was no reply. Repeatedly they addressed, speaking loud, but she gave no sign of hearing. My questions, however, though in a low voice, were instantly noticed and responded to.'

---

* 'Deceptive clairvoyance has its supports in collusion or delusion—superstitious credulity under deception—or in accidental hits, aided by a credulous condition of mind.'

Another case, Miss P., Scoresby found 'after several minutes trial no sensible effect produced. We then commenced looking at each other's eyes and in less than two minutes my young friend's eyes were closed. My every whisper was heard and generally responded to: but Mrs P.'s voice was not noticed when she spoke directly to her daughter, addressing her by name. Extraneous sounds, indeed, made no impression on her, nor did they seem to be heard.'

A personal account by an unnamed subject gives us some idea of Scoresby's powers of mesmerism:

'Last Thursday afternoon we went to Mrs Phillip's and found Mrs Ward, Miss Ward, Miss Louis and Dr Scoresby sitting in aweful array. I must own I felt nervous—preparations are always alarming, and Dr Scoresby I regarded as one does a dentist. However, the moment I was settled on the sopha with my hands in his, all apprehension vanished, a calmness, a delightful resignation to his will came over me. My eyes were irresistibly drawn towards his and in vain did I combat against the superior power of my mesmeriser. A pleasant thrill ran from my finger ends throughout my body towards my feet—my heart bounded with joy and I tasted bliss such as mortals know not. The faces and figures of those around me dissolved, one melting into another until the last vision of them seemed to vanish in Dr Scoresby's eyes. He was no longer Dr Scoresby to me, but my all, part of myself— what he wished, I wished.'

None of the subjects remembered anything afterwards. In many cases certain ailments were cured by the hypnosis. His investigation of the phenomena was undertaken in a truly scientific manner and never before or since has hypnotism in relation to magnetism been so closely investigated. He hypnotised, with varying effects, some fifty volunteers. Among the list of these occur the names: 'Mrs Ker—effect good. Miss Georgiana Ker—slight effect.'

But in no other way was the effect 'slight' with regard to this 'blue eyed Scottish maiden' who lived at the Castle, Torquay. The friendship between her and the lonely widower with the magnetic attraction soon deepened into mutual love—to the great delight of all their friends, with the sole exception of Georgiana's brother, who considered the pair ill-matched. One month before Scoresby's sixtieth birthday they were married and a new era of domestic happiness began for him and for Georgiana, the seven happiest years of her life, as she later told Lady Franklin.

The years of strain at Bradford had tired Scoresby out and he was unable to make any valuable scientific or literary contribution in the immediate post-Bradford time. But very shortly after his third marriage his active mind was re-charged and he started writing once more. He wrote a life of his Father (the capital letter still in evidence) and called the book quite simply *My Father*: it is very fine and brings the elder William Scoresby very much to life; for the general reader it gives a most lively account of whaling and the subject is not approached in as serious a way as in the *Arctic Regions*.

When writing *Sylvia's Lovers*, Mrs Gaskell drew much on Scoresby's *My Father* for her material.* Her hero, Kinraid, was a 'specksioneer' (a Scandinavian term for the chief harpooner), and there are many whaling tales related in her classic book which is set in Whitby, or rather *Monkshaven* as she calls it.

A sufficient distance of time had elapsed between the appearance of *My Father* and his death (1829) to allow the bitterness to subside; he had resented his Father's re-marrying so soon after losing his wife— the mother whom Scoresby adored. Now Scoresby was in the same position and at last he understood and was able to take an objective view. This may be an appropriate place to remark that Scoresby's own biographer, his nephew R. E. Scoresby-Jackson, published his *Life of Dr Scoresby* only a year or two after his death, and the book has thus suffered, all these long years, by being too hastily put together—not always accurately—and by the writer being obliged to be deferential to his contemporaries.

Having been unsuccessful in his Hampton Court efforts, Scoresby decided to retire permanently and devote his time to writing. He rented a house in Torquay, Sparkwell Villa (which he re-named Grosmont), but not without some trouble, for the owner of the house agreed to let it to him for £100 a year when he had already offered another person first refusal at £80 a year. This person, a Mr George Atkinson, was incensed and did his unsuccessful best to oust Scoresby. Letters flew back and forth and were printed in the local paper. It was Bradford all over again. Scoresby carefully compiled a 25-page pamphlet setting forth the facts and denying Atkinson's charges. He was already installed in Sparkwell Villa, which exactly suited him, for it had ample room for his organ and his library, and so, possession being nine-tenths of the law, Atkinson had to retire and Scoresby, for once, won the day.

In all this controversy Scoresby was greatly helped by his friend the Rev. R. R. Wolfe, the incumbent of Upton Church, with whom he had a most happy relationship. He often relieved Mr Wolfe in his preaching duties and eventually was licensed by the Bishop of Exeter

---

* Mrs Gaskell met Scoresby in 1856 and was surprised to hear that he had been the Rev. P. B. Brontë's Vicar. She was then engaged in writing Charlotte Brontë's life; she noted that he told her many tales of the strange ways of the Haworth people. She did not actually mention whaling, but it is probable that he talked to her about it.

Scoresby's house at Torquay

as Lecturer at his church. The post held no salary, but this was relatively unimportant to Scoresby, although he was by no means a rich man, having spent a great deal of his private income on the Bradford schools, an investment which showed no return in actual money. The important thing was that he now had a church, the duties were very light, and he could do exactly as he pleased which, of course, was always his very best.

With this light occupation and his new-found domestic happiness, Scoresby's ever active mind was enabled once more to bear fruit. He had a riding accident in 1851 and broke his leg. This meant that he was compelled to keep still; but only in body, not in mind. Being the man he was, he 'contrived a variety of machines and apparatus, to the astonishment of the doctor. A carriage or couch which runs me from room to room, removes me out of bed, acts wonderfully; a child can push me along. My leg is lifted for dressing with a tackle I made when a boy!'

Compelled to remain still, Scoresby closed his eyes. But his mind could not be still. He watched and wondered about the after-images which he saw and he wrote papers for the British Association and the Royal Society on *Optical Spectra* and the *Pictorial and PhotoChromatic Impressions on the Retina of the Human Eye*.

Letters amassed to and from Lady Franklin and for a long time Scoresby, a truly kind man, did his best to reassure her that there might still be hope. Certainly he offered her spiritual consolation: 'Your writing so fully and so frankly encourages me to hope that under the Divine blessing I may possibly be enabled to suggest something

Sir John Franklin

in the way of support and consolation which may not be altogether useless during the interval of anxious suspense before you.' He goes on to reassure her that 'all has been done that experience and liberality could devise', and recommends that she should stay in London and not go to Canada, emphasising his advice with Biblical quotations: 'Stand still and see the salvation of the Lord' and 'In quietness and confidence shall be your strength.'

It was not Lady Franklin alone who sought Scoresby's advice. In 1851 the Admiralty wrote to him: 'The Arctic Committee being aware of your great experience in all matters connected with the Polar

Seas and of the value that consequently attaches to your opinions thereon, have desired me to send you a series of questions which have been submitted to the officers of the greatest experience in the recent expeditions, and I am to request you to be good enough to give the subjects your *most careful* consideration, furnishing me with the result thereof, for the information of the committee:

1. Do you suppose it probable that Sir John Franklin or any portion of the crews composing his expedition still survive? If so, in what direction?

2. What are your grounds for forming that opinion?

3. Should a further search be decided on, what measures do you recommend for this purpose and in what direction?'

The combined answers to this questionnaire, and those of Scoresby, were very hopeful, and induced the Admiralty to send out yet another search expedition. In America, too, they were deeply concerned and several expeditions were sent from there, some privately financed. Parry wrote to Scoresby from Gosport, where he lived in retirement: 'Richardson and I are of opinion that some testimonial *from England* as a Nation, should be offered to that noble fellow, Mr Grinnell, for his unexampled liberality and benevolence in fitting out an expedition to look for Franklin, at his own individual expense. And we further think that it would be appropriate and becoming if it originated with us Arctic Men. There is no doubt that it would be largely responded to—and our subscriptions need not exceed £2 each, as everybody knows we are all poor men.'

Scoresby lectured on the Franklin mystery and wrote letters to the press about it. Letters flowed in giving advice where to search, Boothia, Melville Island, Prince Regent's Inlet, Smith's Sound, the list of names was endless. Nor were suggestions, sensible and fanciful, found wanting. The searchers should have boats on skis; they should carry rockets—the louder the better—which could be let off 'as often as convenient—thus the wanderers might know from what direction to expect help'; they should take balloons with 'a car large enough to hold one man with a telescope'; 'Give them the aid of a couple of small steamers; freight coals for their use by the Whale ships of the season.' Everyone wanted to help and no one more than Scoresby himself. No fewer than forty expeditions looked for the two ships, but every member had perished by the time the cairn was found with its last fatal message. The end of the story was not told until 1880, when the skeletons of the crews were discovered by Lieutenant Frederick Schwatka, of the United States Army.

The British Association continued to occupy the greater part of Scoresby's scientific life. Since he had complained to Sir Roderick Murchison matters had improved, and Scoresby was able to make

his voice heard. He read a paper on the Atlantic Waves in 1850, and at
the meeting in Hull, in 1853, no less than four of his papers were read:

> On the Surface Temperature and Great Currents of the Atlantic.
> On Deep-Sea Soundings and Errors from Strata-Currents.
> On the Popular notion of an Open Polar Sea.
> On the Prevention of Railway Accidents by collision.

The following year there were two papers, both bearing a relationship to each other:

> On the Loss of the *Tayleur*, and changes in the action of compasses
>   in Iron Ships.
> Inquiry into the Principles and Measures on which Safety in the
>   Navigation of Iron Ships is to be looked for.

The magnetism of iron ships was no new problem to Scoresby. He
had worked on it for many years and his findings and suppositions
are to be found in his two volumes of *Magnetical Investigations*. From
his experiments, he deduced the inference that a great part of the
deviation in iron ships is caused by the retentive magnetism, which
at first is very powerful from the great amount of hammering to which
the iron of such a vessel is subjected to in building, but which is altered
as soon as the vessel is exposed to blows or strains. The experiments
further showed that with such retentive magnetism is united a large
amount of transient induced magnetism.

The *Tayleur* was a fine new iron ship of 2,000 tons. On her maiden
voyage she met severe weather in the Channel and she was wrecked
on the Irish coast. Scoresby put forward the supposition that the
battering she had received in the storm had altered her magnetism
and caused the deviation which had driven her out of course.

By a happy coincidence, this meeting of the British Association was
held at Liverpool, where Scoresby had ministered at the Floating
Church nearly thirty years before, and at whose docks and shipyards
he had already become a familiar figure as he made observations and
experiments to support his theories. After the British Association
meeting he was invited to lecture to the Liverpool Underwriters
Association and he was asked what remedies he would suggest to put
this serious matter to rights. The main points of advice to captains
he put into a 'somewhat rude rhyme':

> The watchful *look out* let not cease;
> Nor *observations* never miss;
> Reckless, speed not, in 'wildering *fog*;
> Make use of *lead* as well as log;

> Be of compass changes wary,
> Running near to dangers chary;
> On duty personally attend;
> On Providence, Divine, depend.

But above all, over and over, he maintained that the only safe and dependable way was to have a compass aloft, well away from the magnetic influence of the mass of iron in the ship. He also said that he himself would be prepared to take a long journey in a new iron ship in order to make experiments to prove his theories.

William Scoresby in later life

CHAPTER 22

THE *ROYAL CHARTER*

'I have given the description ... to put on record for any who may
hereafter read them, the impressions made on my own mind.'

Not for nothing had Captain Flinders* complained: 'The compasses
in the Royal Navy and to this day are the worst constructed instruments carried to sea.' Despite the rebuffs Scoresby had received in
1839 from the Admiralty Compass Committee, he was still deeply
interested and concerned about the state of compasses. In his retirement he was able to give much thought and study to the question.
He knew about deviations in northern latitudes well enough; but
mariners and scientists alike were uncertain about what happened
when a ship crossed the magnetic equator. Great confusion and controversy arose, because by then ships were sailing in ever-increasing
numbers to far-off places beyond the South Atlantic and round the
Cape of Good Hope and Cape Horn and, indeed, to distant Australia
and New Zealand. In wooden ships the effect on the compass had
been minimal, but now ships were built of iron, and it was this very
iron which caused the immense deviations in the compass and consequently many wrecks. Mariners knew that the polarity of the ship
became inverted when she crossed into southern hemispheres, but not
to what degree. Scoresby investigated this in theory and though he
was fairly certain that his forecasts would be right, he also wished
to prove in practice that they were valid. Being the man he was, he
wanted to do the testing himself. And so it was that, in the summer
of 1855, he wrote to his friends, the Rathbone brothers of Liverpool,
to ask if they could 'find a suitable iron ship of a first-rate or good
class, either sailing or steaming, voyaging to Australia (or New Zealand), and if with the owners of such ship I could make a favourable
arrangement so as to put me to little cost (for I have already spent
many hundreds in this branch of the public service), I am disposed,
God willing, to undertake such a voyage in order to verify and

* Captain Matthew Flinders, RN, 1774–1840. Explorer and navigator.
Inventor of the Flinders Bar on the compass, which is made of soft iron and
compensates mainly against the magnetic force exerted by the predominant
mass of iron presented by the bows or stern as the case may be. He was a
cousin of Sir John Franklin.

complete the investigations I have been so long pursuing, on the important object of the compass action in iron ships.'

The ship would have to have wooden masts with 'some reasonable arrangement for compass aloft; with such appliances of azimuth compasses and previous swinging of the ship for determining the state of the compasses, as a prudent management might demand'. Remembering his experience with a seasick gentleman crossing the Atlantic, Scoresby asked for 'a small separate berth'.

The Liverpool Shipowners Association were quick to accept Scoresby's offer and suggested the *Royal Charter* as a suitable vessel. But her owners jibbed at a single cabin. There was no such thing; Dr Scoresby could only have a shared cabin. It looked as if the whole idea would fall through. But, wrote the Association's chairman, S. R. Groves, 'Throughout the whole community of Liverpool there is but one feeling, and that is to give you every aid.'

Very shortly, the money to pay for the extra berth had been raised in the City, Graves' Shipowners' Association, the Underwriters' Association and the Liverpool Compass Committee being the principal subscribers. Scoresby made preparations for his long journey. There was no difficulty in borrowing instruments; it was very different from the twenties, when he had been rebuffed by the Admiralty. Now, they bent over backwards to help and lent him 'one of the best azimuth compasses, pocket chronometer, Fox's dipping needle and gimbal table, with an ample selection of charts etc., applying to the tracks in which we were expected to sail'.

At almost the last moment, Mrs Scoresby decided to accompany her husband; she was very nervous, but she felt her place was beside him and Scoresby himself tried not to influence her in either direction, but it need hardly be said how delighted he was at her decision. Thus the empty berth in the cabin was filled.

The 3,000-ton *Royal Charter* was built in Scotland, in Hawarden, under William Patterson, of Bristol (who also built the *Great Britain*, which latter ship has survived to the present day and is now a museum piece). She was launched in September 1855 and then towed to Liverpool, where she had her engines installed, and was rigged, fitted out, and finally loaded. The Scoresbys joined her at Liverpool and the maiden voyage started on 18th January 1856. It does not appear that she had any trials before leaving, for after only six days' sailing there was trouble when they ran into a storm and 'the water flowed down in such quantities, that all the third class, and most of the second class and some of the first class were more or less flooded'. The captain was ill and had been confined to his cabin since they left port, due to 'over exertion in his efforts to get ready for sea, and cold'. Scoresby became a sort of liaison officer between the ship's officers and the captain, visiting him frequently and reporting on the state of the ship. On the first Sunday at sea Scoresby took it upon himself to assemble 'some 60 to 80 of the passengers' and perform Divine Service, giving an extempore address on 'the interesting story of our Lord's walking on the sea, of his pitiful concern for his toiling disciples, and consoling salutation: "Be of good cheer: It is I: be not afraid."'

The flooding grew worse. The captain 'hesitated on the question of putting back. My own mind, as an old sailor, was well made up on the point, but fearing in any way to influence him in a step which might seriously compromise the owners' interests, and damage the character of the ship, I told him I should volunteer no opinion until his own decision was taken; but meanwhile, I would go below into all departments of the passengers and then report to him the results of those impressions.'

When he went below he found 'Everything presented a picture of wretchedness and damage. Dirt and water defiled, especially in the third-class, every cabin and berth. It was most pitiable to see the prevalent suffering. Wives, children, and young women, wet throughout their dress, up to the knees, without possibility of drying their petticoats; a woman, without shoes or stockings, and wet up to the knees, was baling out water as it ran from side to side on the floor of the berth. In many cases the upper berths near the ship's side had been deserted, and the bedding removed half saturated. Bags, boxes, articles of culinary or domestic character, were heaped together drenched in water. It was lamentable to witness the small property of the poorer emigrants thus damaged or destroyed; in some cases their "little all".'

'Reporting to the captain the results of my observations, he made up his mind immediately to put about and make for Plymouth, then within a good day's run. I had now no hesitation in expressing my decided conviction that this was the only course he could wisely and safely pursue.'

It took almost three weeks for the ship to be off-loaded of ballast and made securely water-tight. On 16th February they once more set sail, Scoresby and his wife having spent a fortnight at Torquay in the meantime. One extra passenger embarked with them, Lieut. Chimmo, 'an officer who had done good work in surveying the Southern hemisphere, having, under Admiralty orders, taken passage in the *Royal Charter* "on particular service"'.

Scoresby made compass readings and comparisons twice or thrice daily. He also noted the state of the wind and weather as meticulously as he had done when he was master of a whaler. He was pleased with the speed of the ship and its graceful design. In the south Indian Ocean he particularly noticed the quietness of the vessel, travelling

at speed only under the power of sail—for the engine was only used
when the wind failed. 'Whilst so scudding at the rate of about 15 knots,
I was led to remark, in the middle of the night when in bed, the
astonishing quietness of the ship's action. She often went for minutes
together, at this great speed, with hardly observable motion or rolling—though a sea with 20 to 22 feet waves was agitating the waters.
Sometimes the quietness had something in it quite impressive. During
10 or 15 minutes (about 2 a.m.) when I was giving special attention
to the fact and counting in intervals of quietness the seconds of time,
I noted special intervals of 10 and 20 seconds in which not a roll could
be perceived nor the creaking of a single joint or fastening could be
heard. There was absolute stillness within board as in a ship in dock,
or—in the Greenland seas—of perfect shelter from ice. Fifteen knots
were being run with only the token of a slight vibratory tremor in
the ship—which from experience I had learnt was the sure sign of
a rapid speed—when everything else seemed to indicate entire rest.'

Nor was it only at night that there was silence. By March 1st they
had reached latitude 12° 56′, longitude 20° 26′ W (off the coast of
West Africa, that is,) and Scoresby wrote: 'I was much struck with
the stillness and strange solitariness of the regions which we now traversed within the northern tropic. Often when I looked scrutinisingly
around not a symptom of organic life, beyond the little world comprised on board the *Royal Charter*, was anywhere to be seen! Not a
gull was tempted to watch our progress to fish for the oft-dispersed
slops of the cooks and stewards. Not a whale, or porpoise, or other
inhabitant of the ocean, for long periods together appeared. Nothing
could be traced moving in sea or sky, and during much of this day
not even a cloud. Sea and wind, in the early day, seemed to sympathise
in the characteristic repose. In the high northern latitudes I had been
accustomed to a perpetual accompaniment of birds in the air and
water, of creatures of various kinds and magnitude, from the great
whale down to the animalcules which swam amid the Arctic ices. But
here there seemed to be an absence of all; and it was not until towards
evening that the solitariness was broken, a few flying fish emerging
occasionally from the surface water, and after their habitual limited
progress again disappearing.'

Well might Coleridge write: 'So lonely 'twas, that God himself
scarce seeméd there to be.'

But the respect shown to the albatross by his ancient mariner was
not shared by the passengers of the *Royal Charter*. When they reached
latitude 35° 3′ S they were followed by these birds, 'presenting a new
scene in aerial life after the deadness of almost the whole of our track
from entering the tropics. Graceful and majestic on their expansive
and elegantly shaped wings, the albatross floats in the air and follows

without effort the fastest sailing ship.' 'The shooting at albatrosses, which in great numbers follow the ship, appears to be a prevalent usage in many ships of our class voyaging to Australia and other considerable southern latitudes.'

And here it is that we find an insight into Scoresby's extreme sensitivity and delicacy of character and undoubted humanity and we realise—if we have not done so before—that the killing of whales—though necessary for a livelihood—had been repugnant to him. He goes on to say: 'The after part of the poop was yesterday occupied with "sportsmen" and lookers on, who with rifles or other guns were every now and then firing at the unconscious elegant birds gracefully hovering about our rear. I fancy 50 to 100 shots were fired, happily with rare instances of their taking effect; but in one case I saw, on being induced to look astern by a general shout, a poor stricken bird struggling on the surface of the water apparently mortally wounded. This useless infliction of injury and suffering on these noble looking birds, where there was no chance of obtaining them as specimens for the museum, nor for any other use, was to my feelings and, I believe, the feelings of many others, particularly painful. The inducement was "sport", the object, practice in shooting. But in attempting remonstrance, it was curious to hear the excuses for the cruelty on these confiding or unfearing creatures;—"they were savage birds"; "they attacked their unfortunate associate as soon as it was clear of the ship, to prey upon it"; "a boy who had once fallen overboard was attacked by an albatross, therefore"—it was inferred—"it was proper to shoot them". I quietly applied the argument to the case of dogs. I had known a dog attack a person and injure him; it was therefore proper to amuse ourselves as we had opportunity by shooting dogs! But the case was not admitted to be in point.'

Travelling through the tropics was a new and unpleasant experience for the Scoresbys. Their room was airless and humid and uncomfortably hot, the temperature seldom dropped below 80° and the candles at night made it hotter than ever. It is extremely difficult always to remember that their only lighting was candles, so much do we today take electric light for granted. Yet this was little more than a century ago. After they crossed the equator into the southern hemisphere Scoresby noted: 'To us, inhabitants in previous life of northern latitudes, a new phenomenon broke strikingly on our attention, viz. the appearance of the sun performing its daytime progress to the northward, with the astronomical peculiarity of meridian observations being taken with the face of the observer turned toward the Arctic pole! Everyone knows the fact; but its first realization, nevertheless, is a striking incident.'

At night time they watched the 'splendidly star lit sky' from the deck. Did Scoresby, we wonder, remember being 'with my Mary under the bespangled canopy of a star lit atmosphere' more than forty years before? 'The warm temperature of the air,' he wrote, 'rendered protection even from the dew, which was but moderate, unnecessary. The sky from the horizon below the Southern Cross, adorned as it is by the great luminosity of the milky way, and the rich assemblage of stars in the direction of Orion, and beyond it, presented a most glorious spectacle, and an emphatic demonstration of the Eternal Power and God head of the Great Creator. The glory of the scene was enhanced by "shooting stars" of apparently large magnitude.'

Sundays were regularly employed by Scoresby taking Divine Service, at first in the saloon and then, as it grew warmer, under an awning rigged up on the deck. But not all the passengers were as eager to attend as they had generally been on the Atlantic crossings: of these, Scoresby rather sadly writes: 'Without indulgence in verbal profaneness or intemperance; without any distinct violation of the proprieties of conversation or the volunteering of infidel or ungodly principles or views,—there was such a thorough negative in their manner or conversation as to religion or spirituality—such a marked avoidance, whilst not professing to object conscientiously to the Liturgy of the Church, to assembling themselves at our or any Sabbath day ordinances, that no reasonable exercise of christian charity could evade the painful conviction of the state of men of whom it is written, "God was not in all their thoughts."'

Our observer did not fail to record details of the food served and noted the menu just as he did in Paris and America:

'The admirable service and provision may be worthy of some little notice. The saloon passengers are 54 in number, which with four officers of the ship, makes an amount of 58 to be provided for. Two tables, separated only by the missen mast, run down the centre of the saloon, extending together to 50 feet in length. The dinner is served up in silver plate. The bill of fare for February 21st, which is a fair sample of the ordinary provision, ran as follows:— 2 joints of roast beef; 2 roast and 1 boiled mutton; 2 roast and 2 boiled chickens; 4 dishes of mutton cutlets; 4 dishes of mutton currie; 1 ham; 2 tongues; 2 roast pork and apple sauce; 2 mutton pies. Vegetables— potatoes, carrots, rice, cabbage etc. Pastry—4 plum puddings, brandied; 4 rice puddings, 6 fruit tarts, 4 open tarts, 2 sago puddings. Dessert, various.'

There was no shortage of fresh milk, for there were two cows on board. The list of dishes offered at breakfast is quite enough to make any landlubber feel queasy: Mutton cutlets, Irish stew, sardines, rice porridge, stewed mutton and ham.

Nor did Scoresby fail to notice the efficiency of the catering service, regardless of the state of the weather. 'Everything cooked with the same effectiveness and completeness in storm as in calm—fresh provisions, unfailing and abundant—pastry and puddings always ample and good of their kind; so that in speaking of the servants and cooks as part of the ship, and of the ship as a thing or creature of life, I may say that the *Royal Charter* had no consciousness of bad weather, and made no signs of complaining in storms or heavy seas.'

The whaling captain did not fail to notice the conditions on board for the crew. In the tropics, where the stillness and heat were all but unbearable for the passengers—who only had to sit still—he noted that: 'The men connected with the engine were in a most painful and serious degree the real sufferers. No ventilation could be obtained in the engine room, wind sails could not be expanded, and the glazed covering of the hatchway above could only be partially removed. In the coolest part of the engine room, on the platform just below the hatchway, the temperature was 93°; and near the furnaces, where firemen and stokers had to work, the thermometer rose to 130°. Some of the men fainted, but their small corps could not be dispensed with, and they bravely persevered, returning to their trying post as soon as sufficiently recovered. The Captain treated them with much discretion and judgment, as well as kindness. He allowed them altogether fresh provisions, and beer, porter, or weak brandy and water, carefully administered after their period of work.'

Being the man he was, Scoresby very naturally wondered what could be done to help them. 'Entirely removing the sliding windows would do much; and it would not be difficult, I think, to affix a ventilating trunk and fan—the fan to be worked by the engine—for forcing the air down under such atmospheric stagnation.'

For many of the passengers Scoresby felt a scorn almost amounting to contempt. This arose from their complete indifference to all around them; their lack of feeling towards the gallant crew, and their inhumanity in shooting sea birds for 'sport'; together with their complete lack of any religious feeling whatever, and no sense of imminent danger. This last was apparent when the ship was in an area where icebergs could be expected. No one knew their danger more than Scoresby and he was appalled at the careless indifference shown by some when icebergs were sighted: 'The mixture of feeling and contrast of conduct among the passengers was very striking and surprising. Some naturally timid, thoughtful, reflective, were in much serious anxiety at the realising of a peril hoped to have been escaped; whilst others, after a crowding of the decks in the excitement of the moment, seemed to see nothing in the formidable unmapped islands but objects of curiosity, and returned in brief space to their cards and play and recreations,—indulging in as much unsubdued levity as if they were enjoying the best circumstances of a sea voyage or the perfect security of a social party on shore! It might have appeared severe to have searched for a text expressive of my own feeling, with the knowledge and experience of ice navigation, of this exceeding inconsideration and reckless levity of some whose disregard of everything serious, or aversion even to the ordinances of religion had shown itself under much variety of conversation and incidental intercourse; but the text in Eccl. vii 6 was forced emphatically and repeatedly upon my recollection.' ('For as the crackling of thorns under a pot, so is the laughter of a fool; this also is vanity.')

His concern for the crew shows itself again and again in the narrative. He tells of an unusually high crossing of heavy seas which struck the ship in the middle of the night; 'Some of the passengers were awoke by it, one thought (the first impression) that the ship had struck against a piece of ice! But beyond the shock and the coming in of a small body of water upon the main deck, the result was perfectly indifferent, and the effect was regarded by the lookers on only as an amusing incident of sea life to the poor drenched sailors who happened to receive it in the shape of a shower bath.'

After the extreme discomfort of the heat and humidity in the tropics it was difficult to readjust to cold weather. Scoresby was 'somewhat surprised to see the sailors, men and officers in regular costume of our Greenland crews. Caps with protection for the ears for the helmsmen; mittens, strong water and wind proof dresses from head to foot, and, still more characteristically, large fishermen's boots.' When snow fell 'snow balls were made, and amusement extracted out of the (to us) ungenial curiosity'.

There were no stoves and the passengers shivered together in the unheated saloon. 'The heating of the saloon may be a difficulty', wrote Scoresby, 'but surely not an insurmountable one. I never before sailed in a ship without stove or stoves; yet we are told these Australian vessels, changing the temperature from 84° to near freezing in 20 or 30 days, and having to encounter severe frost, storm and snow in returning by Cape Horn, do not need stoves! I cannot see any difficulty in heating the saloon by a heating apparatus in the engine room, where the distance to be conveyed, of hot water or air, would only be a few yards to the forepart of the saloon.'

'We had', he records, 'a very unquiet night and comfortless day.' But there was worse to come for they ran into a tremendous storm, 'one of those more terrific disturbances of the elements which, though by no means unfrequent in certain tropical regions of the globe, involve risks of no ordinary kind to ship and passengers'.

'In attempting to describe gale after gale, and tempest after storm, I have not contemplated these grand operations of the elements or

their effects at sea, as anything remarkable in their kind, or as exhibit-
ing any phenomena unfamiliar to the sailor or to the practised voyager
across the great oceans of the globe,—but I have given the description
as part of a particular journal, written not for sailors or experienced
sea adventurers, but to put on record for any who may hereafter read
them the impressions made on my own mind, and the results of some
habit of observing and experience in noting the more remarkable
features and phenomena of storms at sea.'

Scoresby was suffering from a cold and sore throat and 'could not
venture to brave the storm on deck as I could have wished, or do
more than observe the effects of the furious storm from the "companion" and poop deck, and after some abatement of the wind from
the mizzen rigging'. It was no ordinary storm, it was indeed, a
cyclone. 'No one experienced in scudding before a fierce gale and
heavy sea, and knowing how the safety of the ship depended on the
steering, could contemplate the possible failure of the helm of the
Royal Charter when so scudding under the violence of this terrible
cyclone and tremendous sea, without much anxiety. This well apprehended risk it was which gave character and sharpness to the picture
of energetic life about the helm. There you saw four men—the best
class of seamen—supported by others on either side of the deck, keeping the wheel in active play, as they endeavoured to counteract any
sideway tendency of the ship's head. Every man there was a picture
of energetic manly life. You saw in his face an expression, to be read
of every one, that he felt in the management of the wheel he held
the destinies, under Providence, of ship and human life in his hands.

'Then there was the Captain, standing a few yards forward of the
helm—his figure and features expressive of an intelligent perception
of his responsibilities and his reliance on his experience of direction
in difficulties and perils,—his position partly sideways, so as to be able
with equal facility to watch every movement of the ship's head and
every turn of a spoke of the wheel—and thus giving guidance to the
helmsman in usual emphatic words, "Starboard! starboard!—steady
so—port a little—meet her again—mind your starboard helm", and
so on.

'Were I a painter, there is no scene which, since my abandonment
of Arctic adventure, has come under my personal observation that
I should more earnestly attempt to place on canvas than the poop
deck of the *Royal Charter* during the height of the hurricane. First,
in the afterpart of the ship, looking upward, we should have the
mizzen mast of the ship denuded of all sail with the cordage swelling
out forward with the force of the wind—then the ship herself cast into
an oblique heel towards the port side, the stem raised high by a mountain like wave—then the living pictures at the helm—the attending

officer and the directing Captain standing sideways, in the foreground
of all. Then the mistiness of the storm-drift—the sun throwing a lurid
glare through an aperture in the dense masses of cloud flying above,
eliciting in the sea-spray of a breaking crest a striking and brilliant
segment of a prismatic arch; and finally, beyond this, astern, an
approaching squall shower, thrown by the contrast of the penetrating
sunbeams into the aspect of consummate threatening and blackness!'

But the picture Scoresby has given us in words is far more vivid
and credible than any painting could ever be.

His severe cold confined Scoresby to his cabin, and prevented him
from making compass observations after the storm has passed, but
'Lieut. Chimmo undertook to obtain a set of comparisons of the three
fixed compasses, when the following results were obtained:

Compass aloft	Steering Compass	Companion Compass
E 17° N.	E 21°½ N.	E 25¼° N.

'These results were interesting and important, as showing what
I had always expected, that whereas the increase in the westerly deviations, on a south easterly course, had been moderate (about 16° in
the steering compass), that it was probable that other differences,
possibly much greater changes, would be found in other directions
of the ship's head. This single experiment showed at least a marked
change in the deviations of the adjusted compasses, for though the
quantity (compared with the compass aloft) was not great, the *sign*
of the difference was changed.'

On the following Sunday, it being the last—they hoped—of the
voyage, Scoresby was glad to be well enough to take Divine service
and he took as his address part of Psalm 107:

They that go down to the sea in ships, that do business in great
waters;

These see the works of the Lord, and his wonders in the deep.

For he commandeth and raiseth the stormy wind, which lifteth
up the waves thereof.

They mount up to the heaven, they go down again to the depths;
their soul is melted because of trouble.

They reel to and fro, and stagger like a drunken man, and are
at their wit's end.

Then they cry unto the Lord in their trouble, and he bringeth
them out of their distresses.

He maketh the storm a calm, so that the waves thereof are still.

Then are they glad because they be quiet; so he bringeth them
unto their desired haven.

O that men would praise the Lord for his goodness, and for his wonderful works to the children of men!

It was more than gratifying for Scoresby to find that his theoretical predictions about the ship's magnetism—for the testing of which he had undertaken this voyage—were being proved correct by his regular observations. 'On many occasions I had made trial of the magnetic condition of the top of the ship's iron plating, especially on the poop and forecastle. The *indications* of the results have already been noticed, but now I found them perfectly decisive.' All the plating had reversed its original polarity. 'All standards, an anchor stock standing upright, the entire tops of the iron capstans, had all changed—the tops now having northern polarity instead of southern. The extent of this change in the general fabric of the ship's hull outside, I hope, please God, to be able to determine at Port Philip. The results to me were especially interesting, as corresponding with my theoretical views so often and particularly published, and so much resisted by some men eminent in science. I had never contended indeed for more than what the present experiments might serve completely to vindicate, viz., that in a voyage of this description, the reversal of the dip must *tend*, under the mechanical straining and violence to which a ship is always more or less subjected, to a reversal of the original organic polarities, and that such tendency must produce a sensible change; but to what extent in respect to quantity, I did not venture to predict.'

As soon as they entered the smooth channel leading to Port Philip, Scoresby, oblivious of his years, nipped down the ladders just then put out on the ship's side and made 'hasty but important' observations which verified absolutely his theory. There was a complete inversion of the original polarity, exactly as he had forecast.

Fifty-nine days after leaving England the *Royal Charter* dropped anchor in Hobson's Bay—'the roadstead of Melbourne'—thus making a record sailing time between England and Australia. 'And here', says Scoresby, 'every devotional heart must have been fervently lifted up to God for the abounding mercies in preservation which we had all experienced.'

CHAPTER 23

THE LAST YEAR

'Every principle I had asserted was completely verified.'

Scoresby and his wife went ashore in a small boat to Sandridge and from there they took a train up to Melbourne. 'Much having been described to us during the passage out of the enterprise, extraordinary progress, and fine scale and plan of the city, it accorded more with my conception of it, except as to being much finer in the width of the streets and the costliness of many of the newer buildings, than almost any strange place in a distant country I remember to have visited. But my familiarity with the progress of prosperous cities and new populations in the United States prepared me for the variety of building, from wood or corrugated iron to fine substantial edifices of cut greenstone or basalt, granitic rock, and well-dressed and executed freestone.

'All seemed stirring, progressing and enlivened by prosperity. It seemed almost strange, at our antipodes, and in a city built on a reclaimed desert, and having risen from a population of some 400 to near 80,000 in less than twenty years, to witness the same dress, manners, and classes of population as at home; and it was a surprise to me *not* to witness passers-by in silk and satin dresses, of costly material and incongruous or vulgar colours, as I had been led to expect. There was no such thing to be seen wherever we walked,— many well-dressed and several genteel-looking women in the streets, but all in quiet and sober habiliments.'

The broad streets, though not 'completely paved or maca-damised' impressed them and though the bullocks and buffaloes were novel, the carriages were 'of the manner of English, with smart and handsome horses'.

Scoresby thought Melbourne was 'a fine city, fitted for the chief city of a colony, destined probably in the order of Providence to be a great and wealthy country; and considering the recent date of its commencement, the progress made, notwithstanding the costliness of the work of artisans and the high rate of wages for labour, presents something very remarkable in the history of the cities of the world. It is like a city raised by the power of an Aladdin's lamp.'

Their preliminary calls, with letters of introduction from the British Secretary of State for the Colonies, were abortive, for neither

the Governor nor the Bishop were in town. The senior partner of
the shipping firm which had given Scoresby the passage, William
H. Hart, was in his office, however, and he extended an offer of
hospitality at his home at Balmerino whenever Scoresby was able.
In the meantime he had to stay by the ship until he had opportunity
to swing her.* It was not possible to do this immediately, for she
was 'in a great state of confusion' discharging her cargo and
Scoresby had to content himself with taking bearings and deciding
which peaks of the distant hills he would use for points of observation.

He had 'opportunity for another class of observation of great
interest, and calculated further to support or to contradict my
published theoretical deductions. The ship's head turning very nearly
south magnetic, the terrestrial induction was equal on both sides. I
was thus enabled to get a series of observations on the ship's external
magnetism at the accommodation stairs, about 100 feet from the stern,
under circumstances for which I had long been earnestly looking. The
results were conclusive and, as to my published anticipations, I may
say triumphant.'

When the ship was eventually unloaded, the weather changed and
rain and fog set in, making observation impossible; it was three weeks
before they were able to swing the *Royal Charter*, but at last it was
done and Scoresby was pleased with the result, which proved without
doubt his theory that the only satisfactory and accurate compass
direction to be relied upon was that of the compass aloft.

He found that the error in the *steering compasses*, because of their
fine position in the *Royal Charter*, 89 feet from the stern (a large mass
of disturbing iron) as well as being placed some feet above the upper
plating of the poop deck, was not so great as those generally found
in iron ships: Still, it was out one and three-quarter points.

The *standard compass*, unadjusted, 'gave results, under my personal
observation, of such singular beauty as to consistency and precision
as must render them, when mathematically worked out in connection
with sets of observations in England, available for very important
scientific deductions.'

The *compass aloft* 'gave results that were admirable'. There could
be no doubt 'but that this compass had acted throughout with most
reliable accuracy'. The deviations of this compass were 'far less than
than those of the steering compasses of any ship built of wood in which
I ever sailed'.

There were only three weeks more to spend in Australia. Scoresby
had letters of introduction to the Governors of New South Wales and
Tasmania, and Mrs Scoresby was invited to visit a friend now living
* See Appendix.

in Sydney; but, since travelling to these places would have occupied
so much time, they decided to remain in Melbourne. Ten years
earlier, Scoresby might have undertaken all the travelling,—he had
covered hundreds of miles in the States—but now he was approaching
seventy and he was no longer able to do so much.

The *Journal of a Voyage to Australia* is some three hundred pages
long and only three of them are concerned with the time spent at
Melbourne, and we are left, tantalisingly, without any detailed
account of his stay there. All we are told is: 'The interval has been
spent in unmixed enjoyment and satisfaction. Our first visit was at
the hospitable residence and with the friendly household of W. Hamilton Hart, at Balmerino on the Gardener's Creek road; our next was
with his Excellency Major-General Macarthur, the acting Governor
of Victoria, at Tourac, three miles from Melbourne, where we were
made acquainted with a refined and charming society in an almost
continuous series of social dinner parties. Among the ladies and
gentlemen connected with the military staff, the public officers of the
city and government, and belonging to the legal and clerical professions and the mercantile classes, there were many from whom we
parted with real regret.'

The work Scoresby did on the compass was his last, for he was at
the end of his useful scientific life. Recognising the worth of that life,
the University of Melbourne gave him an honorary degree.

He was taken by his host to see the gold working at Anderson's
Creek: 'We visited two descriptions of diggings, one was the alluvial
in which they washed the gold, an operation so simple that all the
party requires is a bowl and cullender, and a thing like a cradle. The
other mode is to sink a shaft until the miner gets into an auriferous
vein.'

When he was only twenty-one, watching the working of the lead
mines at Alston, Scoresby stood at the threshold of his adult life. Now,
towards its close, he observed the gold workings in Australia. So had
his life been spent, progressing from the lowly lead to the noble gold.

Australian gold formed part of the homeward cargo of the *Royal
Charter*, which left Port Philip on Sunday the 28th of May. The journey was marred for Scoresby by a severe injury to his knee when he
slipped and fell quite early in the voyage. For a time this prevented
him either from making observations, or of holding religious services;
it also meant that he was unable to officiate at the burial at sea of
a passenger, a stonecutter from Australia who was 'ill of a consumptive
disorder when he came on board'.

Three weeks later, however, he was watching the waves and estimating their height and he records: 'The height being a question
of some interest, I contrived with difficulty to get into the mizzen

rigging, and in a position where by eye had an elevation of about 32 feet, found many waves intercepting the horizon.' The same week he notes that he is able to return to his clerical duties.

On the 4th of July, there being four Americans on board, eight guns were fired as a salute and 'a delicate and delicious punch, of which the basis was sparkling Moselle, instead of water, was liberally distributed by those gentlemen among the saloon passengers at luncheon, and a most liberal provision of champagne was placed by them on the table at dinner. Toasts were drunk, and speeches with snatches of songs or choruses were made after dinner,—all, as the good habit of the Americans is, being in the greatest good humour and pleasantry.'

July 11th brought them to 'an interesting position in our voyage—an epoch in our adventure—the crossing of the *Royal Charter*'s track in her outward voyage, and thus completing the circuit of the globe'. Allowing for the time spent in port, this meant that it had taken them seventy-six days to 'sail round the world'.

'As on the outward voyage, we found the approach to the tropics marked by a striking absence of the birds wont in other regions to follow our track. Life began to wane and solitude to grow upon us. On first going on deck in the morning, two birds only were seen, and these keeping at a great distance—a contrast to the close and intimate association of the Cape pigeons, Cape hens, gulls, etc which had hitherto accompanied us.'

For the first time in his life Scoresby was able to observe a 'vertical moon, 13 days old, shining gloriously in the tropical sky over our heads. Personal shadows were absorbed within the outline of the thickest part of the body.'

The experiments which Scoresby made for the dip gave results which confirmed 'strikingly and beautifully, former theoretical deductions'.

The growth of barnacles on the ship's bottom somewhat impeded her progress and Scoresby employed his active mind in thinking of various ways of removing them, suggesting a sort of 'windscreen wiper' arrangement on the keel.

The only signs of life in these desolate waters were a few whales blowing, and Scoresby was able once more to impress upon his fellow passengers that it was not water, but air which they were expiring. 'The error is not only a popular one, but even to this day is supported by many of our most eminent naturalists. It is difficult to find a work embracing the natural history of whales in which this error is not propagated. Several passengers, whilst deferring to my knowledge and experience in respect to whales, affirmed their unequivocal and decided impression that they had witnessed the ejection of columns or jets of water from whales.'

The passengers passed their time in the usual ways, walking the deck for exercise, the ladies 'working' at their sewing or knitting; they held concerts, dramatic recitations—the story of William Tell and portions from Shakespeare; and even a mock trial. Crossing the line was observed without ceremony on the part of those 'forward'. 'But performances and exhibitions of various kinds were got up amongst the gentlemen "aft" which were the occasion of much lively excitement; and from the universal good feeling and propriety of everything, no small real gratification and enjoyment to the general body of our associates. Dancing followed and was continued for a considerable period.'

Scoresby christened an infant born on board, the son of a gold digger, but he does not mention his name. He notes the lack of external life in the tropics:

'No appearance of living creatures beyond the precincts of the *Royal Charter*. The continued abandonment of the tropical waters by birds, so abundant generally throughout the other regions of the globe, gives them a singularly desolate character. Looking abroad for days and sometimes weeks together, nothing appears but the sky above and a sterile, desolate area of waters, unchanging in magnitude, form and character, bounded always with the same sharp circle of the horizon.'

But there were plenty of birds on board, for the passengers and crew had brought with them 'numerous cages of birds'. There were around a hundred parrots—'in which a great traffic has been carried on by the ship's servants. Many having been sold as high as two guineas a pair. A great number perished by fighting amongst themselves, whilst not a few have escaped, but only for a worse fate.'

Travelling rapidly northwards, he notes: 'Though no birds were to be seen to give animation to the dull, cloud-canopied atmosphere, the sea was more full of life than we have yet seen within the tropics. Sharks, cetaceous dolphins, flying fish, bonetos, were seen in extraordinary abundance. The dolphins' active gambols made them irresistibly amusing to our passengers, whose impulsive shouts and exclamations drew all from their seats to watch the play. In hardly any case did they content themselves with coming up to the surface and rolling over like the porpoises, but, as if overstocked with energy and life, they rose completely clear of the water and descended snout foremost into a brief concealment below.'

Two weeks before reaching port they met with a French vessel who, in reply to signals 'Peace or War?' answered 'Peace—Peace', which 'called forth a general cheer from our crowd of passengers. The grateful news was celebrated at dinner in an abundant supply of champagne for general use, contributed by one or two of the passengers, and after dinner by a salute of 21 guns, by order of Captain Boyce, followed by hearty cheers of those on deck, the resounding of which yet rings in my ears whilst writing this part of my journal. May the peace be graciously consecrated and sustained, under the Divine blessing, for the benefit of the world, the advancement of civil and religious liberty among the oppressed nations, the controlling of ambitious selfishness and wrong in the mighty of the earth, and the extension of the Redeemer's kingdom.'

After watching a Roman Catholic Archbishop giving his blessing to the passing French ship, while its crew fell to their knees, Scoresby comments, rather sadly, on the absence of a like respect in the Anglican Church for its ministers: 'In many cases, not only is no respect paid to the minister's official position, but not unfrequently a less value attached to his judgment on subjects than would generally be conceded to a master in any other profession, such as that of medicine or law.'

A week later, Scoresby made his usual observations and stated:

'Good sights were again obtained by the sun at setting. The ship's head being N. 55° E. by the standard compass, and allowance of $\frac{3}{4}°$ westerly for the deviation taken from the Melbourne tables and curves reduced, as on courses between N. and E. the change appears to have been in the proportion of one-third. This gave the variation 22° 31' W., or, by a final sight of the sun 23° 6' W, the mean being 22° 49' W. The variation by the Admiralty chart appears to be about 24° 20' W.

'These results serve to show that the eliminating of the local attraction, even in iron ships, so as to obtain useful and satisfactory determinations for the variation, is by no means so difficult as might have been apprehended, and as in my personal anticipations I thought it would be.'

He regretted that the compass aloft had not been adjusted so as to have been visible with a telescope from the deck and suggested a 'bold graduation of the card into degrees' so that this could be done.

At heart, Scoresby was still the whaling captain, thinking of the welfare of the crew. He welcomed a fresh breeze which enabled the ship to travel under sail, thus relieving 'our engine men from their long spell of exhausting duties'. 'In the evening the breeze freshened and the ship resumed her outward habit of running at a speed of 13 knots or upwards. There was something very exhilarating, and, to a sailor's feelings, I may say charming, in this quiet performance of what in other classes of ships would be deemed wonderful, this splendid feat is accomplished without apparent effort or strain on ship or spars. The fast clipper reminds me of the high-bred and high conditioned horse, which in bounding with the swiftness of the wind over the downs, expends no apparent effort.'

Though Scoresby completed his magnetic observations and swung the ship on its return to Liverpool, he did not complete the *Journal of the Voyage*, which breaks off five days before reaching port (August 14th).

The *Journal* was edited by Scoresby's friend, Archibald Smith, himself an expert on magnetism, and the following note, which ends the book, was sent to him by W. W. Rundell, who assisted Scoresby in his final observations:

'The deviations about which you enquire were obtained in the Mersey, by means of the magnetic bearing of the Vauxhall chimney, which had then been recently painted on the Dock walls. About 22 observations were made, as opportunity allowed, the same day the *Royal Charter* arrived, and it was agreed by Dr Scoresby and myself that we would sleep on board, so as to continue them at daylight in the morning, as the ship was to be docked very early. By the Doctor's ready thought in hailing a steam tug to pull the ship's stern round as far as possible against the tide, additional points were observed; and by good fortune we were able to observe the remainder as the ship was turned into the London Basin, on her way to the Wellington Dock. As you may suppose, it was a subject of much congratulation that, by a little energy and perseverance, the reswinging of the ship on her return to Liverpool has been effected; and Dr Scoresby repeatedly remarked that had it not been for the bearings printed on the walls his experiments would have remained incomplete.

'Dr Scoresby had charge of the Admiralty compass, and gave the signal for each observation, while I undertook to give the ship's head correct magnetic for the same moment, and to read the steering compass. One of the subordinate officers read the companion compass, and a seaman was sent aloft to read the mast compass, but through the sluggishness of the last compass the readings were of no service.'

There is little left to tell. The voyage had drained Scoresby's strength. The immense responsibility and importance—at the time—of his investigations, had worn his already tired frame beyond the limit of recovery. But he was not a man who would easily admit defeat.

They returned home to Torquay first, where he worked hard at his *Journal* of the voyage, writing a preliminary exposition on magnetism to the actual journal some hundred pages long, setting forth the principles of magnetism and compasses and giving the reasons which had influenced him in undertaking the voyage, of which the following is rather neat:

'There were other results of inductive research on magnetical phenomena in iron in their bearing on safe compass guidance in iron ships, which neither home experiments, nor the information hitherto obtained respecting magnetic changes on such ships abroad, were sufficient, either to establish or refute them. Nor could the extent of the operation of influences tending to the inversion of a ship's magnetism in far southern latitudes, be gathered from the deductions of science. If, indeed, it had been practicable to put an iron ship to the test of experiment, as in the case of iron bars and plates, so as to turn it upside down, and in that position subject it to a thorough hammering, or other mechanical action, we should then have had the asserted principles of the complete inversion of the ship's polarities by the reverse operation of terrestrial induction under mechanical action put to the test, and the truth or error of the theory satisfactorily determined.'

GROSMONT INSTITUTE.

IT IS INTENDED THAT THE

ANNUAL

OF THIS SOCIETY BE HELD

On TUESDAY Evening, October 28th, 1856,

WHICH WILL BE PRESIDED OVER BY THE

REV. DR. SCORESBY,

TEA ON THE TABLE AT 5 O'CLOCK,

After which addresses will be delivered by the distinguished and talented Chairman, and other Clergy and Gentry.

Miss IRVING and part of the Members of the Whitby Amateur Philharmonic Society, have kindly consented to give their services on the occasion, accompanied by MRS. RIPLEY on the Piano.

Tickets, including Tea, ONE SHILLING, to be had of MR. DREWRY, the Secretary; and MESSRS. HORNE & SON, Printers, Whitby.

Grosmont, Oct. 15th, 1856.

In November Scoresby and his wife went to Whitby, where they stayed with his sister Mary Clark. Whilst there, he gave a lecture on his recent tour. He was able to say to the audience:

'Every principle I had asserted was completely verified. The compasses were adjusted on the very ingenious principle of the Astronomer Royal, the errors being compensated by antagonistic magnets in England. Exactly as I had said before the British Association in 1846, these compasses not only ceased to be useful, but they went further wrong than any others on board. Every principle of a compass aloft, as the only means of a safe guidance, was fully established. If he cannot combat with an enemy, a wise general gets as far away from him as he can. In our compass aloft, we had our perfect guide and standard of reference at all times.'

From Whitby they went on to Edinburgh, where Scoresby was persuaded to give a course of four lectures on the Arctic Regions. After two of them he broke down and the others were postponed for a day or two. But he was not a man to spare himself or give in easily and he insisted on delivering the two final lectures. The following day he was taken ill and had a haemorrhage while they were at Polloc, staying with Sir John and Lady Maxwell. He recovered sufficiently to return, in easy stages, to Torquay.

He did not have a great deal of faith in doctors, usually preferring his own remedies. He crossed swords with the one who attended him when he had erysipelas, who had been heard to say 'I had rather attend ten fools than one philosopher'. Early in the year he said in a letter:

'In some particulars I feel better and get on better; but I do not yet attempt any duty on the Sunday—my greatest deprivation. Doctors I have not yet consulted. Some would blame it as a mistake or error; but I feel that when I begin I must leave off self-administering and get into a certain bondage I do not like. Probably, however, I shall take advice soon.'

The decision was forced upon him by another attack, when Mrs Scoresby called the doctors in. They diagnosed heart disease and held out little hope of recovery.

Within a month, on 21st March 1857, William Scoresby had heard the one clear call and was well prepared to see his Pilot face to face. Quietly, he slipped from his moorings and set out on his last voyage.

CONCLUSION

Scoresby-Jackson, in the biography of his illustrious uncle which was published only a year or two after Scoresby's death, tells us that: 'Torquay presented a saddened aspect' on the day of the funeral. 'Great respect for his memory was evinced among the middle classes of the town by the closing of the shops during the sad ceremonial. The vessels in the port testified the reverent sympathy of the seafaring public by having their flags half-mast high, whilst the respect of the immediate friends of the departed was displayed in the swelling of the procession by upwards of twenty private carriages. The bells of Upton Church proclaimed in muffled peals the sad event of the day, whilst the mourning drapery with which the interior of the church was clothed filled up the measure of the prevailing gloom.'

Why was this so? we might ask, for it was not to be wondered at that a man who had undergone such an arduous and active life—more especially during his Arctic years—should develop heart disease in later life. He had never been robust and the wonder is that he was able to do so much without injuring his health long before he reached his sixties. Torquay was proud that such a man should have chosen to end his days there, but it was not merely demonstrating its respect for a kindly retired cleric. In his day, Scoresby was recognised as being in the foremost ranks of eminent men and it was because of this that the town mourned his death.

When we look at Scoresby's life, the first thing which strikes us forcibly is the amazing promise shown by him in his early youth. His immediate family may have taken this for granted, but to have been appointed captain of a whaler at the age of twenty-one, with all the responsibility implicit in the appointment: to control the burly, rough and tough Greenland sailors, almost all older than himself, was a formidable task in itself and points to his ability to command and gain respect; to equip a ship with stores enough to last a year if need be was no simple task; nor guiding that ship through treacherous northern waters; yet at the same time to carry on with his scientific work—well enough when his Father was in command—was certainly remarkable. For we must not forget that while observing, measuring, recording and continuously and patiently carrying on his researches, Scoresby was catching whales. The men of the northern whale fisheries were redoubtable men. They had to be to fit the task they had undertaken. Though the ships were wood, the men were iron. Whale fishing was an heroic struggle with gigantic denizens of the sea in those

days, not the mechanised, soulless destruction of whales from huge
floating slaughter-houses it later became, and which today—if
continued—will soon render the whale an extinct species.

How can we sum up the career and arrive at a just estimate of the
character and achievements of such a man as William Scoresby? The
tremendous drive, early maturity, wide interests and commanding
grasp of all he undertook are in marked contrast to the narrow profes-
sionalism which has grown since his time. This fact, while adding
much to the interest and significance of Scoresby for our own time,
does make it difficult to arrive at a clear picture. Men of great dis-
cernment and ability in his own day, such as Banks and Jameson at
home and Rosily, Humboldt and Ampère abroad, knew his worth
and recognised his abilities and achievements.

How does such a man come to be undervalued after his death?
No single great discovery in science stands to his credit and that is
undoubtedly the principle cause of his comparative obscurity. He was
born just a little too late to mature during the period of Banks's presi-
dency and of Cook's voyages, for Scoresby was of a type similar to
Alexander von Humboldt and had gifts of command, exploration and
research at a very early age which could have carried him far in the
period of exploration and expansion dominated by the personality
and force of Banks and by the genius of Cook. He might have achieved
for the Arctic what Cook did for Australasia. But what he did was
not inconsiderable and should by no means be overlooked. It was
no less than the founding of Arctic science and the beginnings of
oceanography. The record of the achievement is contained in his two
volumes of *An Account of the Arctic Regions*. Well might Sir Alister Hardy
describe it as a classic of whaling literature and a quite outstanding
pioneer work on the science of the sea.

We recently visited the new Maritime Museum at Hull and on
being admitted to an inner sanctum noticed a copy of *Arctic Regions*
open on the desk. 'Aha!' we exclaimed, delighted at seeing the familiar book, 'so you have a Scoresby too.' 'Oh, yes, indeed,' said our
guide, reverently picking up the volume, 'this is our Bible.'

The book came into Banks's hands only a few weeks before his
death, and a little later Arctic exploration and discovery passed
largely to naval men who, while possessing much courage and ability,
had few, if any, of the scientific insights of a Scoresby, nor his unique
experience of navigation and conditions in the Arctic, for he had, since
the age of thirteen, voyaged regularly in the northern whale fishery
and in his formative years had the extraordinary advantage of the
guidance and experience of one of the leading whaling captains of
the time, namely his own Father, William Scoresby senior. However,
after Banks's death Scoresby had no powerful friends in the Royal

Society, and not being a naval man he could not count on the support of naval authorities—indeed, it seems probable that one of the most influential naval civil servants of his day, Barrow, was actively hostile to Scoresby's interests. Be that as it may, Scoresby no longer voyaged among the icebergs and the whales of the northern seas and the rapid growth of Arctic science—which had seemed possible from the splendid beginnings he had made—never came, and not until our own century did Arctic research really get under way.

Scoresby was one of those many-sided men—a type the eighteenth and nineteenth centuries seemed to produce, but which in our own times are all too rare. He had qualities and gifts 'seldom united in one man'. A courageous whaling captain; a skilled navigator; an able surveyor and draughtsman; a naturalist and an acute observer; a forceful and graphic writer. We may wonder why such talents were not fully utilised and why the science of his time failed to provide more opportunities that would have led him to still greater achievements. The answer lies partly in the fact that the science of Scoresby's day was moving away from exploration and observation of natural phenomena and products and it was actively engaged in developing a new chemistry and physics which would provide the basic information for the new industrialism; its leaders were typified by Sir Humphry Davy. In such a new climate of interest and endeavour, the achievements of Banks came to be undervalued and Scoresby's neglected. It was a considerable shift of focus and the light of the new science shone on different types. Perhaps in a society differently organised this might not have happened. But whatever the conjecture might be, Scoresby went into the Church and his tremendous drive and ability were harnessed to pastoral duty, social reform and educational endeavour. In the midst of this most worthwhile and very arduous activity Scoresby' met the young James Prescott Joule. At this time, 1842, Joule was almost unknown.

'I had the happiness of forming the acquaintance of Dr Scoresby.' he wrote later. 'He became greatly interested in the view I was at that time beginning to take of the relation between heat and other forms of force.'

Scoresby was fifty-two at the time of the meeting, Joule was less than half that age, only twenty-four. The older man's immediate interest in Joule's most original ideas is very striking. Receptivity to new ideas is not usually a characteristic of middle-aged men. Here we discover a new facet of Scoresby's character: appreciation of the ideas of a young scientist—non-academic and working alone in a private laboratory—still to gain recognition and to make his way in the world of science. We know that the acquaintance ripened into friendship and a mutual high regard of the two men one for another; they worked together on a piece of research and, as far as Scoresby's many duties would permit, were scientific collaborators. Apart from discussion on science and the details of their experimental work they talked much on the philosophy of science and on the true aims and objects of scientific research; we have commented earlier on the value and significance of this and feel very strongly that their approach and their conclusions have a bearing more than relevant to our time.

Scoresby believed that scientific and technical development should be directed by the friends and not the exploiters of nature and that they should contribute to the 'enhancement and betterment' of human life. He saw that to build a better society one must start with the individual and with education. During his stay in Bradford he worked very hard to improve the educational opportunities of the factory operatives and finally—after immense effort in a town hostile to the established church and rampant with 'dissenters'—succeeded in building no fewer than four new church schools. This was no small achievement in a mere half-dozen years. Imagine such efforts going on in all the major cities of Victorian England: perhaps some of the more pressing social evils of our own day might thereby have been obviated. Whatever modern educationalists might think of the instruction given in such schools, at least they inculcated a sound morality and a worthwhile amount of basic knowledge upon which ability, if it were present, could well build.

Another and most important activity of Scoresby, sustained with great pertinacity throughout the whole of his working life, was the study of the marine compass, especially the design of the compass needle and the production of steel which would take and maintain a high degree of magnetisation. After the introduction of iron vessels he was very active in his studies of the behaviour and reliability of compasses in such vessels and his last long sea voyage to Australia was undertaken to make detailed studies of the compass in these new conditions. His unique combination of practical experience as a navigator and surveyor with scientific insight and training made his findings in this field invaluable, and much he wrote and advised did pass into seafaring practice almost unnoticed, for it was so close to the problems and requirements of his day and so suited to the needs of the class of men he understood that, like much good work of its type, it was almost taken for granted.

Although there have been great advances in marine navigational methods since Scoresby's time and much that he wrote is now only part of the history of the subject, it is yet a part which should not be forgotten, for Scoresby grappled successfully and tirelessly with the problems of the design of compasses and compass needles and of the reliability of compasses in iron ships—urgent and pressing problems of his time—and like all good scientists, he was anxious to put his knowledge and experience to practical use.

We have commented on Scoresby's open-mindedness and ability to appreciate and understand new ideas. He was even willing to investigate mesmerism and performed many experiments with suitable subjects, trying to discover if any relationship could be established between the terrestrial magnetic field and mesmerism. In his interest in these psychic and border-line phenomena he was a pioneer investigator on the scientific side, a forerunner of Sir William Crookes and Sir Oliver Lodge. No positive results were obtained; research still continues with mesmerism and telepathy and allied phenomena. Who knows what the future may reveal?

We would have a most incomplete and unreal view of Scoresby the man if we failed to appreciate the deep religious faith which underlay, directed and informed all his life and work. This real faith was part of his character long before his entry into the Church. It was the substratum out of which grew his courage, singleness of purpose, command of life and of men, seen in his astonishing early ability.

It was no ordinary man who voyaged in the Arctic, who began to discover secrets of nature amid these frozen wastes where others had only battled with the elements, who carried with him all his life a deep conviction that mankind can only move forward by patiently searching divine and scientific truth. In the pursuit of this moral and intellectual ideal he did not spare himself, his time or his money, and in terms of the world's wealth he died a poor man.

William Scoresby is assured of a place in the history of science by his pioneer work in the Arctic and for the science of the sea. But equally important for our own times is his example as a man of culture and of faith.

> For all that nurtures human life
> And for mankind the future holds,
> Is what the gifted mind unfolds
> Despite man's greed and strife.

APPENDIX—for landlubbers

In case there should be any readers who are as ignorant of all things nautical as we were when we started this book, we give a few definitions, kindly supplied by Capt. C. H. Hooper, R.N.

AMPLITUDE and AZIMUTH are methods by which observations of celestial bodies are made in order to ascertain the error (and thus the deviation) on the compass at any given time.

AMPLITUDE is the distance in degrees from the East point of the horizon at which a heavenly body rises, or from the West point at which it sets.

AZIMUTH is the arc of the horizon between the meridian of a place and a vertical circle passing through a celestial body.

BESET is the term used when a ship is completely surrounded by ice and unable to move through it.

COURSE—*True course or bearing* is that which is taken from or applied to a chart direct.

   Magnetic course or bearing is obtained after applying Variation to the True.

   Compass course or bearing is obtained after applying both Variation and Deviation to the True.

DEVIATION in the compass is caused by magnetic disturbance or influence or interference.

DIP is the amount of angle a magnet will incline from the horizontal towards the north or south pole respectively. It will be horizontal at the magnetic equator, inclining to maximum as it moves towards either pole.

FLINDERS BAR. A soft iron bar usually placed vertically on the fore side of the compass which compensates mainly against the magnetism from the predominant mass of iron in the bows or stern.

BINNACLE. The wooden structure which houses the compass, which in turn is slung in gimbals allowing fore-and-aft and athwartship degrees of freedom when the ship is in motion in a seaway.

LUBBERS LINE is a vertical line clearly marked on the middle of the forward inside rim of the compass bowl which permanently indicates the ship's head.

SPECKSIONEER. A Dutch word meaning the chief harpooner on a whaler.

STANDARD COMPASS is the main compass in a ship and all observations are taken with it and all courses set by it. In present-day ships it is situated generally in the open above the wheelhouse clear of all obstructions.

STEERING COMPASS is in the wheelhouse and is the compass by which the helmsman steers the course. Other compasses can be situated amidships or right aft at the secondary steering position.

SWINGING. The turning of a ship to ascertain and correct deviations on thirty-two points of the compass. The ship is taken to a suitable place and turned slowly and with care through 360°, the deviation on each point being noted whilst so doing. A record of the deviations on each of the thirty-two points of the compass is carefully noted on a DEVIATION CARD and is of vital importance to the mariner thereafter; it is kept in a prominent place in the chartroom for immediate reference when required. After adjustment and swinging, the compass will remain correct for all parts of the world, north or south hemisphere, until the vessel is drydocked or undergoes a major refit.

VARIATION is the divergence or variation of the earth's influence upon the compass needle, differing in extent according to the latitude north or south of the magnetic equator.

GUNTER'S CHAIN. A decimal scale used in surveying and navigation. Derives its names from an English mathematician and astronomer, Edmund Gunter (1581–1626). He is also said to have invented the 'portable' quadrant—a forerunner of the sextant.

SEXTANT is an instrument used for measuring angles. It is used in navigation and in surveying for measuring altitudes of celestial bodies and their angular distances. It is an instrument of double reflection created by two mirrors appropriately positioned and has a telescope and graduated arc and vernier for reading very small intervals. As its name implies, it is one-sixth part of a circle and is the successor to the astrolabe and quadrant used in earlier times. John Hadley is said to have invented the quadrant and later the sextant.

THEODOLITE. An instrument used in land surveying for the measurement of angles both horizontal and vertical, being neither more nor less than an altitude and azimuth instrument, proportioned and constructed so as to be conveniently portable. For observations it is usually set up on a tripod stand.

BIBLIOGRAPHY

The Life of William Scoresby. R. E. Scoresby-Jackson. 1861
The Scoresbys and Greenland. T. Sheppard. 1939
The Whaleman's Adventures. H. T. Cheever. 1850
Quest for Franklin. Noel Wright. 1959
Portrait of Jane. F. J. Woodward. 1951
The Search for Franklin. L. H. Neatby. 1970
Sir John Franklin's last Arctic Expedition. R. J. Cyriax. 1939
Explorers of the World. W. R. Clark. 1964
The Arctic World. W. H. Davenport Adams. 1875
Great Waters. Alister Hardy. 1967
The British Association. O. J. R. Howarth. 1931
Sir Joseph Banks—The Autocrat of the Philosophers. H. C. Cameron. 1952
Britain's Heritage of Science. Schuster & Shipley. 1920
Reason and Chance in Scientific Discovery. R. Taton. 1957
British Scientists of the 19th Century. J. G. Crowther. 1935
Scientists of the Industrial Revolution. J. G. Crowther. 1962
Memoir of James Prescott Joule. Osborne Reynolds. 1892
Great Men of Science. Phillip Lenard. 1933
Victorian Exeter. R. Newton. 1968
North West Passage. Richard Hakluyt.

BY WILLIAM SCORESBY:

An Account of the Arctic Regions. 1820
The Loss of the Esk and Lively. 1826
Memorials of the Sea: 1. *Sabbaths in the Arctic Region.* 1830
                        2. *The Mary Russell.* 1830
                        3. *My Father.* 1851
Memorial of a Dutiful and Affectionate Son. 1835
Magnetical Investigations. 1852
Journal of a Voyage to the Northern Whale Fishery. 1823
Journal of a Voyage to Australia (Posthumous). Ed. by Archibald Smith. 1859

INDEX